IND. OHIO

ILL.

MISSISSIPPI R.

Thurs., Ju...
Wesley...
The Oaks...

D1188127

OHIO R.

...RIS

U R.I

KENTUCKY

OHIO

MISSOURI

GALLATIN

NASHVILLE

Fri., June 28, 1844.
Encounter with
U.S. Marshal.

TENNESSEE

...SAS

DALTON 1864
RESACA 1864

S. C.

ARKANSAS
POST 1863

X KENESAW MT. 1864
...A 1864
JONESBORO 1864

MISSISSIPPI R.

ABERDEEN

MISS.

Fri... ...
...ert James McGowen.

...July 2, 1844.
Jas McMurrey.

GEORGIA

JACKSON

NATCHEZ — Mon., July 15, 1844

— Down river via steamer.

FLORIDA

LAKELAND — Wed., July 17, 1844.

OPELOUSAS

LOUISIANA

Sat., July 20, 1844,
Meet Maj. Tarbone
and Jack Spangler.

Gulf of Mexico

Diamond Six

3-7843-0018-1952-0

DIAMOND SIX by WILLIAM FIELDING SMITH

EDITED BY GARLAND ROARK

DOUBLEDAY & COMPANY, INC., GARDEN CITY, NEW YORK

To my wife, Ella Frances,
our daughter and son, Starlett and William Fielding,
whose enthusiasm and encouragement
made the writing of DIAMOND SIX a
pleasant task.

Library of Congress Catalog Card Number 58-8109
Copyright © 1958 by William Fielding Smith

Author's Foreword

DIAMOND SIX is the true story of a man who carved his destiny out of the wilderness that was Texas in 1844 after being forced to leave his beloved state of Kentucky at the age of fifteen for the killing of the man who murdered his father. It is the story of the Diamond Six cattle brand and the people, some famous, some little known, who stepped down out of the pages of history to play their parts in the making of a great land.

DIAMOND SIX is the story of Wesley Smith, my paternal grandfather, who, as a loyal Texan, fought hard for the Southern cause in the cruel and bloody War of Secession and remained strong and unbowed before the invaders during the long, bitter, and distressful days of Reconstruction. History knows Wesley Smith as a Southern patriot, Texas Ranger, sheriff, gun fighter, planter, and cattleman. To those who treated him justly he was a kind and considerate man; a cruel, relentless, and unforgiving enemy to those who sought to hurt him and the ones he loved.

DIAMOND SIX is also the story of my grandmother, Margaret Arnold Smith, a Connecticut Yankee who became a pioneer Texan.

FOREWORD

This chronicle of Wesley Smith's eventful life was handed down to his son and my father, Eliphlet Arnold (Bubba) Smith, who in turn related it to me many times. It is as true as Bubba's account, as true as the old papers, letters, and documents used in its preparation, and is set down truthfully and faithfully.

In writing DIAMOND SIX, I have made few changes from my earlier recordings of the story, these being mostly dates in slight error or conflict. Nor have I in any way attempted to spare Wesley Smith by omitting events or to justify his deeds by injecting my opinions. Related herein are his loves, his hates, his ambitions, his frustrations, and his battles with circumstances and the lawless element of his time, 1844, when this story opens, to 1902. However, I respect his memory and have endeavored to emulate him during my years at the helm of Diamond Six Ranch, because I believe he justified all the things he did.

WILLIAM FIELDING SMITH

Point Blank, Texas
1957

Contents

Contents

1. The Stranger

JOHN WESLEY SMITH was both merchant and plantation owner of Paris, Kentucky, during the years when the frontier was moving west. He was no visionary, but an intensely practical businessman who believed in freedom and the right to pursue and labor for the future. He talked the cause of Texans in their fight to overthrow Mexican oppression in 1836, and his sons, then seven and nine, listened and learned the meaning of freedom and independence. They learned also that their father was sincerely religious, that he had an abounding faith in people and a love for his neighbors, that he supported President Andrew Jackson's policies on one hand and opposed them on the other. It was a man's duty and privilege.

Smith lived at a time when the way of life in Kentucky was almost wholly Southern. There were land and slaves, a culture emanating from the past aristocracy and economy. He imparted his knowledge of these things, together with his opinions and ideals, to his sons so that they might through a better understanding fully appreciate their heritage, that they might step into his shoes when the time came and carry on. He was a good parent, a good citizen. In the pages of history there is no mention of him, though he is collectively recorded in the accounts of those solid Americans who rose to new situations in a big way, and in doing so laid new foundation stones. He was just another man, but he was a necessary one.

As the years passed, John Wesley Smith continued to prosper. His store had grown in size. Tall rows of shelves bulged with packages and bolts of cloth, shoes, hats, gunpowder, shot, and ammunition. Pistols, rifles, and shotguns graced the walls, temptingly visible from the hide-bottomed chairs surrounding the big potbellied stove in the center of the building, as were fine hand-tooled saddles, bridles, and harness made famous by Kentuckians. At the end of one of the long counters sat the usual barrels of pickles, sugar, crackers, vinegar, and flour. The store helped feed and clothe Paris, Kentucky, and environs. It had weathered and shaped many social and political issues. This was the general store.

The home of the Smiths was typical of the wealthy Southern planter's abode in those antebellum days. The Oaks, it was called, was an enormous brick house of two stories, painted white. Its half-circle portico was supported by six large fluted columns. In a spacious setting of ten acres of lawns and gardens, shaded by great spreading oaks, the Smith house was an imposing place, a mansion dedicated to good living and the hospitality of those great years. The Oaks was the nave, the center, of the Smith plantation, acres upon acres of bluegrass where fine cattle roamed, fields of cotton and corn where the "darkies," as the slaves were called, sang and worked contentedly.

As the spring of 1844 turned into young summer, John Wesley Smith had every reason to look back over the past with the pardonable pride of a man thankful for his many blessings. In a land of good government, despite the increasing sounds of strife between the industrial North and the agricultural South, one's possessions seemed secure. A way of life, useful production, and the pleasure of its traditional living seemed to reach beyond the present, on into the future. There were his sons, Joe seventeen, Wesley about to turn fifteen. Wesley was born to the land, Joe to the store. They did not disappoint their father. Seldom did he look at either of them without a smile on his face. Often the smile would fade pensively away. It was then that his thoughts were of his wife, who had died shortly after bringing his younger son into the world. The years had been lonely without her, though the boys, a part of her, lessened the hurt and somehow filled his heart with fond memories.

All things considered, John Smith admitted that life was worth living. He was able to shed a wise and benevolent influence on the civic, religious, cultural, and political life of the community. He was raising his sons to be men, not mollycoddles, to take their places in society as citizens with ideals shaped for the betterment of mankind. This was the paramount aim. He continued to carve at this niche, more lovingly than dutifully, with the comforting realization that the things worth while he instilled in his sons would be passed on, an annuity payable to future generations. Both of his sons showed the effect of his unassuming guidance, the example placed before them. They were industrious, polite, quick to learn, persevering. They possessed initiative. They had their faults, of course; Joe was a little too hotheaded; Wesley, who looked older than his years, tried to act the part at times. But one did not shape a tree in a day.

So John Smith went about his business with calm, watchful eyes on his store, the cattle in the bluegrass, the young corn and tobacco, his many slaves, the community, and his sons. All looked promising and he could not foresee any interruption in the good plan of life.

Then came the day of June 6, 1844.

The dawn crept up pink in the clear sky that Thursday morning. The mist hanging in the layered distance clung to the woodlands in quiet defiance of the lifting sun. The town of Paris came alive early, as was its habit, seemed to yawn and stretch as it drank in the cool air and surveyed the beginning of another day. A rooster crowed and another answered. A lazy, early-morning breeze stirred the dust in the streets and played gently in the trees. A fine summer's day lay ahead, and the town greeted it with a natural unawareness of the strange pattern fate was weaving in its midst.

Paris could set its clocks at half-past six sharp when John Wesley Smith opened his general store. It was no different this day. Accompanied by his seventeen-year-old son Joe, he entered the store and, after a perfunctory glance around, moved directly to his office. There, in a matter of minutes, he usually brought the past day's business up to the present before moving behind the counters with the alert, inquiring attitude of a businessman examining his wares. He did so this morning, even as Joe followed the normal routine of making the store ready for business.

At seven the Negro dray boy hitched his horse at the rail behind the building and entered the store with the same words as the day before: "Mawnin', Mistuh John. Mawnin', Mistuh Joe."

"Good morning, Sam," said Smith, without turning from a shelf he was examining. "Wesley with you?"

"On his burfday, suh?" It was more an exclamation. "He fifteen today, Mistuh John, an yo' knows Polly ain't 'bout to let him outen de house without feedin' him all she can cook."

John Smith raised his brows and admitted it was so. Smiling through his short beard, he looked at Joe and opened his mouth to speak.

Whatever he was about to say remained a part of him, for entering the store were two men, one a close friend, the other unknown to him. Lewis Traylor, banker of Paris, was a large, though lean man of forty with ruddy face and direct eyes. It was the unusual expression on Traylor's face, a pin-pointed light in his eyes and a tightness about his mouth, that forestalled Smith's greeting and sent his curious glance on to the man he had never before seen.

The stranger appeared to be in his early thirties. Clean-shaven but for a thin, closely cropped mustache, which stood out in contrast to the heavy Kentucky beards; he was tall, wiry, meticulously dressed from gray beaver to highly polished boots. Beyond the purely physical impression, he exuded an air of self-assurance and determination, a bearing in itself impressive and, thought Smith, somewhat militant; or, giving the man benefit of doubt, coldly inscrutable. Perhaps he just looked that way; he might be the type of person who would speak in a warm, friendly manner and change over upon introduction. In any case, Smith knew the error of early judgment.

Traylor cleared his throat. "John, this is Mr. Benjamin Tobin. Mr. Tobin, Mr. Smith."

Smith shook hands warmly, spoke his pleasure, and took mental note of the other's strange indifference.

"I'll come directly to the point, Mr. Smith. My call

here concerns a matter I think we should discuss privately."

The stranger's clipped tone irritated John Smith. "Very well, we'll go to my office." He turned to Traylor. "Come along, Lewis, if you have the time."

Pausing to confer with Joe regarding grocery deliveries, he stepped from behind the counter and ushered the pair into his office. When they were seated, Smith drummed his fingers lightly on the chestnut-oak table and looked at Tobin, who forthwith named the company he represented and launched into his subject:

"I am a lawyer from Albany, New York, here for one purpose, to settle the conflict in boundaries and titles between land owned by my employers and the land you claim title to on the Green River southwest of Owensboro."

Smith had scarcely said, "I didn't know any boundary or title conflict existed," when the sounds of a galloping horse drew his attention. The three men watched a big blood bay stallion come to a sliding halt at the hitching rail, saw a tall young man clad in fringed buckskins, wide-brimmed white hat, and soft, polished boots swing from the saddle and enter the store.

"My younger son, Mr. Tobin," Smith said proudly. "Before we talk further, I'd like you to meet both my boys." Rising, he called out: "Joe, you and Wesley come in here a moment."

The lawyer did not rise when the boys entered, nor did he change his cold expression one iota when Smith presented his sons.

"Sir," he said, "I happen to be a very busy man. I suggest we get on with the business at hand, since you are only one of the land-grabbers I must deal with this week."

John Smith's face underwent a rapid change. The beaming smile was replaced by a look of utter calm that hid the anger seething within him.

"All right, boys," he said quietly, "you'd better go."

Joe Smith stood a moment, glaring at the stranger. In contrast to his glittering eyes and compressed lips, his younger brother's expression and bearing might have indicated that he had not heard the insult. A hint of a smile lingered on Wesley's face as he led the way out of the office. It did not go unnoticed then, and it was not forgotten by any of the three men who saw it, father, friend, and sudden enemy.

Traylor and Smith also saw in the stranger's face a look of strong determination, more like sustained menace, and knew at once they were in the presence of a man who invited trouble, who seemed to bypass politeness purposely, as if he were lowering himself by dealing with inferiors. Smith waited, however, as did Traylor, for a word of apology. They waited in vain.

John Smith closed the door unhurriedly and, ignoring Tobin, walked to the window at the far end of the office where the banker stood chewing his cigar. He gave Traylor a heavy clap on the shoulder as if to relieve himself of pent-up emotion. Then he whirled to face the lawyer.

"Mr. Tobin," he said slowly, "listen carefully, for when I have finished we will both know exactly where we stand. I have never stolen anything in my life, never cheated any man out of the value of anything. Now about the land you mention, my father helped Daniel Boone buy large tracts of land from the Indians for Richard Henderson, president of the Transylvania Land Company. In return for his services, my father was rewarded in land, the land you question. As you know, the Virginia government was also buying large tracts.

"This land was monumented on every line, and the deed to my father contained a description of the monuments. In 1778 the commissioners were sent to Kentucky to examine land titles. As you also know, the government nulled Boone's titles to land secured from Henderson's company. Boone left in disgust, saying, 'I've learned that this thing you call civilization is but an improved plan of overreaching your neighbor.'* So my father rebought his land from the Virginia government. And now you have the gall to speak of me as a land-grabber."

Tobin did not move a muscle of his face or body as Smith paused for breath before he continued:

"We know that without water from Green River any land you and your outfit might see fit to give me would be worthless for cattle range, should I be foolish enough to agree to partial settlement. I tell you here and now, Mr. Tobin, that it is my intention to keep every damned last acre of that land. Now leave quietly and quickly, if you value your cheating Yankee hide, and don't ever come back into this building again."

Without any word, the lawyer continued to eye Smith. Then he got to his feet and moved slowly out of the office. His very silence, the set repose of his face seemed to carry more threat than a volley of words. Smith watched him go, with a feeling that he was not done with this arrogant visitor. Then Tobin was gone and the air cleared and the flush of anger fell away.

"Damn it all, John," began Traylor, "if I had even dreamed——"

* Paper entitled "Early Bourbon Families," compiled by Franklin Warren Houston, 1895.

"Oh, forget it, Lewis, and let's have a drink." John Smith smiled broadly at his friend as he produced a small stone jug and two glasses.

He did not pour at once. Instead, with glass poised in hand, he looked through the window. The morning was yet young; the big tree stood in the same place at the end of the hitching rail; the same sights and sounds of hundreds of yesterdays reminded him that nothing had changed. Yet there was a change. It was in the very air he breathed—a change he could not deny, one brought to Paris on the early breeze of the morning by a stranger.

2. A Birthday Present

JOHN SMITH had no sooner replaced the jug and glasses than Wesley slipped quietly in and took a seat on the high bookkeeper's stool. He asked about Tobin and listened attentively while John Smith related all that had happened, and following that to the argument between Lewis Traylor and his father, which began with the banker's thoughtful remarks:

"John, I reckon you know you've got a fight on your hands. You'll probably lose it too."

He recalled facts: John Smith's father had obtained title to his land when Kentucky was a part of Virginia; since then there had been treaties with the Cherokees, lost records, land suits, and all sorts of manipulations in Washington, many of which favored the land companies.

"Take my advice, John, and go slow. The outfit Tobin works for is big. Maybe you should strike a compromise."

Smith looked his friend squarely in the eye. "As lifelong friends," he said, "we've weathered some pretty rough times together. You don't mean what you're saying." He brought a fist down on the table. "Lewis, I say this—if that land company's power is bigger than our Constitution, and the goat-headed politicians in Washington insist on running the affairs of the individual state, then I'm for quitting the Union."

"That's treason, John! Now you listen to me."

"You listen. Our fathers helped settle this territory. They came here for land and got it—lots of it. Now do you mean to tell me it's not worth fighting for?"

Traylor sat silent a moment. "I guess you're right," he said, resigned. "It may be a fight that will see us both badly hurt, but here's my hand on it."

Wesley grinned when the pair shook hands in pledge of their alliance, then reminded his father that this was the day designated for his biweekly tally of the cattle they had driven from the Green River pastures. So saying, he departed.

Upon reaching the field where the Negroes were chopping and plowing the young corn, Wesley reached into his saddlebags for peppermint candy and dropped a handful into each waiting hand and bonnet. It made little difference that buxom Aunt Polly, slave herself, called them "field niggers"—far below "house niggers" in her foolish but accepted caste system—he loved them all and knew they loved him. Only Aunt Polly made rules, only Aunt Polly broke them to suit her whims. But he loved the bossy old tyrant. She had nursed him as a baby, had been the nearest thing to a mother he had ever known.

When the Negroes began to sing once more, adjusting the speed of hoes and plow mules to the rhythm of the music as they gradually worked away from him, Wesley turned his horse in the direction of the pastures. In his mind was the incident of the morning, and he felt instinctively that Tobin would do his utmost to repay his father for the tongue-lashing he had received. However, since he could arrive at no solution of the trouble, he shook his head to dispel all disturbing thoughts.

Thinking the steers they were finishing for market would probably be grazing toward the water of Little Sandy Creek at this time of day, Wesley gave the big stallion rein and thrilled to the leap as the fine animal took the rail fence in his stride. Upon reaching the trail leading from Paris to Lexington, he slowed the horse and moved up the water's edge at a walk so that the cattle would not become alarmed and scatter.

Suddenly he drew the stallion to a halt. Several hundred yards up the trail and coming directly toward the creek were two riders. Evidently they had not seen him, for as he watched they pulled up at the fence, dismounted, and began taking down a section of the rails. Wesley moved his horse quietly into a grove of chestnut oaks that bordered the stream, dismounted, and led the stallion down into the bed of the creek where they would be protected by the high bank. From his point of vantage he watched as the pair rode a little way upstream toward a herd of big red steers.

Screened by the creek bank, Wesley followed and slipped up to within earshot. Daring a peep over the bank, he recognized one of the men. Benjamin Tobin.

"When can you move these steers out, Judd?" he asked his companion.

"Tonight. Right after dark."

Tobin ordered the man called Judd to drive them northeast toward the Licking River sixteen miles away, then turned his horse toward the gap.

As Wesley stood a moment irresolute, his stallion threw up his head and trumpeted. Instantly both intruders spurred their horses into a dead run. Without any thought other than that of protecting what was his, Wesley brought up his pistol and fired. The man called Judd whirled in the saddle but, slumping forward, held his seat. Then they were gone.

Wesley did not follow them; he knew the danger of being shot from ambush. Giving the stallion his head, he began the four-mile ride back to Paris. He had passed the cigar factory, the Robin Inn, and the stage stop between the two saloons when he saw something that caused him to draw up sharply.

There, in a surrey driving away from the livery barn, sat Benjamin Tobin. Incredible, for how could Tobin have reached town ahead of him and changed clothes? Yet here was Tobin, and he was moving past without showing any sign of recognition.

Minutes later Wesley entered the store and walked directly to his father's office, Joe on his heels. He told them what had happened, and out of the heavy silence that followed, Joe informed Wesley that it could not have been Tobin at the creek, since he had seen Tobin a half hour earlier in the bank, "making a deposit of five thousand dollars in favor of someone named Judd."

"Judd! That's the man I shot! Let's go find Tobin," breathed Wesley.

John Smith's hand fell on Wesley's shoulder. Their eyes met and held, and the father said, "No. Not now."

Smith sat down thoughtfully. "Take it easy, boys. Joe, smooth the temper out of your face. We'll put a watch on the cattle tonight. In the meantime, Wesley, I want you to ride out to the Weavers' place and tell Tom about this. Tell him I want him and his boys to help us out tonight, and that they are invited to supper at The Oaks.

And if you see Tobin, don't say anything to him. Understand?"

As Wesley nodded, his father studied him, admiring all he saw in the tall, broad-shouldered boy. A flicker of hurt crossed his eyes as he thought of his son, just fifteen on that day, having shot a man. Justification did not enter into the heart of John Smith—that was for the mind— the heart grieved that fate had decreed it. Then reason took over.

"What made you shoot that man, Wesley?" he asked. When no reply was forthcoming, just a strong look, as direct as one man could give another, Smith dropped his gaze. "Never mind, son. I know why."

Tom Weaver and his two grown sons arrived at The Oaks about an hour before sundown, the elder Weaver in a surrey drawn by two handsome bays, the boys on stocky cow horses. John Smith, from his seat on the veranda, rose and gave a slight nod to two stableboys lying in the grass at the edge of the driveway. They jumped to take the horses as the men dismounted.

"Just a minute," said Weaver, moving to the back of the vehicle, where he drew a long rifle from a quilt. "Figgered it was best to hide it from prying eyes through town."

They walked into the house. As Joe and Wesley entered the parlor, Aunt Polly waddled in, took their hats, and departed, to continue her supervision of the evening meal. The men ranged themselves about the big room, and Wesley told again of his meeting with the cattle rustlers. After a lengthy discussion, supper was served.

It was almost sunset when they rose from the table and began preparations for the night. Attention was directed to rifles and pistols, and shortly they trooped out the big front door of The Oaks to where the stableboys held their horses. It had been decided that Joe and Wesley would ride with their father and Tom Weaver, taking a route directly across the fields and pastures to the spot where the steers were thought to be. Weaver's boys would ride up the Paris—Lexington road and, after mending the fence where the rustlers entered, would take cover in the trees along Little Sandy Creek. All would rendezvous behind the creek bank and bring their guns to bear on any intruders.

As they mounted, Aunt Polly's huge frame stood in silhouette in the doorway. "Mistuh John, yo'all take good care o' my boys. Hear what I say?"

John Smith heard. His pause seemed more eloquent than any reply.

Darkness quickly settled over the countryside. A thin fog rolled slowly over the pastures. Presently a big moon edged over the horizon and began a fast, steady climb into the sky and the stars began to wink on. A slight breeze eddied the fog, and it swirled away into the trees along Little Sandy Creek.

When they reached a spot about a hundred yards from the course of the creek, the four drew up and Wesley pointed to a bright patch of moonlight between them and the trail, at a herd of fine red steers they had come to protect. As they looked at the cattle standing motionless in the light of the big yellow moon, it seemed they were gazing at a painting instead of an actual scene on a Kentucky plantation. Then the prearranged call of a night bird broke the spell; another night bird answered, a signal that the Weaver boys had reached their position, that all was in readiness.

They waited and continued to wait. The moon had pushed its way high into the heavens when finally Tom Weaver moved close to Wesley's father and said softly,

"Those fellows wouldn't come any later than this, because they have sixteen miles to drive these critters and they want to do their driving during the night. What do you say we call it a night?"

The words were scarcely spoken when the cry of another night bird signaled that the rail fence was being taken down. The rustlers had come. Before the defenders were able to see the horsemen, the cattle nearest the trail began to mill about and push farther into the pasture. Suddenly a steer, frightened by the approaching riders, bolted directly through the herd and set all the cattle in motion, causing a small bunch to wander close to the creek bank under which their guardians stood.

Then the Smiths and Tom Weaver saw the rustlers, eight, nine, perhaps ten of them, all riding slowly so as to cause as little movement as possible in the herd. They were heading directly toward the men standing below the creek bank.

Without waiting for the signal to shoot, Joe suddenly threw up his rifle and fired. The rider nearest him whirled in his saddle and thudded to the ground. Joe's shot caught his companions unaware, and before they could bring rifles to bear the two rustlers closest to the creek spurred their horses into the gloom of the trees and headed downstream in an effort to gain the safety of the trail. Then the firing became general, stampeding the steers.

One of the raiders wheeled his horse toward the gap in the fence in a frantic effort to escape, but three others spurred their mounts directly into the withering fire coming from the creek bank, shooting as they came. Before the first man reached the shadows all three were shot from their running horses and killed.

The fight ended as quickly as it began. A heavy quiet,

weird and unreal, settled over the countryside. Tom Weaver suddenly remembered his sons down the creek in the path of the outlaws who had run away. "Good God!" he exclaimed. "My boys are down yonder." He dashed off, followed by the others, all reloading their pistols as they ran.

They found the two young men sitting on the bank of the creek with a badly wounded man at their feet. As he shuddered and rolled over dead into a patch of moonlight, Wesley recognized him as the man called Judd.

"Well," said John Smith wearily, "that about cleans up a dirty night's work, except for notifying Marshal Hazelett. That damned Yankee will probably try to jail us all."

Tom Weaver offered to notify the marshal as he went through town, and soon he and his two sons set out across the big pasture toward the gate on the trail. Smith and his boys rode directly to The Oaks. As they dismounted, Sam emerged from the shadows and Aunt Polly came to inquire about her charges, Joe and Wesley.

"We're all right, Polly," said John Smith. "Just a little tired and sick over what we had to do tonight. Make some coffee and bring it to the parlor, please." Then he turned to Joe. "I want you to take Sam and a wagon to meet Hazelett. Wesley will stay here with me. Let's have our coffee while Sam hitches the wagon."

Polly soon arrived with coffee. Little was said between the father and his sons as they drank. Then Sam came with the wagon and Joe departed.

Wesley and his father sat in silence several minutes before the latter rose wearily and unbuckled his gun belt. Wesley did the same. They were walking out of the room when they heard a noise on the veranda. Thinking Marshal Hazelett had probably made a mistake regarding the place he was to meet Joe, Smith walked to the door, opened it, and looked out. Standing directly behind him, Wesley saw in that instant the parlor lamp light reflected along the length of a shotgun barrel.

The gun was leveled at his father, and he made a desperate effort to pull him inside. He was too late. A blinding flash and a terrific roar filled the room. Back of that flash Wesley had seen the face of Benjamin Tobin.

John Smith's body whirled from the impact of the load and he sank to the floor at his son's feet. Wesley took one long stride to the table where the lamp sat and, cupping his hand, blew out the light. Then he jerked his pistol from its scabbard and, jumping over his father's body onto the veranda, fired in the direction of running footsteps until his gun was empty. Then he ran back to his father, calling desperately for Aunt Polly.

The waiting for a hurrying rider to return with Dr. Randall seemed an eternity to Wesley. The doctor came, but he was too late. Already Aunt Polly had closed the eyes of her master with big black fingers and raised the coverlet over his face. As the doctor entered the room where the body of John Smith lay and saw Wesley and Joe and the black mammy with faces buried in the coverlet, he backed slowly away and closed the door.

3. From Boy to Man

JOHN WESLEY SMITH had carved his niche in life but had left it unfinished, the tools lying where he had dropped them. The pattern was visible, and in it one saw and felt the design of life. But his departure seemed too sudden, surely an error of destiny. All in one day he had been forced into the position of leader of a fighting faction, a pawn in a mad, bloody game. There was no reason to it; it just happened. One had to accept it.

His funeral service was held at The Oaks on Sunday, June 9, 1844. It was a warm, bright day, and the dead man's hosts of friends filled the big parlor to overflowing long before the service began. As the crowd continued to swell, the men gave their places to the ladies and moved quietly to the veranda.

The windows in the back wall of the parlor opened onto a large rose garden that had been planted by John Smith's young wife. Here among the flowers stood the slaves, heads bared and bowed in complete silence, an occasional tear rolling down a black cheek.

At the appointed time Reverend Milo Walker came

into the room, followed by Lewis Traylor and the murdered man's two sons. Traylor and the boys slipped
quietly onto a davenport near the hallway door. As they
seated themselves, Aunt Polly, dressed in her shiny black
taffeta, edged in behind them and stood with kinky head
bowed low on her ample bosom.

Standing straight and firm beside the black casket,
Reverend Walker belied his silvery hair and seventy-six
years, and when he spoke his voice was not that of an
old man but of a strong and courageous soldier.

"My friends," he began, "fifteen years ago, almost to
the hour, I stood in this very room and said the burial
service over a brave and wonderful young woman. She
was the wife of the man we are here to pay our last
respects to this morning. There are many of us here who
well remember when this fine young couple came to make
their home in our community. Both vibrant, full of life,
happy, and honest. And we felt better and cleaner for
their having come our way. Although John Smith was
blessed with the goods of this world far and above the
average man, he remained meek, humble, and reverent
in God's sight. In my long years of service to the Church
I have wondered many times why so many fine, righteous
people have been taken from our midst long before their
promised span of threescore years and ten."

As the old minister talked, the servants outside the
back windows began to hum softly. There was no individual sound, but a blend of harmony that only Negro
voices can lend to a spiritual such as "Swing Low." The
music seemed to float into the room as though it issued
from a distant organ.

"Speaking not as a servant of God, but as friend to
friend, I want to tell you that I have observed not only
this man but many more like him, who came to this

bountiful state of Kentucky and fought hard and honestly to win from this good earth the right to live and prosper. There have been other men, with distorted ideas of honesty and decency, who have been just as determined that these builders of a new land would not gain and hold their rightful belongings. On the one hand, it is only healthy and natural that differences of opinions arise on political questions and issues. Doubtless there are some among you that differ on these things. But I dare say, my friends, there is not one among you who would resort to violence, thievery, and corruption in order to achieve your purpose.

"All of you gathered here were friends of this man. If you have differed with him on political and social questions, I pray your forgiveness for the theme I have taken, but as I walked into this room and took my place here at my dead friend's side I thought of the valiant fight he, and so many more like him, waged against the loss of individual rights which they came to this section of our great nation to achieve. So it has been down through the ages, Christian men and women pioneering and building the land, those who are weak and cowardly and greedy following in their wake to snatch from them the hard-won trophies. The way of life, here and in other Southern states, is something our Northern neighbors would like very much to have, but they would not be capable of comprehending the responsibilities that accompany it. They refuse to see the real kindness, understanding, and generosity of the Southern man. They see only what they want to see, a man with a whip in one hand, a gun in the other."

Little murmurs ran through the crowd. Reverend Walker heard them. It gave him a grim satisfaction to realize that the crowd was reacting just as he had planned.

He had known and loved John Smith for many years and he was determined to use his death as a whipping post to stir the people of Kentucky.

"John Smith," he continued, "will not be here to see the day, not too far in the future, when the Southern states will grow weary of the injustices they are bearing. No, John Smith will not be here to see that day, but his death at the hand of paid assassins will be another weight on the scales which will hasten the hour. Let us then, no matter what our political views and personal aspirations, reaffirm and rededicate our lives on the predicate that we are really free men. Let us give our neighbor the privilege of thinking for himself, acting for himself, so long as his thoughts and actions are based in integrity."

He raised his hand high to give the benediction.

"O merciful God, bring your blessings to this home. Bless these fine young men who will live here. Bless their servants and their friends. Give them the strength to face the world with courage and honesty, and help them in their efforts to carry on the good work their father did in the time allotted him on this earth. And, Heavenly Father, teach us all understanding. Bestow upon us the capacity to accept the cruelties of fate but, O God, please consider that, being human, we can only measure these cruelties with man's own yardstick. We beseech your eternal blessings on our friend. May he rest forever in your sight. Amen."

Wesley seemed lost in a trance. Every word Reverend Walker had spoken blended with the things his father had said to him over the years. There was no confusion of mind in Wesley Smith then, but a clear picture of the close past and all that the future entailed. He was a boy in years, a man in hurt and grief and in the acceptance of a responsibility.

4. Destiny's Hand

THE day of Tuesday, June 11, 1844, was one Wesley Smith would never forget. It began wet and blustery, as if the elements sounded a warning of all that was to follow.

Joe left early to open the store, and Wesley, in bed, watched the wind-lashed rain beating against the windows. The torrent of water reminded him of Joe's unbridled fury when he learned of his father's murder. Thinking of his brother's vow to kill Tobin, Wesley realized that, unless he intervened, Joe in a sudden passion might rush blindly into a trap set by Tobin, who would kill him and claim, with some justification, self-defense. This must not happen, he told himself over and over.

The memory of the funeral lingered all too fresh in Wesley's mind. John Smith had been placed at rest beside his wife in the little churchyard on the outskirts of Paris, and Lewis Traylor had driven them home. Lingering over coffee at The Oaks, Traylor had renewed the pledge made to John Smith on the day of Tobin's visit. "And heaven help me, I'll never back away from it."

"I'll never back away from it," promised Wesley.

[31]

Wesley began his breakfast alone. Brooks, the butler, served him in silence. Dude Justice, the overseer, came to talk about certain operations. Alone again, remembering with a sudden pang of hurt that his father was dead, he pushed the food away, rose, and buckled on his gun belt.

The rainstorm ceased before Wesley mounted his stallion, though water ran brown and strong in the ditches along the trail as he rode toward Paris. Long narrow lakes separated the corn rows flanking the road, and at the ford a gushing stream flowed over the trail. He entered Paris as the Lexington stage pulled up at the freight office. The handlers were changing the "six-up" for the twenty-mile run to Lexington, and Wesley paused to study the passengers emerging from the coach.

A distinguished white-haired man with side whiskers was helping his wife to the ground. Then he was handing down a pretty brown-haired young lady whose radiant expression, together with a delightful rustle of her petticoats, caused Wesley to straighten in the saddle for a better view. She was worth a long second look, he mused, combing his hair with his fingers and adjusting his hat in an act of unconscious preening.

He did not see the white-haired gentleman light a cigar, turn, and collide with one of the four darkly tanned men in homespun moving toward the coach. Wesley's first inkling of trouble came when the roughly clad man struck the other to the ground. In another moment the older man was up and fighting. Then, by some miracle of chance, he was sitting astraddle on his assailant.

When one of the remaining three men drew a knife and rushed to the aid of the man on the ground, Wesley spurred his horse forward. As the stallion's hoofs struck the ground in their midst, the ruffians fell back.

"Nobody likes that kind of knife play, mister," said Wesley evenly. "Now get on the stage, all of you, and don't look back."

The man on the ground got to his feet slowly and fixed his baleful gaze on the young horseman.

"Just a damned boy. I'm a mind to pull you off that horse and learn you a lesson."

He made a step to do just that, though something in the pair of calm brown eyes and the half-smile on the boy's lips checked him. It was then he saw Wesley's hand resting easily on the butt of his pistol.

The old stage driver's drone, "We're gonna roll, we're gonna roll," broke the tension. The men climbed aboard, and the horses responded to the driver's whipcrack.

"Young man," said the white-haired stranger, "allow me to thank you. My name is Eliphlet Arnold. This is my wife and our daughter Margaret."

Following the introductions, Arnold asked if Wesley was, perchance, John Smith's son. He saw the boy's look of pain and heard that John Smith had been buried Sunday morning.

"But, son, your father wrote me only a few weeks back inviting us to Paris."

"The invitation stands," smiled Wesley, daring another look at Margaret Arnold.

As Wesley ushered the Arnolds into the store office, Joe and Lewis Traylor stood, the latter beaming before rushing with extended hand to renew an acquaintance of several years. The banker had once visited in the Arnold's Connecticut home.

Traylor briefly described the circumstances that had led to John Smith's death and, to the surprise of both Traylor and Wesley, Arnold seemed horrified that such lawlessness still existed even here in Kentucky, which he

considered the very fringe of civilization. That man
would kill man to settle differences of any sort was beyond his comprehension, and he gave them to know
that he did not approve of the manner in which John
Smith and Tom Weaver and their sons had killed the
cattle thieves.

Although Wesley could not understand how any man
could fail to recognize the importance of defending his
possessions, he was glad Joe had occupied himself with
chores in the store, for such an opinionated expression
would have provoked his brother to speak rashly. Wesley
realized that words were cheap and he was determined
to remain calm in the company of the pretty girl at his
side.

Margaret Arnold evoked in Wesley strange and con-
fusing emotions, causing no end of speculation as to just
what was happening to him. He heard himself praised
for his part in the fight at the stage office and then heard
Traylor hotly defend the course of action taken in the
fight with the rustlers. All the while he was stealing
glances at Margaret Arnold.

Finally he asked if she would like to see the store, and
she in turn whispered to her mother. Once in the store
with her, he began to feel at ease in her company, and
it seemed they had scarcely exchanged a few words and
glances when Margaret's mother came to advise they
were ready to drive out to The Oaks.

A little later Joe and Wesley stood watching the surrey
carrying the Arnolds turn onto the main road.

"Pretty little girl, isn't she, Wes?"

Wesley jerked his glance around to Joe's grinning face.
"What do you mean, little? She's nearly as old as I am.
Lives in Haddom, Connecticut. Her people don't like it

there, so they plan to move to Savannah, Georgia, as soon
as——"

"Boy!" Joe interposed. "You really found out all there
was to know."

Feeling the color diffusing his face, Wesley turned
toward the store. He had not taken two full steps when
Joe's hand on his arm brought him to a halt.

"Look, Wes, I've got to talk to you about Tobin."

"You stay away from Tobin, Joe."

"That's what I want to talk about. Listen, I know I've
got a quick temper, one that has caused you to pull me
out of a lot of scrapes. But this is one time I have sense
enough to know we must work together.

"Tobin is coming to town this afternoon. I heard Ned
Barker tell Mr. Traylor he saw him on the Lexington road
and that he sent word he might just come in and kill Mr.
Traylor."

"For what? Why? There's no reason for that, so it must
be a trap of some kind. You stay at the store, Joe. Inside.
I'm going out and see that Aunt Polly has everything
fixed for the Arnolds. Now, no matter what happens, I want
your promise that you won't leave the store."

"I promise. You be careful too, Wes."

It was approaching noon when Wesley dismounted to
open the gates at The Oaks. He was thinking that the
bell calling the slaves to the midday meal would ring
any minute, when he looked up the Lexington road and
saw a rider approaching at a leisurely gait. Curious, he
put the latch chain back in place and waited.

There was something vaguely familiar about the man
coming on so nonchalantly. Wesley stood with eyes
fixed on the rider until he drew close enough for identification. Then he felt a surge of hot blood at his temples.

The man was Benjamin Tobin, and he rode with his gaze on the trail, as though unaware of Wesley's presence.

Wesley loosened the big revolver in his scabbard and took a few short steps to the edge of the trail. As Tobin drew near he called, "You, Tobin, pull up!"

Tobin looked up with more surprise than recognition in his eyes. His next expression seemed nothing short of contempt—and that brief—as he rode on past Wesley without any change of pace.

Wesley bounded into his saddle and soon drew alongside Tobin. "I told you to stop, you murdering coward! Now get down off that horse!"

"What do you want of me, boy? If it's robbery, I have but little money on me——"

"You know mighty well what I want. I'm going to kill you for murdering my father. Now get off that horse or I'll shoot you off." He laid his hand on his gun.

Tobin's face went white, but he dismounted and leaned against his horse for support. "I didn't kill your father, boy. That I swear. Besides, I'm unarmed. You speak of murder. Now would you murder me?"

"I can fix that," said Wesley as he slipped to the ground. "I'll get you a gun."

He walked quickly under the stallion's neck to his saddlebags with a total disregard of Tobin, who stood with his back to him. Wesley had not quite produced the gun he had promised when Tobin whirled, a small pistol in his hand, and pulled the trigger. A great wind jerked at Wesley's sleeve as the lead tore through his buckskin jacket.

His own gun flashed, and instantly a look of fear and bewilderment spread over Tobin's face. Then he collapsed and fell heavily, face down in the muddy trail.

Wesley took a backward step as Tobin crashed into the

mud. The big stallion quivered and breathed excitedly but did not move as Tobin's horse bolted up the trail, drawing an eddy of blue gun smoke in his wake. The boy looked down at the dead man and felt suddenly sick.

He managed somehow to get his revolver back in its scabbard and grasp the pommel of the saddle with both hands. The strength left his legs and a weakness crept up his body until his hands released their hold and he dropped to his knees in the muddy trail. He wondered vaguely where his strength had gone. Where was his command of mind and muscle; where was the satisfaction he had anticipated in killing this man beside him? Suddenly he retched and it gagged him horribly. Closing his eyes tightly, he reached for the handkerchief he carried in his waistband.

As he moved his arm, something stung his shoulder and he realized that he had been wounded. In the excitement he had not noticed it before. He managed to put a hand to his shoulder, and it came away sticky and crimson, but the sight of his own blood seemed to bring back some of his strength. He fought to regain his feet and, thankful that the bay stood still, pulled himself weakly into the saddle, and headed for the plantation gates.

Wesley finally opened the gates by leaning far down in the saddle. Then, leaving them open, he let the stallion go in a swinging gallop toward the big house on the hill.

That was the last he remembered until he opened his eyes in his own bed to the wailing of Aunt Polly, who kept saying over and over, "They done killed my boy, done killed him!" He was thankful for Mrs. Arnold's presence of mind then, for she was working to stop the flow of blood. There seemed no interval of time between her dressing the wound and the arrival of Joe, Traylor, and Dr. Randall.

The doctor declared Wesley lucky. It was just a flesh wound, he said, but a close call. A little rest after the loss of so much blood would see him up and about within a few days. With his departure, Wesley looked at Joe.

"We saw Tobin's body on the trail, Wes. You made a good job of it, but I'm sorry he hurt you."

Wesley shuddered, closed his eyes. Upon opening them, he said, "I hope I never have to shoot another man as long as I live."

"Amen." That was Lewis Traylor's speech.

When Wesley awoke, only Margaret and Aunt Polly were in the room, a tray of food and steaming coffee in the latter's hands.

"So yo' did wake up. Thank de Lawd. Now I'se gonna feed my boy."

Wesley said he could feed himself, though Aunt Polly remained firm until Margaret asked if she could do it. Wesley did not object to this, so the old Negress agreed. She stood a little apart, watching, a crafty, white-toothed smile forming on her face. Suddenly she burst out laughing.

"Lawdy, Mistuh Wes, yo'all don't act like yo' just been shot. More like a love bug done bit yo'."

Still laughing, she ambled out of the room, leaving Wesley red of face and Margaret staring at the tray of food.

Wesley broke the embarrassed silence between them by saying, "Don't pay any attention to Aunt Polly. You never know what she's going to say next."

As he stole a glance at Margaret, she looked up at him and in that moment he was wondering if Aunt Polly hadn't been right after all. When Margaret left him a little later he continued to think about it.

After a fitful sleep Wesley experienced a strange feeling of exhilaration, then wonderment. Perhaps he had

dreamed it, Margaret's presence in his room and the shooting of Tobin. Perhaps the loss of blood did that to one.
The same joy and the same sense of dread assailed him.
Margaret and Tobin, conflicting emotions, all in one morning; it seemed a little too much.

As he lay in his bed and listened to the noises of the
house, he tried in vain not to think of Benjamin Tobin.
His conscience was clear, since he had fired only after the
man had shot him. The knowledge that his own revolver
was still in the holster when Tobin's bullet struck him
gave him little peace, though he knew he had followed
the code, that he was not a murderer. He refused to think
of these things and concentrated on Margaret. She
evoked happy thoughts and he welcomed them.

It was just as well that he crowded the shooting of Tobin
out of his mind that afternoon; Margaret not only gave
him a brief respite from worry but completely shadowed
his mind from concern about the immediate future. Not
once did Marshal Hazelett or the laws created for such
offenses enter his thoughts. When they did, it was sudden,
in the shape of the marshal himself.

Hazelett was a tall, swarthy-faced man with cold eyes
as black as his flowing tie and wide-brimmed hat. His
knee-length boots and gun belt, supporting two heavy
pistols, were equally black. Only the silver star on his
waistcoat and the glitter in his eyes were bright.

He was ushered into the bedroom by Joe, Traylor, and
Arnold. After politely asking the ladies to leave the room,
he stood with thumbs in belt, looking at Wesley.

"Did you know that Benjamin Tobin had a twin
brother?" he asked.

"No, sir. Why do you ask that?"

"Because Benjamin Tobin was playing cards at the

Robin Inn the night your father was shot. He was there for several hours. I know, because I was there."

Wesley felt sick and cold until Traylor told Hazelett that Benjamin Tobin was responsible for all that had happened; that his brother, if he had one, was simply a hireling.

"But, Marshal," Traylor went on, "why don't you ask this boy who fired first, he or Tobin?"

"Tobin shot me before I drew my gun, Mr. Hazelett," Wesley broke in, "but I'll admit——"

"Shut up, Wes!" Joe cried.

"I'll finish your remark for you," said the officer. "You were about to admit that you forced Tobin to draw his pistol first, knowing all the time you were going to outdraw him and kill him. It just happened that he drew faster than you expected and you got a little flesh wound. You murdered him and I'm placing you under arrest. Don't attempt to leave this house without my permission."

He turned to leave the room but found Traylor, eyes blazing, blocking his way.

"Just a minute, Hazelett," he said. "You're going to listen to me. Wesley Smith killed the man responsible for his father's death. Benjamin Tobin murdered John Smith as surely as we are in this room. As one of this boy's many friends, I do not propose to stand idly by and allow you or any other hireling of Tobin's thieving group to persecute a youngster who has acted in defense of himself and his family. Now get out."

Eliphlet Arnold said surprisingly, "That's right."

Hazelett, now thoroughly angry, moved to the foot of the bed and glared at Wesley a moment before almost spitting the words between clenched teeth:

"I want to tell you something, boy. In my book you murdered a man in cold blood. You're going to stand trial for murder if I have to chase you all the way to Texas and back. I'll be back for you day after tomorrow and you'll go before Judge Fowler for arraignment."

He stood a moment to let his words sink home, then stalked out of the room. He left in his wake a heavy silence and a dark outlook for the future, for he represented law and order, however biased and twisted his version of it might be.

Wesley sank back on his pillow with a strange mixture of feeling and emotion. In conflict with the teachings of his dead father, to respect not only the law but its physical arm, was the growing conviction that his appearance before the pompous judge would be tantamount to years of imprisonment even if he escaped with his life. As these things ran through his mind, the words of Tobin sounded again out of memory: "I didn't kill your father, boy. That I swear."

The day had begun in storm. It was ending in storm, for if Wesley could believe Tobin and Hazelett, he had killed the wrong man.

5. As Fate Willed It

On the morning of Thursday, June 13, 1844, Wesley arrived at the store at around seven. This was the day Hazelett had promised to take him before Judge Fowler, and he had given the situation careful study, debating on the course he should follow. It was as if his dead father had risen from the grave with patient advice, so deeply instilled were his teachings in the boy; he seemed to speak to Wesley, telling him to abide by the law, that he would win despite all Hazelett and Fowler could do. Wesley intended to go before the judge voluntarily, before the marshal could invoke arrest. The very fact that he did not on that day, or ever, go before the judge was due to circumstances beyond his control.

The moment he entered the store Joe beckoned urgently from the office door. Tom Weaver awaited him and without any preliminaries plunged into the matter that had brought him to town so early. Weaver had been in the Robin the night before and had heard enough to convince him that the land company's crowd was determined to see Wesley convicted of murder.

"Now I know John taught you boys not to run away

from anything or anybody, but there comes a time when a man has to run in order to be able to fight back. You think about it, and remember this, the old-timers around here don't intend to let a thing like this happen to you without a fight. So if you're determined to stay, you'll have lots of help, but there'll be a heap o' trouble."

Weaver added, "It's up to you, Wes. You make the decision."

Joe stood on one foot, the other resting on a chair rung, his gaze fixed anxiously on his brother.

After a thoughtful silence Wesley looked up. "I don't want any of you in trouble on my account, Mr. Weaver. But if I run away I'm guilty to all but my friends who know the truth. Maybe I'm wrong, but I believe I can talk to Judge Fowler. Maybe he won't even hold me for trial after I tell him the truth about the whole thing."

"Now I know better than that," said Weaver, bringing a fist down hard to a palm. At that moment Marshal Hazelett appeared in the doorway.

"Good morning," he said gruffly, looking at Wesley. "I'm as good as my promise. I've come to take you before Judge Fowler on a little matter of murder. Ready to go?"

"I'm ready, but I'm going by myself, Mr. Hazelett. You're not going to take me."

"Well, now," the marshal said. "Since you won't go with me, guess I'll just have to take you, sonny."

Just as he dropped a hand roughly on Wesley's shoulder, Joe leaped forward and swung a fist to his jaw. Hazelett went down. On his back, he reached for his pistol, but Joe kicked his hand savagely, sending the gun spinning into a corner. In another second Joe sat atop Hazelett's stomach, his fists pounding the officer's face.

Slowly Weaver got up and pulled Joe to his feet. When

Hazelett did not move, but lay unconscious, Weaver stroked his chin.

"Well, boys," he said thoughtfully, "looks like both of you will have to get out of the country for a while. Hazelett is a bad man, and if you stay you'll have to kill him or get killed."

"How can both of us leave, Mr. Weaver?" Wesley asked, raising a hand in protest. "Everything we own is here!"

Placing a big hand on the shoulder of each boy, Weaver replied calmly, "How can either of you stay now?"

The cold truth struck home then. Wesley looked at Joe, who was still breathing heavily as he glared at the marshal. Hazelett was stirring. "All right, Mr. Weaver. But will you get Mr. Traylor and meet us at The Oaks in about an hour?"

"Sure, son, but what about him?" Weaver pointed at Hazelett.

Without a word Wesley removed a handkerchief from his waistband and gagged the marshal. Then he bound Hazelett's hands and feet with heavy wrapping twine from the dry-goods counter. When the job was finished, Weaver laughed and said he would send someone to "find the bully" in an hour or so.

"Maybe Sam here," he said, turning a glance on the frightened Negro.

"Naw, suh, not me! Don't know nothin' 'bout it. I'se goin' to fetch the horses."

Hazelett was regaining his senses when Wesley knelt to test the thongs binding him. His cold black eyes conveyed hate and threat, and Wesley studied him unhurriedly.

"I didn't want to do this, Mr. Hazelett," he said softly. "When I came here today it was not to resist arrest but to go see Judge Fowler by myself. You know I'm not a murderer. And now I'm going to tell you something else, mister—don't you ever come after me again. If you do, I'll probably let you find me."

Joe, Weaver, and Traylor reached The Oaks ahead of Wesley. They were busy rolling camp packs when he arrived. Aunt Polly was calling the Arnolds down to breakfast in the big dining room, and Wesley decided to join them, as did his brother and the two friends. Minus any appetite, but knowing with a pang of regret that it might be a long time before he would taste Aunt Polly's cooking again, Wesley tried to eat. A heavy silence hung over the room until the big Negress said:

" 'Tain't none o' my business, Mistuh Wes, but I'se got to know where yo'all is goin' and how long yo' gonna be gone, 'cause I'se got to run this heah place whilst yo'all is gone."

"I don't know, Aunt Polly," he replied gravely. Then he looked at the banker. "I suppose you know more about Father's business than anyone else, Mr. Traylor. And Mr. Weaver knows more about crops and slaves than anybody around Paris. What I'm getting around to is this—Joe and I would sure appreciate it if you gentlemen would run the store and The Oaks for us until we can come back."

Traylor folded his arms on the table and said, "Tom and I talked about it on the way out here, Wesley. It's quite a responsibility, but it's also our duty. That's the way we feel, isn't it, Tom?" With Weaver's reply, he continued, "Now don't you boys think it would be a good idea to call Dude Justice in here and tell him we are going to be in charge?"

The boys admitted the wisdom of the banker's suggestion, and Wesley walked out of the room to dispatch a boy on the errand. As he turned from the front door he saw Margaret and, knowing she had followed him, led her into the parlor.

He was about to speak when Joe's cry broke the spell: "Wes! Somebody's coming through the gates—could be old Hazelett."

Margaret pushed Wesley toward the door with "Hurry—and take good care of yourself," just as Weaver and Traylor ran into the hallway, the former ordering Joe and Wesley to their horses.

"If it's Hazelett, we'll try to detain him. You boys come to my place after dark. Sam will be there with the packs and Lewis will bring you some money. Now get going!"

Aunt Polly barred the way, tears streaming down her black cheeks. "Mistuh Wes, Mistuh Joe," she cried, hugging them close, "dis ole nigger don't know what she gonna do widout yo'all, but please take care o' Aunt Polly's boys. The Lawd bless yo' both. Bless yo'!"

The two brothers departed amid hurried farewells and rode a back trail to the edge of a wooded knoll across the valley back of the house. The big white house under the bright summer sun stood majestically on the high, flat-topped hill a half mile in the distance. Surrounding it were green fields and pastures broken only by trees, zigzag rail fences that seemed to march up and down the hills, the neatly painted slave quarters, and grazing cattle.

They looked long and wistfully at the scene spread out before them, as if intent on capturing a permanent picture of the only home they had ever known. Only God knew when they would ever see it again. Something of what both felt was put into trembling voice by Joe:

"Damn Hazelett! Damn him to hell!"

They rode on into the timber, where they remained until late afternoon. As they emerged into the open, Joe raised a telescope and identified the Negro on horseback leading pack animals as Sam. Then slowly, watchfully, they rode toward Tom Weaver's place and intercepted

Sam. After telling him he was to accompany them, they ordered him to continue south and leave plenty of sign.

Toward dusk they discovered a number of riders approaching Tom Weaver's place. Through the telescope Wesley watched Hazelett, at the head of ten armed men, ride up to Weaver's home. The distance, even under the glass, was too great to observe any details, but they saw Hazelett dismount and follow Weaver into the house. Several of his men rode completely around the building and others went into the big barn. After long minutes the marshal came out, mounted his horse, and rode to the door of the barn. Six of his men had gone into the building. Now only two came out.

"Well, well," Wesley said, smiling, "he has baited his trap. Now all we have to do is ride down there and fall into it."

Joe said nothing, nor did he so much as look at Wesley.

"I told Hazelett not to ever come after me again," continued Wesley. "I told him I'd probably let him find me. But, Joe, I don't want to shoot him or anyone else." What he said next brought Joe's glance around: "Except the man who murdered our father."

Soon Hazelett and all but the four men secreted in the barn departed. When day darkened into full night, Wesley left Joe with the horses and crossed a rail fence into the trees along a creek. Emerging on the opposite side, he made his way cautiously through the screen of trees to the opening in front of Weaver's house. There he saw Tom Weaver edging toward the creek and hailed him in low tones.

"That you, Wesley?" Meeting with the reply he wished to hear, he said, "Stay low—Hazelett planted four men in the barn."

Soon the pair were joined. Weaver unbuckled two belts heavy with gold. "Five thousand dollars in each one, Wesley. Now, where are you boys going?"

"I don't know. Just south, Mr. Weaver. Probably Texas."

Weaver said nothing for a full minute. "Well, it's a tough, rough place, I hear. But Texas offers a lot of opportunities, son—if you survive. You'd better be on your way. Write Lewis and me when you can—and the little Arnold girl. I put her Savannah, Georgia, address in your belt. She cried when you left, Wesley."

Wesley looked deep into the night, then held out his hand. Weaver took it, held it as he gave advice: they should ride at night and keep off the main trails until they were three or four days from Paris; Hazelett was determined to find them.

"God bless you and Joe, son."

Wesley swallowed hard. His eyes seemed to cloud up and he was afraid his voice would tremble if he tried to speak. So he pressed Weaver's hand hard and turned away into the night. He did not go directly to Joe but stood for some time on the other side of the creek, looking down toward where Texas lay, far off and beckoning. Then he looked toward Paris and The Oaks and Margaret Arnold.

What had happened? he asked himself. Why had fate singled him out, crooked a finger at him? There was no answer.

6. On the Road to Texas

THE Smith boys rode at night and with each sunrise
ate the breakfast that Sam prepared over a smokeless fire.
Bacon, beans, biscuit, and hot coffee tasted good in the
open. While Sam spread their bedrolls the boys hobbled
their horses and turned them loose to graze. They slept
by day and began packing about an hour before each sunset. Then as the shadows crept over the misty blue hills
they swung into their saddles again.

After four days of riding back trails they decided there
was nothing to be feared from Marshal Hazelett and ven-
tured boldly onto the main roads. Traveling was easier,
and they encountered only one band of Indians, a hunting
party of friendly Coushattas. Soon they were riding days
and sleeping nights.

On the afternoon of Friday, June 28, they entered the
town of Gallatin, Tennessee, to buy supplies and learn
what they could about the Republic of Texas. At a hitch-
rail in front of a general store they dismounted and
climbed the steps to the store gallery. Sam followed them
inside after securing the horses, and stood behind Joe

while Wesley passed the time of day with the storekeeper.

"Now, Sam," said Wesley at last, "you tell the gentleman what we need to run us for four or five days. Feed us good, Sam."

"Yassuh, Mistuh Wes." As Sam named the needed supplies, the merchant stacked them on the counter until the order was completed.

Wesley wandered about with Joe, looking at the various items in stock. He knew this store was making Joe homesick.

He extracted several gold coins from his money belt while in the back of the store. Then he adjusted his jacket as they made their way to Sam and the supplies, and watched the Negro walk out with the first load. When the merchant turned the paper on which he had added their bill, Wesley looked at the figures and dropped two of the coins on the counter. The storekeeper was in the act of making change when Sam hurried back into the store, the supplies still in his arms.

"Mistuh Wes," he whispered, "I just seen dat marshal comin' up de street. What we gonna do, Mistuh Wes?"

Wesley thought a moment. "Go right on packing, Sam. Maybe he will ride by and not recognize our horses. But if he does and asks you where we are, tell him we're in one of the stores across the street. We'll be watching, and if he goes to the other side, you untie our horses, for we'll be coming out. When he starts after us, you get out of town as fast as you can, and we'll meet you after sundown about three miles back on the trail. Be sure and leave some sign. Don't build a fire. We'll find you, so just stay put."

Sam turned and walked out to the horses as Wesley and Joe moved slowly to where the merchant stood straightening the stock on his shelves. The storekeeper was evidently unaware of Sam's recent state of excitement, for he gave the brothers an affable smile as Wesley swung up on the counter to sit where he could command a better view of the street.

"Which is the best way to Texas?" Wesley asked.

"Most folks," replied the man, "head for Natchez over on the Mississippi. From there they either ferry across the river and take the Old Southern Trail through Shreveport, Louisiana, or they take a boat down to Lakeland, Louisiana, and go into southeast Texas over the Atascocita Trail. The first way will take you into Nacogdoches, Cincinnati, Huntsville, and on to the west. The other goes into Houston and Harrisburg and on west to San Antonio. Which part of Texas you aiming for?"

Before Wesley could reply, Marshal Hazelett rode up to the hitching rack, dismounted, and tied his horse. He did not once look toward their horses, but when Sam raised an arm and pointed across the street they realized that the marshal had engaged the Negro in secret conversation. Hazelett stood a minute looking at the stores before putting a long cigar between his teeth and moving casually across the street.

As the officer moved up the steps of one of the stores, Sam quickly pulled the slipknots and threw them over the horses' necks. Joe and Wesley walked quietly out of the store without a backward glance at the merchant, sprang into their saddles, and raced back up the trail to the north.

They looked back in time to see the marshal run into the street and level one of his revolvers. They saw the puff of smoke as he fired and heard the whine of the slug as it passed. He did not fire again but ran to his horse.

"He'll come after us, and Sam can get the pack horses out of sight," said Wesley as they turned a curve in the trail. A short distance ahead they made a second turn. At the bottom of a little hill Wesley pulled his horse into a creek and headed downstream. They rode perhaps fifty yards out of sight of the trail, then reined the mounts out of the running water. Without a word both boys dismounted and held their horses with a close bridle to prevent them from neighing as the officer rode by. They heard Hazelett's horse gallop down the trail, hit the creek with a splash, and head on north.

"Wait here, Joe," Wesley said. "He will probably stop on that ridge up there and come back." He passed the reins to Joe and slipped away up the creek toward the trail.

As Wesley had surmised, Hazelett drew up short a little distance up the trail and began backtracking. He was no amateur at reading sign, Wesley realized, for he studied the water for silt and red sand swirling in the current, sure marks left by horses. After a minute's inspection from the saddle Hazelett reined his horse about suddenly and raced downstream.

Taken by surprise, aware that he could not warn Joe before the marshal tore down upon him, Wesley fell flat in the brush until Hazelett passed, then leaped up and ran after him. Fearing for Joe, hoping he would not attempt to draw against the officer, Wesley forced a sudden burst of speed just as Hazelett stopped his horse at the water's edge. In doing so, the man hunter unwittingly placed himself in the position of the hunted.

Wesley drew his pistol. "All right, Marshal," he called out, "just throw your guns down and don't turn around."

Slowly Hazelett's hands dropped to his holsters. Then, all in one swift motion, he jerked a gun free, fell to the side of his horse, and fired. Almost in the same instant Wesley's gun roared. Hazelett struck the ground heavily and clapped a hand to his shoulder.

Wesley looked up from the fallen man to see Joe standing close with his rifle leveled.

"No, Joe! No!" yelled Wesley. "Don't shoot. Let's see how badly he's hurt."

With Joe's gun leveled at the marshal, Wesley bent to examine the wound. It bled freely, though not dangerously, and he bound it with Hazelett's shirt. There was anything but gratitude in the officer, who glared at Wesley and said:

"You won't get away from me, boy. You should know that I'm going to bring you back if it takes the rest of my life."

"Look, Mr. Hazelett," said Wesley, "I told you once that if you came looking for me I'd let you find me. Well, I kept my word, despite the fact that I let you chase me from The Oaks. Now I'm telling you something more. Trail me one more mile and I'll kill you."

"If I don't do it first," said Joe grimly.

After binding the officer's hands with his own rope, Joe and Wesley lifted him in the saddle and put a loose hobble on the horse's forefeet to hold him to a slow walk.

"Remember, Marshal," Wesley said just before he slapped the horse on the rump, "just one more mile and you're a dead man."

Following this experience with the determined marshal, they traveled only at night until supplies began to run low, then warily entered Aberdeen, Mississippi, one day and tied up at the rail before a large frame building bearing the legend:

ROBERT JAMES McGOWEN, *General Merchandise*

McGowen himself met them with a cordial greeting. A big ruddy-faced Scotch-Irishman, he responded to their questions about Texas with enthusiasm. He had been there and he was going back to stay, he told Wesley. "The greatest place on earth, my lads," he went on, declaring his intention to settle in the eastern part of Texas along a river known as the Trinity. "Wonderful rich country, broad and flat for miles before rolling into green hills."

McGowen was as hospitable as he was voluble. He took them to his plantation home on the Tombigbee, and after a big supper told them about the trails, towns, stream crossings, and all the hazards of the journey, as well as the names of trustworthy people along the way. But most of all, it seemed, he pin-pointed the land they should see first.

" 'Tis the new frontier, lads. That it is. The day is coming when the government will free the slaves. It's ruin for the plantation then. So it's to Texas I'm going, where a man is rugged and has a purpose and thinks and acts for himself."

Joe and Wesley spent several days with the McGowens. They wrote Traylor, Weaver, and Aunt Polly, and Wesley penned a long message to Margaret Arnold.

One night after they had retired, the boys discussed the sale of The Oaks, the store, and the broad acres they owned in Kentucky. They agreed that this trip to Texas would be to find and acquire land they would need and to decide on a town where Joe could build his store. It was to be a permanent move. Marshal Hazelett did not enter into this new picture. After the land in Texas was acquired they would simply go back to Paris, close a deal for the sale of The Oaks and their other properties, including the store, send Dude Justice and Friday Fance, the Negro in charge of his people, ahead with the slaves and personal belongings, and then hunt down John Smith's murderer. Then, with the exception of their many friends, their ties to Kentucky would be severed.

On Monday, July 8, 1844, they were packed and ready to leave Aberdeen for Natchez. They watched the stage roll north, bearing messages to their friends regarding their plans. In the letter to Lewis Traylor they asked him to proceed with the tentative sale of all their properties, including The Oaks. The deeds were to be ready for them to execute and turn over to the new owners on Thursday, December 26, 1844, no sooner. The letters also requested that every effort be made to keep track of Benjamin Tobin's twin brother and the band of outlaws he kept about him. Especially they wanted to know where Tobin would be on the day after Christmas.

Christmas Eve was the day they planned to arrive in Paris, and their letters made it clear that the first order of business was to be an old-fashioned Christmas party at The Oaks that same night. Aunt Polly and the other servants were to prepare a dinner for the eighteen guests they listed. There were to be presents and candy and toys for the darkies.

And then would come the grim business of killing a man. Wesley knew he would have to shoot the other Tobin before he could ever really be at peace. Though the thought of taking another man's life made him sick and cold, he experienced the grim satisfaction that the same thought left him calm and steady. It had to be done. There was no other way.

7. The Six Diamonds

FOUR DAYS out of Aberdeen, they reached the capital of Mississippi. Here in the heart of the Deep South, where men talked politics with aggressive seriousness, Wesley and Joe met another wealthy plantation owner who planned to pull up stakes and move to Texas. The meeting took place in the rotunda of the handsome capitol building; rather, it began when Wesley turned to study the portrait of a Mississippi statesman and collided bodily with a large well-dressed man.

The stranger laughed, as did Wesley, then extended his hand, saying:

"By grabs, youngster, you carry a lot of heft. My name is Jim McMurrey." After the introductions, he rubbed a jaw and studied Wesley curiously. "Wesley Smith? Now where have I heard that name?" Suddenly all puzzlement evanesced. "Now I remember. Sure!

"I wish you boys would step into my office down the hallway," said McMurrey as Wesley and Joe exchanged brief glances. "Maybe we can discuss with a little more privacy this killing I received word of in yesterday's post."

The stranger's disarming smile perplexed Wesley, whose first impulse was to draw his pistol and disarm the man before beating a hasty retreat. After a moment's consideration he realized that such an act would put every officer in the region on their trail. Then it occurred to him that McMurrey had not demanded their guns. He quickly gave Joe a signal to follow. Once in the office, McMurrey smiled broadly at their discomfort and indicated chairs.

"Please have no fear of being arrested, young men," he began. "I am no officer of the law, just a very good friend of Lewis Traylor. He wrote me to be on the lookout for you boys and offer any help possible."

He produced a letter from his desk and passed it to Wesley. Both boys read eagerly every word of the message from their old friend.

At McMurrey's insistence Joe and Wesley spent the night in his home. They met his pretty wife and, after dinner, they talked far into the night. Wesley told their entire story, evoking stormy words from McMurrey, who had been a political leader and a large slaveholder in Mississippi for half of his forty years. In his opinion, the land company was out for more than the acquisition of honest men's property. Since it was no doubt officered by Northerners, its aim could be the abolition of slavery in Kentucky. Perhaps he was wrong in giving a crook any motive other than theft, but he contended that many Northerners who could not use the Negro to their advantage wanted to force citizenship and its multifarious responsibilities upon a race of people who could not be ready for such, even with patient teaching and coaching, for many generations to come.

Wesley was not too well conversed in the economic struggle between the North and South, though his natural sympathies toward the Southern cause had, since the death of his father at the hands of a Northern crowd, increased until it went beyond the meaning of sympathy; his feeling was better defined in terms of bitterness toward all people who opposed the Southern way of life. He was, therefore, an eager listener, one who felt keenly disappointed when Mrs. McMurrey deftly turned the one-sided conversation to other channels.

There was no hurry as the boys prepared to leave the following morning. The sun had quartered the sky when McMurrey stood with his family on the veranda and waved a farewell. As Joe and Wesley swung into their saddles, they assured their hosts they would keep in touch with them. The McMurreys promised to visit them in Texas.

The brothers traveled steadily southwest, and on the afternoon of Monday, July 15, the second day out of Jackson, they rode into Natchez, the most beautiful city they had ever seen. The charming mixture of Spanish and Southern colonial architecture employed in the huge manor houses in and around the city impressed them greatly.

They saw Concord, the enormous home of the first Spanish governor, Linden, Dunleith, and many others. It was here that plans for their homes in Texas began to take on shape and substance.

In Natchez a decision had to be made: whether they should cross the broad, muddy Mississippi and enter Texas through Nacogdoches, Cincinnati, and Huntsville, or go down-river by boat to Lakeland, Louisiana, and reach Texas by way of the Atascocita Trail to Houston and Harrisburg. While they rode slowly along under the moss-draped oaks surrounding the mansions of Natchez, they decided to go down-river and enter Texas on the Atascocita Trail.

After considerable bickering and trading, which Joe
enjoyed, they paid the captain of the *New Orleans* three
hundred and sixty-five dollars for passage and walked
excitedly up the gangplank to begin their first trip on a
river steamer. The horses were installed on the stern near
the great paddle wheel. Sam stowed their gear among the
piles of boxes and bales and crates, then took up his vigil
near the animals to keep them quiet until they became
used to the roar and movement of the boat. Wesley and
Joe were shown to a small stateroom opening onto the top
deck, directly behind the wheelhouse and the captain's
cabin. Sam brought fresh clothing from their packs, and
as Joe and Wesley bathed and changed, the great com-
motion of casting off began.

The pilot and the captain were both yelling orders
through paper megaphones at the top of their lungs, sea-
soning these orders with river jargon and epithets known
only to the river-boat fraternity. The Negro deck hands
began chanting as they coiled the ropes and heavy haw-
sers which had been thrown from the dock to the lower
deck of the boat. A bell rang, the deep-throated whistle of
the *New Orleans* sounded two long blasts, and the tall
smokestacks belched forth great columns of black smoke.
As steam hissed about the big engine and the giant paddle
wheel began to turn and push the boat out into the wide
muddy stream, Wesley and Joe got into their clothes and
hurried out on the upper deck to watch the bustle and
activity.

They leaned excitedly against the rail where a tall, an-
gular man in his early fifties watched nonchalantly as the
steamer moved out into the current. He finally turned and
surveyed the boys leisurely.

"We are going to be shipmates for a few days, young

[59]

men," he said. "So please allow me to introduce myself. I am Marion Nagle, trader, gambler, and soldier of fortune." He smiled and extended his hand to Joe, then Wesley.

The boys grasped his hand warmly, since it was a pleasure to meet anyone who might lessen the feeling of growing homesickness. "I always thought a gambler tried to hide the fact, Mr. Nagle," Wesley said.

"That is very true of many in my profession, son, but everyone on the river knows what I am. They also know I am an honest man. I never sit in a game of any sort without advising the participants of my profession."

They talked for some time, though Joe and Wesley appeared more interested in the huge cotton plantations they were passing, larger than any they had ever seen. Nagle's information regarding the land and landowners added greatly to their enjoyment.

After the evening meal Joe and Wesley wandered about the big steamboat, peeping into the boiler room to watch the Negro stokers feed pine knots and cordwood to the furnaces under the boilers. Steam eddied about them and rolled up the hatchway, bringing with it the hot smell of burned oil. They visited the stern, where Sam was attending the horses, and sat near the huge paddle wheel and watched the foamy wake. The fine spray from the paddles finally drove them back and they climbed up to the hurricane deck, directly in front of the pilothouse. Pausing before an open skylight, they looked down into an ornate room on the deck below where a poker game was in progress. Around a table sat Marion Nagle and five other players.

The boys leaned idly against the rail and watched as the game progressed, enjoying the cool wind that swept up the river and the pleasant sounds of the water lapping at the bows as the big stern wheel forced the steamer down the river.

Suddenly Joe grabbed Wesley's arm. "Look," he said softly, "that man is cheating!" He pointed to a large, neatly dressed stranger directly across the table from Nagle.

They watched the game and the suspect intently for some time before anything further happened to justify Joe's remark. Finally the big man picked up the cards dealt him and called the opening bet. Two of the men threw in their hands and the others, including Nagle, called. There were no raises. The man whom Joe thought was cheating held his cards close to his face with both hands and slowly parted them with a thumb. The brothers could see that he held four hearts and a spade. He flipped the spade out of his hand face down on the table and called for one card. It was dealt to him and he placed the four hearts he held atop it and brought them all up together. Each of the remaining players took three cards, except Nagle, who drew two.

The big man again held his cards close to his face and spread them slowly with a thumb. Joe and Wesley saw that he had drawn another spade. He held what was known as a "busted flush." Keeping the cards spread, he lowered them, face down, to the table with his left hand and dropped his right arm to his side, as if stretching his muscles. His hand, however, went to the inside of his right leg and came up to deftly place a card in his left hand and remove the offending spade he had drawn. With another unnoticed movement of his right arm the spade disappeared, and he raised his cards and spread them close before his face. Joe and Wesley discovered that he now had the six of hearts in his hand to fill a queen-high flush.

The man who had opened the pot now came forth with a sizable wager. The big man raised, and all other players, except the opener and Nagle, threw in their hands.

Nagle carefully contemplated the faces of his two opponents for several moments before placing fifteen twenty-dollar gold pieces in the center of the table. "I call the fifty dollars," he said, "and raise two hundred and fifty more."

Wesley and Joe heard. As they leaned forward to see what would happen, the opener threw in his hand, leaving only Nagle and the big man in the pot. After nervously drumming his fingers on the edge of the table for some time, the dishonest gambler counted out the raise and slammed it savagely onto the table, his guttural voice sounding one word:

"Call."

Nagle smiled and lowered his cards face up on the table. He held three kings and two sixes. One of them was a six of hearts. The other gambler, careful not to rise and expose the cards hidden under his leg, slowly turned his cards face up near Nagle's hand.

"You would win this pot," he grated with condemning ease, "if you weren't a damned cheat. Just look at that six of hearts in his hand, men. I held that card on the deal."

As he spoke he made a rapid recovery of the hidden cards and flipped them under the table near Nagle's feet. Then he made a move to draw a gun tucked in his waistband. Nagle had anticipated this, and a small but very efficient-looking little pistol appeared in his hand. He said:

"Gentlemen, I have never cheated any man out of anything. Now, my friend," he addressed this remark to his accuser, "please turn around and drop your gun or I shall have to kill you."

The fellow hesitated a moment before doing as he was told. Then he said, "This Nagle is lying. Why don't some of you search us and see who has cards hidden about him?"

"That won't be necessary," called Wesley from the upper deck. "My brother and I saw the whole thing. That man there is the one who has been cheating." He pointed to Nagle's accuser.

"Which one do you mean?" called one of the players. "We can't see you up there." They were all looking up toward the boys, but the flares had been placed so that the upper deck was in semi-darkness.

"We'll come down there," replied Wesley, and he and Joe walked rapidly to the stairs that led to the lower deck. They explained what they had seen, and when one of the players pushed the table back, there near Nagle's seat were a dozen or more cards. But another card stuck accusingly out of the big man's boot. And he, the first to see the evidence that would sign his death warrant, gained the rail in a sudden rush and dived far out into the boiling, muddy waters of the Mississippi.

A fusillade of shots followed him from a half dozen guns as the *New Orleans* plowed her way southward. Then the incident was forgotten and the remaining players sorted the cards and continued their game.

It was very late when Nagle rapped on their cabin door. Wesley answered sleepily. Upon entering, the gambler stood a moment before he said, "You young men probably saved my life tonight, so I had to come by and tell you how much I appreciate what you did. I should like to show my appreciation further by giving you this to help start that fine plantation you are planning in Texas." He dropped a little buckskin bag on the table and turned to extend his hand.

"What's in that bag, Mr. Nagle?" Wesley inquired.

"The money I won tonight. Around twenty thousand dollars." He smiled. "I consider my life worth a great deal more than that, but it should go a long way toward the purchase of that plantation."

"No, Mr. Nagle," said Wesley. "You are a very generous person, but we can't accept money for what we did tonight. No, sir. Someday our trails may cross again, and in that case——"

Nagle looked at the ashes on his cigar, then up at Wesley. "I surmised as much," he said. "But here is something I have treasured for years. I want you to have them."

From his wallet he emptied six large flashing diamonds on the table top. "Wear these for me and let them help you remember that you once knew an honest gambler."

Without another word he rose and stepped out of the cabin, quietly closing the door.

"Well, I'll be damned!" Joe said, looking from the diamonds to his brother.

They did not see Marion Nagle again until the boat slid alongside the wharf at Lakeland. Later, when Sam had taken all gear and animals ashore, the gambler placed an arm about the shoulders of each boy and wished them Godspeed.

Wesley produced the diamonds and extended them to Nagle. "You might need these one day when your luck isn't so good."

The gambler chose to ignore both the gems and the remark. "I'm going to Texas soon and I'll look you up," he said. "When you get settled, write me at this address in New Orleans and tell me where you are located."

As Joe and Wesley mounted their horses and moved off down the dusty street, Nagle waved a farewell and sauntered into a tavern where, they suspected, he would engage some of the hangers-on in a game of chance while awaiting the *New Orleans'* departure.

8. The Sabine Incident

THE MEETING with Nagle seemed, but for the reward he insisted on giving them, just another incident on the road to Texas. And yet, had the young Kentuckians remained one day longer with the McGowens of Aberdeen or the McMurreys of Jackson, Nagle would not have entered their lives, nor would they have met with the same crowd on the American side of the Sabine several days later.

Both boys had learned a great deal that summer. The shock of trouble and tragedy, the uprooting—these things, combined with travel and new faces, evoked in them an unconscious change in expression and bearing. The sudden leap from boyhood to manhood was so admittedly sharp that had it not been for the wisdom John Smith had applied to the training of his motherless sons the experiences of the rough country and the time might have been too much for them. But they were of sound stock and sound temperament. They accepted that which came as one accepts a new day. True, they looked back over the short past with feelings of sorrow, loneliness, and justified anger, though never with despair. They dreamed also, with the fresh hope of youth guiding their look into the future. This was manifested on the second night out of Lakeland, when Wesley again studied the six diamonds in the light of the campfire and began shaping a dream out of Nagle's gift.

They had ridden into Opelousas, Louisiana—a bustling town of trappers and hunters, a few farmers, and a host of people on their way to the promised land of Texas—hoping to find stagecoach accommodations. Upon learning that no west-bound coach would be available for several days, they mingled with families re-outfitting for the trek to the settlement of Atascocita on the Trinity River in Texas, and others who talked of going on to Houston, Harrisburg, some even as far as Refugio and San Antonio.

The brothers decided to set out at once. They had supplies sufficient for another week, and it should be only a three-day ride at most to Atascocita. So they rode into the afternoon sun until it disappeared behind the thick virgin pines. Then Sam began his preparation of their evening meal.

After they had eaten and Sam had spread their bedrolls the darky and the two boys sat around the campfire and talked of the happy and carefree days at The Oaks and discussed what they thought Texas would be like.

"I sho does dread dis Texas," said Sam. "Yo'all reckon I is gonna be de onliest nigger down heah, Mistuh Wes?"

Joe and Wesley laughed. "No, Sam," Wesley said, "you'll find plenty of darkies in Texas. Besides, we are going to bring Aunt Polly and the rest down here just as soon as we can. Don't worry, you'll have plenty of company as soon as we get settled, because I know how well you get around."

As Wesley winked at Joe, Sam began to squirm. "Now,

Mistuh Wes," he said, "yo' sho does carry on wid me."

Wesley reached into a bulging pocket and extracted the six diamonds Marion Nagle had poured from his wallet, and turned the stones, watching the facets reflect the light of the campfire. He amused himself in this manner for some time before brushing the carpet of pine needles from the sandy soil and tracing with a charred ember different patterns on the ground.

"Not a bad idea for a cattle brand," he said aloud. Looking at Joe, who leaned against a tree trunk, he added, "Look at this."

Joe recalled the many conversations along the trail regarding the branding of cattle. Although their father had never resorted to this, the people in the South were adopting this simple way of identifying their stock. It was an old trick learned from the Spanish. And now, since the Smith boys favored the idea, Joe studied with interest the design Wesley had drawn.

"A six surrounded by a diamond," he said curiously. "What does that signify?"

"A great deal, Joe, when you stop to think about it. The diamond was Father's birthstone. Mr. Nagle gave us six diamonds. Father was killed on the sixth day of the sixth month."

Joe nodded as he stared thoughtfully at the design. "I see. It does make sense, Wes. And the sixth was also your birthday. But what are we going to call it?"

"Six Diamonds, maybe. No, that's not it." He moved his lips for several minutes. Joe was studying the fire again when Wesley exclaimed, "Diamond Six! That's it."

Sam beamed. "Diamon' Six! Sho'ly do sound good, don't it, Mistuh Joe?"

"Diamond Six," Joe said meditatively, removing his boots. It did sound good, he admitted. Diamond Six had

a solid ring, but first they needed land and cattle. His enthusiasm, never fully kindled, fell away. It seemed so
very unimportant. He yawned and crawled into his blanket. Wesley and Sam did the same, and the campfire died
to a red glow under the whispering pines.

A name and a brand had been born, however, on that
clear warm evening of Thursday, July 18, 1844. It was
something of their own, a dream wrapped up in two significant words. Something to work to and for with a purpose.

DIAMOND SIX.

Two days later the travelers emerged from the Louisiana
pines and halted near the bank of the muddy Sabine
River for their first glimpse of the Republic of Texas. In
midstream a little ferry bound for the Texas shore with
cattle, horses, and two covered wagons was being drawn
by men who seemed to be pulling themselves into Texas
by the steel cable stretching across the river. In the covered
wagons, the sides of which were rolled up to let in the
faint, humid breeze, sat their women and children.

"They're like us, Joe," said Wesley at last. "Pioneering.
And over there is the place. Texas."

"I wonder if that's the part they call 'No Man's Land' or
'The Wilderness.' They say a man in the big thickets and
bayous is safe from the law of Texas and the United
States."

"Probably so, Joe. But that's not the place for us. Once
we're across the river, Hazelett won't bother us."

Walking the horses, they moved past the few log shanties
on the low bluff overlooking the river toward the big log
building bearing a sign, Opelousas Trading Post, crudely
lettered on a pine board. A half dozen men sat on the
low gallery fronting the building, and in the doorway

stood two fashionably dressed men in well-polished boots, gray suits, checked waistcoats, white shirts, black string ties, and tall gray beavers.

Close by the trading post stood two army tents, in front of which were eight rifles, swiveled in stacks of four each. At the side of the tents and in the shade of a big pine lounged a squad of soldiers in heavy dark blue uniforms. Their blouses were open at the throat and almost entirely soaked black with sweat.

Sam had dismounted and led his horse and the two pack animals through the cut in the bluff at the ferry landing. Joe and Wesley still sat their mounts, looking across the river into Texas. Now, more than at any time during the past few days, they were wary of the promised interception by Marshal Hazelett. They were at the very fringe of his jurisdiction and were determined to avoid any mistake that would bring about their arrest and return to Kentucky for an unfair trial.

Under other circumstances neither of the boys would have paid particular notice when two of the men from the gallery got up and sauntered in their direction. But now Texas was too close and they were naturally apprehensive of strangers.

"Careful, Joe," Wesley warned in low tones. "Let me do the talking."

The pair came to a halt near the brothers. The larger and meaner-looking of the two grinned. "Hi ya, boys. Where you bound?"

Wesley eyed the man closely. "To Texas. Why?"

"No reason particular. Thought maybe if you was totin' a lot of money, me and my partner would trail along ter protect ye. 'Sides, sonny, I've seen you somewhere, ain't I?"

"That's right, mister."

The man squinted an eye shut. "You don't sound real sociable-like, boy."

"I didn't mean to," Wesley replied evenly, meeting the other's hard look.

"Now look here, I didn't come out here for that. But I'll let it pass. Where'd we meet, boy?"

"In Paris, Kentucky. You pulled a knife on a man getting off the stage. Remember?"

"Well, well. So you're the damned kid that interfered. I'm right glad to run into you again, young squirt. In fact——"

Suddenly he leaped for the bridle of Wesley's horse. As if prearranged, the other man reached for Joe's bridle reins.

As they made their move, Wesley pulled the stallion up short and dug the spurs into his flanks. The big horse reared, then charged forward on his hind legs. As the murderous forefeet came down, he trampled the man in the chest with his hoofs. A moment later Wesley pulled him sharply to the left and into the man who was trying to hold Joe's horse.

Joe had also spurred his horse forward in an attempt to run down his assailant. The two terrified animals crashed shoulder to shoulder with the hapless man's head between them. As their mounts literally bounced apart, the ruffian collapsed in an inert heap.

The boys rode to a stop, facing the other men on the gallery, four of whom rose menacingly.

"Stay where you are," Wesley ordered crisply. "That's my last word to you." He pulled the stallion's head to the left in order to have clear shooting should the men decide to advance.

Joe had scarcely swung his horse around to flank his brother's when one of the well-dressed men in the doorway walked to the edge of the gallery and spoke in a low voice of complete authority:

"Let those boys alone."

All but one of the foursome obeyed. That one sent his hand flying to a holstered pistol. With the first movement Wesley instinctively made a flashing drag for his gun and fired on the sweep.

Two weak explosions seemed to echo the heavy report of Wesley's pistol. Upon looking up from the man falling to the ground, he saw to his amazement that each of the well-dressed men held a small pistol, which he had heard of but had never seen until now—the deadly little sleeve gun. When his glance fell to the assailant, he saw that all had scored a hit, for three bullets had struck the man in the leg.

They had no sooner disarmed the remaining three and began dressing the wounded man's leg than Joe said, "Look, Wes! Sam has taken out for Texas. And from the looks of the face of that soldier coming toward us, we'd do well to join him."

The soldier came on. A tall, muscular, unshaven man in sweat-caked blue, he spread his mouth in a wide, white-toothed grin that did not quite reach his cold brittle eyes. His expression, together with a mop of sand-colored hair against a darkly tanned face, all of which seemed to put the very devil up for notice, flashed to Wesley a warning of impending trouble. Then the soldier was saying:

"Corporal Spangler, United States Army." Glaring at Wesley and still showing the humorless grin, he said, "Do you just ride around the country shooting people like this?"

"If you'd been watching, you'd know who started the argument," Wesley replied evenly.

"That's enough! You're under arrest, both of you."

"For what? Look here, we——" Turning to Joe, he said, "I suppose we'll have to go with him."

"That's better," Corporal Spangler said. "Pull over to my men and dismount."

Wesley darted a glance at the eight stacked rifles, then at the two men on the gallery, who stood with their sleeve guns still in their hands. The three men they had disarmed made no move to retrieve their weapons. Now Wesley took note of something else—the seven soldiers, all standing near the rifles, were making no move to arm themselves.

Wesley and Joe halted their horses before the soldiers at the corporal's order. His next command, "Now dismount," was the one Wesley awaited.

"Corporal, I've had enough of this."

Spangler tensed. "Have you now?" he asked, making a move to raise the flap of his service holster. He was late, for in another instant he was looking directly into the muzzle of Wesley's revolver.

"Boy," he said, dropping both hands to his side, "just let me remind you that you're resisting arrest by drawing a gun on an officer of the United States Army."

"Raise your hands and tell your men not to rush us. We're resisting arrest but we don't want to kill you if we can keep from it. That's up to you."

Slowly Spangler raised his hands, the sneering grin still on his face.

"Now have one of your men run that rope through the trigger guard of every one of those rifles," Wesley demanded, indicating a coil of rope hanging from a broken limb of a nearby pine.

"I'll give no such order!" stormed the corporal.

Wesley's gun roared and a heavy slug ripped into the

dust between the man's feet. "I'm not going to tell you again."

As Spangler looked into the flashing eyes and observed the tight wrinkled smile behind the smoking pistol, he changed his mind. "Do what he says," he ordered.

One of the soldiers quickly laced the end of the rope through all of the trigger guards and stood holding it in his hand, looking at Wesley as if awaiting his orders rather than those of his squad leader.

"Now tie a hard knot in the end you're holding and hand the other end to my brother."

With a shrug of indifference, the soldier proceeded to tie the knot. He handed the other end of the rope to Joe, who deftly threw a half hitch on his saddle pommel.

"Now, Corporal," Wesley ordered, "put your back to me, take your pistol from your holster, and give it to me handle first, over your left shoulder. Careful now, and no tricks."

With the other's gun in his possession, Wesley glanced toward the trading-post gallery in time to see one of the well-dressed men push the last of the ruffians' pistols and knives through a hole in the gallery floor. This meant there would be no firearms available to the soldiers when he and Joe entered the Sabine to join Sam in Texas.

"Let's go, Wes," said Joe impatiently.

"You go ahead," Wesley replied. "Take the rifles into deep water and let the rope go. The corporal can get a much-needed bath while he is looking for them. I'll be right behind you."

As Joe turned his horse, the rifles clattered to the ground and began to slide through the dust. Wesley backed his stallion away from the soldiers, covering them with his gun until he reached the gallery where the two strangers stood.

"Gentlemen," he said, "my name is Wesley Smith. My brother and I want to thank you for your help. Now, do you need any help? We certainly intend to stay if you do."

"No worry on that score, son," the older of the pair replied, his penetrating glance full on Wesley. "Where in Texas are you boys heading?"

"Houston first, then up the Trinity."

"Houston, eh. Well, stay at the Capitol Hotel, across Main Street from the Sixty-six Saloon. I'll look for you there, maybe with a proposition you'll like."

Wesley thanked him again. Then he wheeled his horse toward the Sabine as Sam and Joe had done and was soon swimming his mount for the great Republic of Texas.

9. Tragedy in Houston

IN HIS LATER YEARS Wesley Smith never tired of relating to his family and friends his first act after crossing the Sabine River:

"I got off my horse and removed the hat from my head. Joe sat in the saddle watching me as I scooped up a handful of soil and let it trickle from my hand. It was a serious moment in my life, and Joe, when I looked up at him, felt it too. He nodded when I said, 'Well, I'm thankful, Joe.' And he took off his hat when I pledged my loyalty to the youngest nation on the face of the earth. It was a short ceremony but one I'll never forget. Then it was over—or just beginning, I reckon. Anyhow, Joe and I had to look sharp. Those ruffians, and probably the soldiers, might be hot on our trail. . . ."

Screened by virgin pine, the brothers watched the ferry disgorge wagons, teams, and people. The last to step ashore in Texas were the two men who had come to their aid at the trading post. Agreeably surprised, Wesley suggested that they ride at a slow pace in order to allow the pair to overtake them. This they did, and soon the riders came alongside. The elder of the two said:

"I'm Major Tarbone and this is Captain Wade. We're Texas Rangers."

Following an exchange of apprehensive glances between the brothers, the major continued with, "We like to know where people coming into Texas are from. Especially those traveling light."

Wesley studied the pair closely. He judged Tarbone to be in his middle thirties, Wade some ten years his junior. Both were weather-tanned, both sat ramrod-straight in the saddle, and there was no mistaking the poised vigilance and self-reliance in their expressions. The major's sharp blue-gray eyes seemed to declare that he was a man possessed with the courage to back up his convictions, no matter the odds against him.

Wesley considered the possibility of arrest by these men and said crisply: "If you're putting that question to us, Major, we're from Kentucky. I'm Wesley Smith. That's my brother Joe. We came to Texas to find land and buy it and go back after our slaves and belongings."

The major estimated Wesley keenly. "And just what made you boys suddenly decide on Texas?"

Wesley resented the question but checked his temper. Joe burst forth with, "If it's any of your business, we wanted to get away from the land-grabbing Yankees. Anything else you'd like to know?"

"No, son. I'm from New York myself, but I don't agree with all the politickin' in Washington. So, regardless of whether you're telling the truth or not, you're welcome to Texas just as long as you behave yourselves."

It was nearing ten that night when the four riders reached the settlement of Atascocita and stopped before the Liberty Inn. A lantern high on a post bracket at the front of the large building swayed gently in the warm night breeze. As the tired travelers rode up, three Negro hostlers trotted up to take their mounts. After arranging for Sam's lodging, they entered the large dining room and sat down to heaping portions of steak, baked sweet potatoes, hominy, beans, corn bread, buttermilk, and mugs of steaming coffee.

Following the meal, Major Tarbone drew Wesley to a corner of the big room. When they were seated, the major thoughtfully chewed the end of a thin black cigar several minutes before lighting it.

"You know, son," he began, "the way you handled that situation over on the Sabine this morning was pretty commendable. I never saw a youngster, or a man for that matter, as cold and efficient as you were during that melee. It always worries me just a little when I see a young man like you. I watched your eyes over there today, that tight little smile and your steady hands. A deadly combination. Now I don't know what you've done that brought you to Texas. I know there's a reason for it, because one look at you and Joe tells me that you are from a good, well-to-do family, and boys like that just don't travel a thousand miles to find a piece of farming land. Believe me, I have no interest in what you have done. My interest is in what may become of you."

The Ranger smoked in silence as he earnestly surveyed Wesley. "A boy like you will be either all good or all bad," he said finally. "There is no middle ground for a youngster of your temperament. I want to see you turn out all good, for when I was your age I was just like you. I had to choose to go either with the law or against it. That's the reason I joined the Rangers and that's the reason I want you to join them."

As Wesley opened his mouth to reply, the Ranger raised

a hand. "I don't mean that you should make law enforcement your profession. I mean I want you to come into the Rangers until you get completely over what I saw in your eyes this morning. It wouldn't take much to turn you into a killer. I don't want to see that happen to you."

Wesley's eyes had not left the Ranger's face. "Look here, Major Tarbone, I believe I know my mind better than you or anyone else. I also know I could never be a killer. Take that man I shot this morning. I hit him in the leg, just as I intended. If I was your killer I would have shot him through the heart."

He would have continued, for his anger was on the rise, but the ranger smiled good-naturedly and said, "Just a moment, son. Just a moment. Let me finish and then you'll see what I'm driving at. Remember, you are planning on moving to Texas. Texas is a raw, rough, and lusty country. Word is bound to get around about your speed with a gun. When it does, there'll be a wagonload of gun-slingers anxious to establish a reputation, and they'll attempt to make you prove yours. Then, my boy, you will be forced to kill. Not once but many times, for as your reputation grows so will the number of men who will test you. I never meant to imply that you would be a ruthless killer. I meant simply that killing would be forced upon you, and somewhere down the line you would begin to regard human life as cheap. I hope you understand me, son, and will consider becoming a Texas Ranger for a while."

"I understand, sir, and I appreciate your interest in me. Now about the Rangers—I heard of them back in Paris, but I know very little about them."

Tarbone spoke proudly of the Rangers. He told of how Stephen F. Austin employed a small body of valiant men called Rangers as early as 1823 to protect the frontier colonies against the Karankawa Indians. He named incidents in which the Rangers distinguished themselves. On the eve of war with Mexico, he went on to say, the convention of Texans on October 17, 1835, formally authorized a corps of Rangers to guard the frontiers against Indians so that the Texas Army could fight the Mexicans.

"We did, young man, while our ragged army retreated and finally won the victory. After San Jacinto we enlarged and patrolled the frontier, and we kept the Mexicans from coming back. A horse, a brace of pistols, and a rifle—those are the tools we use to punish Indians, Rio Grande free-booters, and Mexicans. It's a damned good organization, son, one made up of men. I'm paying you honor when I ask you to join us."

"And I'm grateful to you, sir," Wesley replied. "But I can't promise yet, since we're going back to Kentucky for Christmas and return with our slaves and other belongings."

"Very well," said Tarbone. "Let's make an appointment to meet at the Capitol Hotel in Houston, say on the fifteenth of January. We'll discuss it then. But it's time we hit the bed if we're to make Houston tomorrow night."

Wesley moved as in a trance to his room and began to undress. He slipped quietly into bed, aware that this was his first night in Texas. Room 3, Liberty Inn, Atascocita Settlement.

"Texas Rangers," he said to himself. So they wished him to become one of them; without even a glimpse into his past, with only a searching glance of his face. They sized a man up here in Texas, and they judged him by his deeds, that and all they saw deep behind a man's eyes.

Wesley lay awake for some time, his mind occupied with the things Tarbone had told him. More like discoveries they were, since he had never resorted to self-analysis. Now able to see himself through the lawman's eyes, he decided to join the Rangers upon his return from Kentucky, if only to declare by deed his leaning toward law and order. Beyond this aspect of the situation, the boy inside him emerged with an infinite childish pleasure that he had been asked to join the Texas Rangers.

Before daylight the ringing of a brass bell down the hallways of the Liberty Inn announced breakfast. The noises of the kitchen together with the preparations for the stage run to Houston, the saddling of horses and the yelling of Negroes trying to bridle the mounts, all blended into a pleasing sound to Wesley. He sat next to Captain Wade at breakfast. Liking the young Ranger for his directness of speech and glance as well as his modesty, and remembering his speed with the sleeve gun, Wesley said to himself, "Now here is a pattern for a real man."

By sunrise the brothers, Sam, and the two Rangers were in the saddle. They crossed the Trinity River by ferry and rode on toward Houston through pine-covered hills and valleys and reached the San Jacinto River at noon. Here, while Sam prepared food, Tarbone recited an old legend concerning treasure at this very spot. It seemed that a Spanish gold shipment, to pay troops stationed at Atasco-cita, was in danger of capture by an enemy, said to be French. The Spanish hurriedly poured their gold into their one small cannon, sealed the mouth with lead, then rolled the cannon into the water. According to the legend, the entire Spanish detachment, with the exception of one man taken prisoner, was annihilated. This man was never able to find the cannon when he was finally released from prison.

Major Tarbone talked of other things. Texas politics, the wooing of Queen Victoria's government by President

Sam Houston, who had played for the favor of Great Britain just to arouse jealousy and alarm in Washington. And now President Tyler of the United States was pressing the question of annexation of Texas. Texans were still arguing for and against becoming either a territory or a state of the United States, even though annexation had recently been defeated by the abolitionists in the U. S. Senate on June 8, 1844.

"For once I'm glad the abolitionists won," said Tarbone. "Texas is doing all right as a republic, in spite of Sam Houston."

When Wesley asked what was wrong with Houston, Tarbone replied, "Since Old Sam isn't here to tell his side, I'll let you find out for yourself, son."

Night had fallen when they crossed the ferry on Buffalo Bayou at the foot of Main Street and rode the four blocks illuminated with lanterns to the Capitol Hotel in the rough, bustling town of Houston. After promising to join the Rangers in the Sixty-six Saloon for supper, Wesley and Joe bathed and dressed, both anxious to see the town. At the appointed time they entered the big saloon and selected a table.

They had scarcely seated themselves when Tarbone and Wade entered the Main Street door. Tarbone waved a hand at them, then slowly, curiously, walked the length of the bar that ran all the way to Fannin Street on the east. Both men walked back to the Main Street entrance, examining every face at bar and tables. Then Wade turned and walked back, leaving the saloon at the Fannin Street door.

"Something's up, Joe," said Wesley.

Tarbone soon verified the statement. "We have a couple of real bad ones in here tonight," he said as he took his seat. "The kind that kill for the love of killing." He paused to light a cigar.

"We just got word that they robbed the bank in Montgomery yesterday, killed several people, and set fire to the town. Wade and I can take the pair of them easily if they do what I think they will. That is, leave by the Main Street door. Wade will be waiting outside and I'll be behind them."

"So that's why Captain Wade left by the other door," said Joe. "He'll go around the block and be at the Main Street door when they leave."

The Ranger nodded. "We want to get them away from the crowd if we can, for they'll make a fight if they think they have a chance. Now, if I leave suddenly, you boys just sit here. We'll get this business over in short order and then get on with a fine supper."

They sat talking quietly for a few minutes until two men rose from one of the tables near the far end of the room and moved into the aisle between the bar and the tables, walking toward the Main Street entrance. Tarbone glanced their way, then turned as if to continue his conversation with Joe and Wesley. When the desperadoes gained the door, he rose and quickly followed them into the night.

The eerie flickering of the lanterns that hung along both sides of the street gave the boys a shadowy but distinct picture of the drama that was being enacted. They saw a man move out of the darkness of the corner of the building and station himself at a spot commanding the entrance to the saloon. By his neat dress and stance they knew him to be Captain Wade.

The two bank robbers hurried from the saloon door and turned north along the plank walk, going away from the position the young Ranger had taken. Then through the open window by their table Wesley and Joe heard Captain Wade's command:

"Put up your hands, both of you."

The men instantly obeyed and began slowly to lift their arms without turning around. Suddenly both of them wheeled. As the man on the plank walk dived into the street for the temporary shelter of a watering trough, the other raced the speed of Wade's first shot to get back into the saloon, where he met Tarbone's bullet squarely in his chest. He fell heavily to the floor just inside the building and died. But not before he had thrown a chance shot that entered the Ranger's side, spun him completely about, and sent him face down across a table near the doorway. A second later Tarbone slid noiselessly to the sawdust-covered floor.

Outside there was more shooting, and Wesley learned minutes later that the desperado who had dived into the shadow of the watering trough had caught Captain Wade looking about for him and charged the Ranger with gun blazing. As Wade fell with a bullet in his abdomen, the outlaw dashed across Texas Avenue for his horse. Eyewitnesses told how Wade pulled himself to his knees with a mighty effort and fired both his sleeve guns at the running man. He found his mark. The bullets were not heavy enough to down the man, however, and he staggered to the rail, slipped the reins, and, as the horse began to run, pulled himself into the saddle and raced off into the night, blood streaming from arm and shoulder wounds.

When Tarbone fell, Joe and Wesley leaped to his aid. "Go to Wade," he commanded. "I'll be all right."

Wesley found the inert form of Captain Wade lying in the street near the saloon gallery. Wade lay still, staring sightlessly into the starry Texas night. Wesley felt his pulse and discovered the young officer was dead. He placed the dead man's hat over his face, picked up the two tiny pistols, smelled them, and found they had both been fired. Pocketing them, he listened to the account of the gun battle and went back into the saloon.

Major Tarbone was sitting at a table, one of the bartenders dressing his wound. "How did Wade make out?" he asked. "Did he get the other one?"

"Captain Wade is dead, Major," Wesley replied gravely. "But I believe he must have shot the man, for both his little guns have been fired."

Tarbone closed his eyes and ran his fingers through his hair. He finally raised his glance to Wesley, though his grief silenced him.

"I think I know how you feel, Major," Wesley said. "I thought a great deal of Captain Wade—enough to trail his killer and bring him back if you'll let me."

Tarbone wiped a lone tear from his leathery cheek and simply stared at Wesley, who realized that the older man was considering his youth and inexperience with desperate criminals in a prelude to refusal.

"Sam is like a bloodhound on the trail, Major. If Captain Wade wounded the man enough to make him lose blood, we can follow him."

Tarbone grimaced and shook his head. "Look, son, you've never come up against——" Suddenly his expression changed as though a fresh estimate of the youth before him swayed his judgment. A queer, mirthless smile played on his face for a moment.

"Very well, Wesley Smith. Raise your right hand."

When the formality ended, he fixed Captain Wade's badge to Wesley's shirt and pronounced him a special deputy of Rangers.

"Wade was my best friend, son. If you can bring that

man in without endangering your own life, I want you
to do it. But for God's sake, be careful. He's dangerous,
and his killing you wouldn't hang him any higher than
he's going to hang when he's caught."

10. The Texts Ranger

WESLEY and Sam, aided by the town marshal, began the search for signs of blood. They were not long in finding them, for the man had bled freely. The marshal left them near the ford on the Montgomery Road, where Sam made an important discovery: Wade's killer rode a horse with a broken hoof on the right front foot.

The Negro's elation was quickly dispelled by fear, however. Thoroughly frightened, he dwelled volubly on the possibility that the gunman could ride a tight circle and pick them off from the rear.

"Mistuh Wes, dat man could kill us right easy like, 'specially wid me holdin' dis lantern for 'im to see by."

Admitting it was so, Wesley decided that the best insurance against ambush was to skirt the ford of the West Montgomery Road by swimming their horses fifty yards downstream. This they did, emerging in the brush and willows lining the bayou and working cautiously back to the road. Here they came upon the tracks made by a broken hoof again and made camp for the night.

They were in the saddle at dawn. Finding the tracks

plainly discernible, Wesley set the pace by striking a long gallop. After an hour of fast trailing he noticed that the broken hoofprints left the road for the trees of White Oak Bayou. Again fearing ambush, Wesley slipped downstream on foot and came upon signs of the outlaw's dry camp of the night before. His bleeding had stopped, which left only the broken hoof to guide them. But this was enough. They followed it until late in the afternoon, on to where it skirted the town of Montgomery and swung into a seldom-used path through tall grass and then stately pines, continuing northeast.

Emerging from the timber, Wesley looked across a clearing at a new log cabin. Smoke from a mud chinmey rose lazily into the hot, humid air. As they approached, avoiding damage to the small fields of cotton and tobacco, a man walked out of the cabin and stood with a long rifle in his hand.

Wesley stopped and hailed him before moving closer. After advising the man of his mission and learning that the settler and his wife had fed the outlaw and dressed his wound, Wesley told the man he was a Texas Ranger and asked why the outlaw stopped at his cabin.

"We was handy, I reckon. He told me he had been shot in a drinking spree in Houston. Warn't none of my business, so me and my woman took him in. After he et and we fixed his arm, he lit a shuck for the San Jacinto River."

He pointed east before saying, "Ain't you a might young to be a Texas Ranger?"

"I can probably answer that in a day or two, mister."

The farmer chuckled and invited him to supper. Wesley accepted, then ordered Sam to check the direction the outlaw had taken. Sam returned a little later, complaining of pine needles and hard ground which almost obliterated the hoofmark.

During the meal, consisting of venison and sweet potatoes hot from the ashes of the fireplace, the host told Wesley of the palmetto in the river bottomland, where "a man could be right next to somebody and never know it."

After thanking the man with words and a coin, Wesley rode in the direction of the San Jacinto River, Sam in the lead to pick up the outlaw's trail.

They camped early that evening, Sam on the first watch. Wesley had no idea how long he had been asleep when he awoke to find Sam gently shaking him and whispering his name. Sitting up, he found the wind strong in the tops of the pines. Lightning flashed and thunder rolled and muttered in the low sky.

"Mistuh Wes," Sam whispered, "don't say nothin', but I seen a man on a hoss—right out there close! Just wait fo' dat lightnin' to flash agin."

Wesley waited, alert and staring tensely into the darkness. Soon a flash of white light accompanied by a heavy clap of thunder lit up the surroundings. In that moment Wesley saw him. Not thirty steps away a man sat his horse, his gaze fixed down the trail toward the new log cabin.

"Get to the horses, quick!" Wesley whispered. "And keep them quiet!"

As Sam hurried silently off, Wesley loosed his revolver in the holster and slipped from tree to tree in the direction of the horseman. Flashes of lightning revealed the man still there, and Wesley approached with vigilance. Then a ragged bolt of lightning and a heavy crash of thunder came as one. In the next instant rain began to fall in torrents.

The lone rider suddenly wheeled his horse and trotted off through the timber. Wesley dashed to the center of the dim trail and saw in the next lightning flash that the man was quartering north. Running to the horses, he helped

Sam tie their sodden blankets and gear to the saddles, then struck out in a wild, blind run through the storm and trees in an effort to circle the rider and cut his trail.

They rode for almost a mile before leaving the pines and sloping down into the thick tall palmettos. Recalling the farmer's warning and hoping to intercept the man before he lost himself in the palmettos, they wheeled their mounts north for about a mile, then pulled up and waited in the heavy downpour.

The first indication of the hunted man's presence was the sound of a horse sloshing through the mud. Then a flash of lightning lit up the scene, this time revealing through the sheets of slanting rain a man struggling to pull a pistol from a holster tied to the pommel of his saddle. It was evident that the man had seen them first.

Instantly Wesley dug his spurs deep into the stallion's flanks. As he charged forward, the outlaw's gun roared and a bullet screamed past Wesley's head.

With the loud report of the pistol, Sam forgot his own safety and spurred his horse cruelly, plunging him into the side of the outlaw's animal. As the horses crashed together, the excited Negro continued to drag his rowels across the horse's flanks, and as a result the crazed animal reared his flailing forefeet and knocked the man out of the saddle. Sam saw him fall and turned his horse in a tight circle, his aim to trample the man before he could fire the pistol again. One forefoot struck the dislodged horseman and jerked a cry from him; still Sam kept his horse turning until Wesley grabbed the bridle reins.

An hour later Wesley and the Negro rode up to the log cabin with the outlaw securely bound to his horse. The farmer came out with his lantern and rifle and gave Wesley his log storage shed for the night. When he learned that the outlaw was one of the men who had terrorized Montgomery, his eyes burned with anger.

The storm died in the night, and with the clear dawn Wesley tied his prisoner to his horse and moved off. The farmer suggested the Fish Trail Road into Montgomery, some eight miles to the west, as the best route, but Wesley was not inclined to parade the outlaw through the town he had helped pillage and burn. So he pushed rapidly through the pines toward Houston and at noon paused on the north bank of Spring Creek to prepare a meal from the prisoner's pack.

Wesley had untied the man's hands and was sitting on a sand bar near the ford when he heard riders approaching. He rose and looked up the trail to see three men jogging their horses along at an easy trot. He was surprised, however, to note that the animals were hot and flecked with lather, as if they had been pushed hard for miles under the broiling sun.

The trio of strangers paused, commented on the hot July weather, and proceeded to water their horses. All were in their shirt sleeves and appeared to be unarmed. They asked if they could have coffee, and Sam poured three cups, which they drank slowly, almost too slowly, apparently uninterested in Wesley's prisoner. Perhaps it was their extreme casualness that caused Wesley to suspect them and glance at his prisoner. He was instantly alerted, for in the outlaw's eyes he saw stark terror.

The desperado looked quickly toward the three strangers and back to Wesley, trying desperately to convey a silent message. His mouth was forming words without sound and his lower lip quivered. Wesley suddenly realized why these men were here. They meant to take his prisoner. He considered drawing his gun but restrained himself, thinking it would be better to withdraw suddenly with his frightened captive and ride hell for leather in the direction of Houston. Although he was forced to admit that these strangers had come in peace and had made no move to indicate hostility, he ordered Sam to bring the horses and told the outlaw to rise.

The Negro obeyed and they mounted quickly. Wesley did not take time to tie the man's hands behind him. He felt foolish then, for the three strangers made no move to rise or to hinder him as he prepared to move out.

"Why the sudden hurry, young man?" asked the eldest of the trio.

"No hurry, sir," replied Wesley, "except that I want to be in Houston before sundown."

"Being as we're bound for Houston, too, do you mind if we ride along with you?"

"It's a public road," said Wesley crisply. "Lead out, Sam."

The Negro rode his horse past the men, leading the animal upon which the prisoner was riding. Wesley followed close behind, and when they crossed the creek and climbed the south bank they spurred their horses into a swinging gallop down the West Montgomery Road.

They had put less than a quarter mile behind them when the three men overhauled them and rode abreast of Wesley, directly behind the outlaw's horse, which Sam was leading. They continued in this fashion until they reached the woods along the run of Cypress Creek. Then, without warning, they were surrounded by a large group of riders who appeared suddenly out of the timber on both sides of the road.

Acting on impulse, Wesley's hand flew to his revolver. He did not draw the weapon, however, but turned his bay slowly, eying every man in the cordon that drew tighter about them.

"What's the meaning of this?" he demanded. "I'm a Texas Ranger with a prisoner I intend to deliver to my commanding officer in Houston. Move aside and let us through. Now!" He bit the last word off viciously as he pulled the big pistol from his holster.

One of the men who had drunk coffee with him back at Spring Creek said in a slow drawl, "Just a minute, Ranger." Wesley turned his horse to face the speaker. "You have a prisoner, yes. You have a man who murdered Ben Simonton and his pretty wife in cold blood when they walked into the bank in Montgomery the other morning. That same man and his band of cutthroats murdered the cashier of the bank. He helped burn our homes about our heads and brought grief and misery to a fine little community. There sits Ben Simonton's brother. Do you have any idea how he feels about this? No, I don't suppose you do. Well, let me tell you. He feels that he should have the satisfaction of seeing justice done for the murder of his brother and his brother's wife."

"You listen to me!" Wesley's voice cracked with suppressed anger. "I intend to carry this man——"

"You listen to me!" roared the other. "We know you could kill one or two of us before we got you, but we don't believe you would pull your trigger one time to save a murdering bastard like him." He pointed in the general direction of the outlaw without taking his eyes off Wesley. "We respect the Rangers," he continued. "We believe you must be a pretty fine young man or you wouldn't have that badge on. But believe me, we're going to have that murdering scoundrel one way or another. Now put your gun away and be sensible, and think how you would feel if you were Rube Simonton here."

He pointed toward the murdered man's brother, who was quietly sitting his horse directly in front of Wesley.

[93]

At the last remark Wesley's mind whirled back to that night at The Oaks when a murderer had taken the life of his father, and suddenly he felt himself weakening. Perhaps he should turn this man over to these people. Certainly he would want to avenge his father's death, so why should this brother be denied the same right? But he could not do this, for he had a duty to perform, a sworn duty. He looked again at young Simonton and saw that he sat his horse stolidly, with no show of emotion whatever. But in that face he saw determination, the kind that caused him to wonder if he could hope to win.

"I'm telling you once more," Wesley said, "that it is my intention to carry this man to Houston, alive and unharmed. I hope you see it my way, for I don't want to hurt anyone. Move out ahead of me, Sam."

"I can't, Mistuh Wes. Dis gentmun is holdin' my hoss."

As Wesley touched his stallion with the spurs and attempted to ride through the group of horsemen to Sam's aid, something struck him from behind and knocked him from the saddle. In falling, he dropped his revolver, which landed several feet away from where he hit the ground flat of his back. Before he could dive for the gun, a half dozen men pinned him where he had fallen.

Wesley made a valiant attempt to fight, but the men held him fast. They sat him up and tied his hands behind him with rawhide cut from the tie strings of a saddle. Then he saw that others of the group had trussed Sam and the outlaw in a similar fashion.

"Sorry I had to hit you, young man," said the elderly man, evidently the leader. "But this devil and his gang of cutthroats have been terrorizing this part of Texas for several years. Now you will be obliged to watch justice administered."

"Let's get this business over and done with," he said, helping Wesley to his feet.

One of the men threw the rope, one end of which they had knotted about the outlaw's neck, over a low sturdy limb and, pulling out the slack, tied it to another tree. Wesley made his way through the crowd and stood facing the man who was about to die.

"I don't even know your name," he said. "Now I never want to know it. I just hope you realize that I tried the best I knew how to save your life. A man just such as you killed my father not very long ago, and someday I'm going to find him and kill him, but I don't want anyone to help me do it. If I could I'd turn you loose right now. Then I'd track you down and either kill you or bring you back to stand trial. I'm not quite sure what I'm saying but, believe me, I'm sorry you are going to die this way."

The outlaw sat silently on his horse, head down, eyes closed. Wesley wondered if the man had even heard him.

Without any word, the group standing in front of the doomed man's horse moved back, leaving a lane some ten feet wide. Reuben Simonton took a step that brought him to the man's side. "This is for my brother, you dirty, murdering sonofabitch!" he yelled.

Then he lashed the horse violently across the rump with his quirt.

In one leap the animal was gone, leaving the outlaw swinging back and forth in a wide arc, his feet scant inches from the ground. The knot had jerked tight as the horse ran from under him, and now he was slowly strangling to death. His face turned from tan to red to purple in moments. His legs threshed about several times, then he was still, except for his arms, which continued to strain against the bonds that held them. His body wheeled slowly one way, then the other, as the swing of the arc gradually diminished. Then, with a single violent rigor, the outlaw died.

Wesley felt himself tremble with excitement. He stood tense without moving, without turning his gaze from the body. As he stood there the leader of the lynching party cut the bonds from his hands and handed him his gun.

"Young man," he said, "I don't think you'll attempt anything foolish. Now go in and report to Major Tarbone just what happened. Tell him we admire your courage and the way you conducted yourself here today. I wish you would also tell him that you have a great deal to learn about life and about men such as this one. Now shall we help you get the man down and on his horse?"

Wesley gave no indication that he had heard, and presently the group rode rapidly in the direction of Montgomery, leaving him to slump heavily to the ground where, for long minutes, he held his head in his hands, trying to think.

The outlaw hanging up there represented something. It was new to Wesley, grisly, terrible. It was justice of a kind, frontier justice. It was brutal, perhaps, and it represented unrestrained violence; and yet the outlaw deserved the rope of decent men. But there was something wrong in the scheme of justice. Fate dealt it and man could not escape it. Man, therefore, should and must control it. By law. As he thought this way he realized, as though in startled discovery, that he was planning to return to Kentucky to deal with the murderer of his father, because the law would not.

Thoroughly confused and shaken by the event, Wesley looked at the badge pinned to his shirt and pondered its significance. Then he rose wearily and asked Sam to help him cut the dead man down. When the awful chore was done, they caught the dead outlaw's horse, tied the body securely across the saddle, and set out for Houston.

11. The Search for Land

THE BROTHERS and Sam left Houston early next morning. They rode north across the open prairie and entered the timber some twenty miles from the rough town of bitter memories. Wesley seemed more reticent than usual, for he had seen death by violence in Houston streets and saloons and another death at the end of a rope. The parting with Major Tarbone after the full story had been told failed to cheer him, despite the fact that the major found no fault with his conduct while wearing the badge. Furthermore, Tarbone could not blame the group from Montgomery. Nor could Wesley blame them. Even so, the pieces failed to fit any pattern he could either condone or condemn. It had been at best a most unhappy experience, which he had concluded with a statement that seemed fittingly proper:

"Major, I don't think I'd ever make a good Ranger."

They rode on, across more prairie, and entered the pine belt at Spring Creek, both boys studying the country with ideas of ownership, neither of them finding anything appealing in the low, poorly drained land abounding in alligators, turtles, and snakes. They met a man in a gleaming black buggy, Sam Lindley, who praised the land east of Danville, and that lying in a triangle between Swartout, Huntsville, and Montgomery. Lindley told them much of the land could still be bought at a fair price.

In Danville they put up at the new Tabor Hotel and for a week searched for land. One day they came upon a section of upland prairie where the grass stood tall and green on the black sandy loam.

"This is the land for me, Joe," said Wesley as he dismounted and picked up a handful of the rich soil.

"Pretty all right, but let's ride the triangle Mr. Lindley suggested, Wes."

Early the following morning they took the trail in an easterly direction, toward Swartout. This was timberland. The pines rose tall and slender as far as the eye could see. However, the grass was short and dry and the farms they passed seemed barren. Toward midafternoon the trail dropped gradually into a rich, fertile valley where the pines were replaced by immense oaks, elms, and pecan trees. Here grass grew in abundance and the fields of cotton, heavy with squares and blooms and bolls, were bordered by rail fences that reminded them of Kentucky. Small areas were planted in tobacco, potatoes, and corn, and there were green pastures and fat cattle.

Far ahead, over the green fields and pastures, was the dim outline of the large town of Swartout on the Trinity River, and downstream a cloud of black smoke poured from the stacks of a river steamer. Here was pretty land; it was good and rich.

They entered Swartout ahead of the *Camilla Belle* and watched her warp in and disgorge passengers and freight. One of the men who walked ashore was the soldier who had tried to arrest them at the Sabine crossing. However,

Corporal Spangler was not dressed in army blue. He walked directly toward them, his teeth flashing white against the dark tan of his face. There was threat in his eyes when he came to a halt before Wesley.

"Well, well! Seems I found you sooner than I expected. Now I'd like you to take off that big gun so we can see just how good you are with your fists."

Wesley was unbuckling his gun belt when Joe stepped between him and Spangler. His fist flashed and Spangler fell heavily. Instantly he was on his feet, and in the furious exchange of blows he gave as good as he received. The grin remained a part of his expression throughout the fight, which came to an abrupt end when Joe landed a smashing blow under Spangler's ear. When the ex-corporal finally staggered to his feet his bloody mouth was still grinning.

"We'll meet again, I hope," he said.

He turned abruptly and shouldered his way through the crowd.

Joe was taken to a doctor, who sewed his cut lip and cleansed his bleeding knuckles. Following this, the boys went to the hotel, bathed and changed clothes, and made inquiries about land for sale. Shortly after sunset they entered the hotel dining hall and ordered their supper. While they waited, a man took a chair across the table from them. Instantly they recognized Robert James McGowen, their friend and host from Aberdeen.

Wesley leaped to his feet. "Mr. McGowen! This is a real pleasure. But what are you doing in Texas this soon?"

"It's the big secret I had to keep from my wife, lads. So I told nobody."

During the meal he said that he had cleared a great deal of land and had built a large colonial home. Now everything was ready and he intended to return to Aberdeen for his wife during the coming week. What a surprise when she saw her new home in Texas! McGowen beamed with eagerness.

"And you, my lads, are going to be my first house guests," he boomed. "This very night, and for as long as you will stay."

McGowen would not take no for an answer. Host in Aberdeen, now host in Texas, he drove them to his home that night. Even in the dark of night both boys felt that a bit of the South they had known had been transplanted on Texas soil. Nestled among great oaks, the big house with its four fluted columns stood like a scene in Natchez in the starry night. Up the long graveled drive, and drawing closer, lights burning behind cut-glass panels and fanlight created prisms of color. Closer, chandeliers could be seen through the tall french windows. They shed a mellow, cheery light on the gold and crimson furnishings.

That night Wesley ran a hand over the fine wood of a chest in their room, turned his gaze on the rich appointments, and said, "Joe, this is what I want. But first we have to find the land to support a plantation."

"And a town to support my store," Joe replied.

For two days they rode up and down the Trinity River in search of the ideal place to settle. Failing to locate land that they wanted, they thanked McGowen for his hospitality and rode in the general direction of Huntsville. Late in the afternoon they came to a neat log dwelling and dismounted to ask directions to the nearest town.

Over the jamb of the door were painted two words: RAVEN HILL. They realized then that this was the new farm home of General Sam Houston, President of Texas.

The only person about the place was an old Negro servant, who directed them to Huntsville. They had scarcely turned their horses when two men drove up in a buggy. They were General Sam Houston and the handsome ex-

Georgian, George T. Wood, who was destined to be the second governor of Texas.

Upon the general's insistence, they remained to partake of his hospitality and spend a pleasant evening at Raven Hill. As the two older men drank their whisky and water and spun rich and interesting tales of frontier life in Texas, Joe and Wesley sat in attentive silence.

As the evening wore on, Houston became less reticent on the subject of Texas entering the Union. George Wood was unalterably opposed to such a plan. Houston strongly favored statehood for Texas, because, he said, the United States would assume the seven-million-dollar indebtedness of the republic. His booming voice became louder and louder as the liquor urged him on. George Wood, keeping his voice low and even, argued that the United States was already taking away the authority vested in the states by the Constitution and that the Republic of Texas was deliberately putting its head in the lion's mouth. The import and export duties alone, he argued, would retire the public debt in a few years. And, if Texas went into the Union, these revenues would be taken by the federal government.

But Sam Houston had sold himself on the idea of statehood for Texas, and he would brook no argument against his theories. Finally George Wood rose and faced his friend.

"Sam," he said without anger, "you're a damned fool. I've known you as a friend for a long time and believe you have better sense than you show in some of your arguments. These young men here," he indicated Joe and Wesley, "have told us that they are coming to make their homes in Texas to get away from the very thing that you are preaching for Texas to stumble headlong into. This republic is far from bankrupt, as you would like to have us believe. We have the potentialities of the greatest nation in the world, and I hope that your arguments won't influence enough Texas people to vote us into servility."

"George!" roared the general, pounding the arm of his chair. "You are the fool! How in hell can Texas ever pay a public debt of seven million dollars? Seven million dollars! Do you understand how much money that is? Texas needs the United States to protect her from another invasion of the Mexicans too. Another war would see Texas ruined physically and financially, and I refuse to be a party to it."

Wood smiled bitterly. "I'm not going to carry this argument any further, Sam. But I do want to make a prediction. If Texas accepts statehood within the next two or three years, she will be fighting to win back her rights within a few more short years."

Although they listened to the heated argument far into the night, Joe and Wesley were in the saddle shortly after sunrise. George Wood had risen also, though the general was apparently indisposed from his bout with the bourbon bottle. The boys asked Wood to convey their thanks to him for a pleasant night and took the trail to Huntsville.

In the two days that followed they passed through the hilly little town of Huntsville and turned southwest in the direction of Montgomery. They saw many farms that had been carved out of the wilderness of Texas, and near Danville they came upon their first Indian village. This was a part of the Tejas tribe, and it surprised the boys that the Indians were living in such close proximity to the white settlers. They moved on and bought provisions at the Richards store in Danville and, before nightfall, rode up to the livery stable in the flourishing town of Montgomery.

The owner told them that since the bank robbers had

burned most of the town perhaps they should bed down in his hayloft for the night. This they did.

Early next morning Wesley and Joe walked through what had been the heart of Montgomery. One of the first persons they saw was young Reuben Simonton, the man who had slashed his quirt across the rump of the outlaw's horse down on Cypress Creek. He was leaning against a gallery post of one of the few unburned buildings, watching them intently.

Wesley stopped, eyed him a moment, then stuck out a hand. "Good morning, Mr. Simonton," he said pleasantly. "No hard feelings about what happened on Cypress Creek."

Simonton seemed to have been waiting for some declaration of Wesley's sentiments, for he smiled and pushed himself lazily away from the post to take Wesley's hand. "I'm glad you feel that way," he said. "Like we told you down there, we had no quarrel with you. You were doing what you thought was right and so were we. But I would hang that dirty bastard every day of my life if I could, even if I had to fight you every time I did it."

Wesley nodded understandingly.

"You can see what they did to Montgomery," said Simonton, sweeping the gutted buildings with a wave of his hand.

As the three strolled down the street looking at the burned town, several other men whose faces were familiar to Wesley joined them. Finally at the end of the street they came to a neat little coffeehouse that had escaped the fire. Before the cups were drained, Wesley discovered that he liked these people; better, in fact, than any he had met since coming to Texas.

Joe shared the feeling also. His eyes were eager and sharp as he studied the burned town later in the day. That night he spoke of a store site and told Wesley that Montgomery was, as far as he was concerned, the end of the quest.

"It's up to you now, Wes."

Wesley nodded. Looking at Joe, he realized that it really was up to him. He and Joe had grown up together, had been almost inseparable. The thought of losing a brother as companion was not inviting.

"Mr. Simonton promised to show me some fine land tomorrow, Joe. God knows I hope it's what I want."

Simonton spent several days with Wesley. In the saddle the pair studied various tracts, one of which was the homestead of the brother who had been killed by the bank robbers. It was good land. It promised much to the man who would work it. The grass was tall and lush, the soil rich. Cotton, cattle, tobacco, corn—Wesley saw them in a dreaming gaze into the future, the same as he saw a great white house, like McGowen's, and heard Aunt Polly's voice ringing in the halls. Then he heard himself saying:

"I'd like to buy it, Mr. Simonton. This homestead and more land adjoining it."

Reuben Simonton smiled. He knew the mettle of this young man who had, singlehanded, defied a host of men. He liked what he saw in Wesley Smith's face. But men seldom speak of the bonds uniting them. Simonton was no exception.

"You'll probably want to build a big house, Wesley. If you do, I'd like for you to check on me. I'm a designer and builder."

"I'll have to sell out in Kentucky first, Mr. Simonton. It'll take most of my ready cash to buy the land I want."

"Pay me later."

That was the extent of their business contract. Wesley acquired several thousand acres of land in the weeks that followed, and Joe purchased the store site he wanted. The people of Montgomery opened their homes to the Smith boys, gave them ideas to incorporate into the design for their home, and offered their services wherever and whenever needed.

It was a good wholesome feeling to be wanted. It was good to find a place to anchor. It was like watching a dream slowly materialize as they watched with youthful eagerness and feelings of pride and ownership while rail fences went up on their own land. On the site chosen for their new home, the house, barns, slave quarters, and outbuildings were laid out. And Reuben Simonton promised to do his utmost to complete the building program before their return in early 1845.

The brothers departed from Montgomery on Monday, November 25, 1844, for Paris, Kentucky. Although this was a part of the plan, they rode away in deep silence. Both of them seemed to realize that they were no longer boys, despite their years, but men riding out of the promising future back into a troubled past where more trouble awaited them.

Wesley looked gravely ahead at the trail that day. Behind his eyes was a conflict of emotions, tender memories of his father on the one hand, hatred of his father's murderer on the other.

12. Christmas, 1844

I t w a s on a cold, dreary Saturday afternoon just four
days before Christmas when Wesley and Joe saw Tom
Weaver's house in the distance. Though both were anxious to see their friend and to get inside out of the cold,
they sat their horses and looked at the familiar land about
them. Any joy at seeing it again was dimmed by the fact
that they had been driven from it. Just as they moved on,
Joe said something in a low bitter voice about their having
to come home branded as outlaws.

Tom Weaver met them with a warm smile of welcome
wreathing his face. After ordering a boy to take their
horses, he placed an arm about the shoulders of each and
led them inside, where he ordered coffee and said he had
been sitting before the fire wondering where they were
and how they were faring. Kentucky had changed, he
said, but so had they. Wesley looked more like a twenty-
one-year-old man than a lad of fifteen. But it was Christmas, he added, and old friends had returned.

Warming his hands, Wesley realized that Weaver referred to the granite hardness in his face, which even Joe

had spoken of lately. But the change from boy to man had been forced on him with a suddenness likely to change anyone. He looked into the fire and wondered about many things: the circumstances that wrought the change in him; where Tobin was, and how he himself would feel when and if he killed the man who had murdered his father.

The fire burned on, crackling and hissing, and coffee was served. Weaver talked incessantly, and as the black steaming brew warmed the boys he advised that he and Traylor had done very well with their plantation. Furthermore, they had found a buyer for The Oaks, two brothers from Ohio. Robert and Ben Blake, though admittedly Yankees, were slaveowners and in complete sympathy with the problems of the South. The offer was a good one, he said, all cash, but the deeds had to be signed in the presence of Joe and Wesley. The Blakes were due back Christmas Day.

Wesley and Joe nodded, neither moving his gaze from the fire. Breaking old ties renewed heartaches.

"That's the way we wanted it, Mr. Weaver," Wesley said at last. "We appreciate what you and Mr. Traylor have done for us."

Then, as if he found relief in telling about the land and their plans in Texas, Wesley talked on until the servants announced supper.

After the meal Weaver drew Wesley aside and, after due deliberation, said, "Son, are you still in the notion of meeting Tobin?"

Wesley frowned, looked into the fire a moment before meeting the other's gaze directly. "I'll tell you, Mr. Weaver, that man's face has never left my mind for a moment since I saw him shoot Father. As much as I dread it, I intend to kill him if it's the last thing I do."

Tom Weaver smoothed his mustache with a forefinger

and nodded. He did not attempt to carry the conversation further.

Next morning Joe and Wesley skirted Paris as they had done upon leaving Kentucky and rode to The Oaks. As they crossed the little stream back of the house and began climbing the hill they heard a scream of delight.

"Heah comes my boys! Heah comes my boys! Git dis house ready, yo' lazy niggers." Setting all the darkies scurrying about the chores she had assigned them, Aunt Polly marched happily and triumphantly through the house to stand, arms akimbo, on the veranda to await the arrival of Wesley and Joe.

As they rode up and dismounted, the old black's haughty manner disappeared and she heaved a great sob as she gathered them into her huge arms. Mist formed in the boys' eyes as the three of them turned to go into the house. Aunt Polly, however, could not miss an opportunity to berate one of her kind, and she turned on Sam with glaring eyes and a sharp tongue.

"Sam. Yo' there, Sam! Git dem hosses off dat drive befo' they messes up ever'thing we done done to get dis place ready fo' Christmas."

As they entered the house a blaze of light greeted them. The big parlor was ready for Christmas. A ceiling-high tree stood in its appointed corner, glittering with little glass figurines, strings of popcorn, and tiny lines of cotton laid carefully along the top of each limb and branch. Around the base of the tree were piles of gaily wrapped gifts. The room was bright from the dozens of shimmering candles, and branches of evergreen were everywhere. The brothers realized then that both Mrs. Traylor and Aunt Polly had indeed been busy making their last Christmas at The Oaks a happy and delightful experience.

The next two days were busy ones for Joe and Wesley.

They personally supervised the readying of the huge caravan that would leave for Texas on Christmas Day. Everything was loaded, from farming equipment, feed, extra harness, and furniture to all the personal belongings of the darkies. The cattle and horses had been rounded up earlier and sent on their southward trek already, with orders to the drivers to proceed strictly to the map and schedule Wesley had prepared, bypassing the towns as much as possible. The wagon train would overtake them before they reached Natchez, where the entire caravan would ferry across the broad Mississippi and proceed across Louisiana in a southwesterly direction and enter Texas on the road leading to Nacogdoches.

Under the direction of Mrs. Traylor and Aunt Polly, the staff of domestics prepared a bountiful meal for the Christmas Eve party. It had been snowing since early morning, and at six in the evening, when the guests began to arrive, the ground was covered in a deep white blanket and the trees around the house and along the drive were bending low with their white mantle. The air was crisp and dry and cold and the roaring flames in the fireplaces at The Oaks were welcomed by the many friends who entered in little swirls of snow with happy cries of "Merry Christmas."

None of the guests mentioned the fact that this would be the last party Joe and Wesley would ever give at The Oaks. It was not until after the big dinner and the distribution of presents that Lewis Traylor, Tom Weaver, and Reverend Milo Walker drew Joe and Wesley into the library. Over coffee, the banker broached the subject of the sale, then the meeting between Wesley and Tobin.

"The way I look at it," said Reverend Walker, "may be wrong in the sight of God, but I say to you, Wesley, since your father's murderer was never brought to justice, and

since you seem determined to kill him, do the deed, but
without hatred in your heart. Kill him as you would a
mad dog or a snake."

This was not a strange or surprising statement from Milo
Walker, for he was first of all a stern realist, a stern man;
his preaching, by comparison, seemed more an adopted
profession. Some men were like that, and none the less
godly for it.

Wesley nodded respectfully, then spoke of the plans employed to entice Tobin to Paris. A message supposedly
from Hazelett had been sent to Tobin asking him to be in
Paris the day after Christmas, and Tobin had sent word
by the messenger that he would arrive at around ten in the
morning.

"I don't want any of our friends present when the
trouble begins," Wesley told them firmly. "Just Joe and I.
Joe will station himself at an upstairs window of the store
to see that nobody shoots me in the back."

The banker stroked his chin thoughtfully. "It's a wise
precaution, all right," he said, "since there is the possibility that Tobin and Hazelett might get together before
the time comes and figure the whole thing out."

Christmas morning dawned clear and cold. The Oaks
buzzed with activity and seeming confusion as the big
caravan formed and began the long trek to Texas. By noon
the last of the many wagons and buggies wound up the
hill back of the house under the watchful eyes of Friday
Fance, who had been named wagon boss by Wesley. Polly,
in her best taffetas and silks, occupied the entire rear seat
of the lead surrey. She had not questioned the move, but
all who knew her realized that her sly old mind was already at work with plans of dominating the new home far
to the south.

Early in the afternoon Traylor, Weaver, and the Blake

brothers arrived to consummate the sale of The Oaks. When the banker and Weaver signed the deeds as trustees of John Smith's estate, the Blakes produced the money. Some time was required for counting so much cash, almost one hundred and ninety-four thousand dollars in gold, but when it was done and most of the big sum was hoisted into Traylor's surrey for deposit to Joe's and Wesley's credit, the Blake brothers said they intended to make an offer for the store. Then Joe and Wesley were left alone to wander through the empty house.

A wave of extreme loneliness came over Wesley then. He was tempted to try to forget Tobin and ride as fast as he could after the caravan. The big home with its many memories against the present emptiness did that to him. He and Joe did not own it now. The big tie was broken. In his money belt was another five thousand dollars, small recompense for the nostalgia that assailed him.

That night Sam kept a fire going in the fireplace and the boys rolled up in their blankets. At six the next morning Sam brought a pot of steaming coffee. Joe and Wesley sat up and looked at each other, their faces grave. This was the day. Four hours separated them from a meeting with Tobin.

No word was spoken between them, and soon Joe gulped the last of his coffee and left for the store. Wesley watched him go, saw him get on his horse and turn up his collar against the freezing weather and ride off toward Paris.

Wesley returned to his blankets and sat with coffee cup in hand. He tried not to think what the morning held in store for him and gradually put the disturbing thoughts aside and dwelled on the many pleasant years ahead in Texas. He also gave considerable thought to

Margaret Arnold and wondered when he would see her again.

At around eight o'clock he dressed in heavy buckskins, buckled on his gun belt, and left the house. He walked in the snow for some time before looking at his watch. It was almost nine o'clock. In an hour he would meet Tobin. The thought startled him. A rabbit sped through the snow across his path, and in a flash he drew his pistol and fired. He missed by several feet, for he had triggered the gun long before it had come to bear on the target. Thoroughly worried now, he slammed the big gun into the holster and began drawing and shooting at a little oak some ten steps away. Not once did he hit the tree. Once his finger even failed to slip into the trigger guard as the pistol flew from the scabbard.

He holstered the gun, trembling violently, and walked rapidly back to the house. After reloading the revolver, he ordered Sam to bring his horse. The coffeepot was still on the fire. He poured a cupful, then another, all the while watching his hands, trying to regain his composure. "Planning to kill," he thought aloud, almost wonderingly. It was not the same as meeting a situation without notice. He could never be a killer, and yet he was less than half an hour from killing or being killed.

Pulling his hat tightly down on his head, he strode outside to Sam and the stallion. Jerking the reins from the startled Negro's hand, he said savagely:

"Put out the fire, close up the house, and go to Mr. Weaver's and wait for me."

He swung into the saddle, dug his spurs into the horse's flanks, and took off in a dead run through the snow for the meeting with Tobin.

Once in Paris, Wesley became alert and watchful. He approached the store cautiously and kept his eyes moving in every direction as he dismounted and tied the reins to the rail behind the store. Glancing up at the second floor, he saw a broken windowpane and he knew that Joe was behind that window with rifle ready.

Not a person was in the streets. Perhaps the weather was to blame. He kept close to the wall and waited. His watch read nine fifty-seven. The seconds ticked away. He continued to wait and then looked at his watch again, wondering where Tobin might be. It was almost ten o'clock. As he stepped away from the building, he saw the back door of the inn open slowly. A man came out and stood for a tense moment.

The man was Tobin.

It was a long shot for a pistol, though Tobin soon corrected that. He walked unhurriedly, deliberately, toward Wesley, no fear whatever in his composed face. His very manner, however, warned Wesley that Hazelett was somewhere near. Instinctively Wesley took two quick steps to his left.

This move very likely saved his life, for as he stepped aside two rifles barked almost in unison and a bullet whined past his head, slamming into the wall at his back. The bullet had come from the side, proving Hazelett's presence. The other rifle had to be Joe's. But he was given no time to verify it. He felt a tug, like a sudden wind, at his sleeve and saw a blossom of smoke from Tobin's gun.

Wesley's revolver roared twice. He saw Tobin falter and lower his pistol, a dazed look of unbelief in his eyes. Then Tobin began to fall, his knees buckling under him.

A movement to Wesley's right took his gaze off Tobin. He threw himself aside and down into the soft snow, then looked around for one of Tobin's men, bringing his gun to bear on the movement he had seen. It was not one of Tobin's henchmen. It was Marshal Hazelett.

Wesley fired and the bullet plowed into the officer's chest. Only then did he realize that Hazelett was already dead. He saw the bullet hole in the marshal's forehead as he sank to his knees and pitched forward on his face.

From upstairs Joe cried: "Stay where you are, Wes, until we see what those men are up to."

Wesley jerked his glance around and saw a half dozen men moving from the inn to where Tobin lay. "Stop where you are!" he commanded. "We want to leave without any more trouble. What about it?"

"We ain't makin' trouble, young feller. Just wanted to see where you got Tobin."

The men advanced to where Tobin lay. One of the group took a card from the poker hand he held and laid it across the two bullet holes in Tobin's chest. It covered both.

The card was the deuce of spades.

Wesley shook his head and looked away. Joe's order to stand watch while he came down saved Wesley from the awful sickness that was fast rising in his stomach.

As Joe came out of the store, Reverend Milo Walker walked toward them from the bank. He went to Tobin and knelt in silent prayer. After closing the dead man's eyes he rose and repeated the performance over Hazelett's body, then walked over to the brothers. His face was drawn and a tear stood on his cold wrinkled cheek.

"Thank God you're both safe," he said softly. "You'd better go quickly, boys. God bless you."

His hand fell to a shoulder of each boy. Then he turned away.

Joe and Wesley were soon in the saddle and rounding the corner by Dr. Randall's office. They raced on past the big tobacco warehouses and toward the little churchyard where their mother and father were buried. Here they drew their horses to a walk and, without a backward glance or any fear of pursuit, stopped before the iron gates and dismounted.

They walked through the undisturbed blanket of white snow. It sparkled in the sunshine and lay blue in the shadows of the large snow-laden oaks. Then Joe and Wesley stood at the foot of the two graves, their heads bowed in silent prayer. Long minutes passed before they raised their faces. They talked of removing their parents' remains to Texas, finally deciding against it, since both father and mother had loved Kentucky and therefore belonged in the little churchyard. They had turned to go when Wesley hesitated, then slowly faced toward his father's grave.

"I didn't want to kill Tobin, Father," he whispered. "I had to. I had to do it!"

Joe's hand touched his shoulder then and they walked slowly back through the snow to their horses. As they stepped into their saddles a wind scurried through the oaks and sent down a heavy flurry of snow to cover the deep tracks they had made across the hallowed ground that held their last tie to Kentucky.

The brothers had planned well; the plan had moved to its climax without flaw or interruption. The acquisition of land and store site in Texas had been followed by the sale of The Oaks and the exodus from Kentucky. Their father's murder had been avenged, and the land-grabbing syndicate had lost its ablest thieves through violence. The Tobin brothers and Hazelett were all dead. To their way of thinking, justice had been done.

Wesley and Joe Smith rode away from Paris, Kentucky, in heavy silence. There was no elation, no feeling of pride at having executed their plan in its entirety, no gleam of satisfaction in their grave faces. The results they had worked to bring about seemed all too sudden, too sharply defined, as sharp as the bark of a rifle. Three shots, two men dead in the snow, shock and bewilderment. The awful anticlimax had set in, it seemed, before the smoke curled from the guns and disappeared. It was loath to depart.

A deep quiet enveloped Joe. It remained a part of him all the way to Natchez. He scarcely ate, and he seemed to bristle when spoken to by either Wesley or Sam. The change in him appeared to be a permanent one, his eyes during the day speaking with despair the words he cried out in troubled sleep at night.

"I killed a man! I killed a man!"

Rousing Joe again, Wesley said as before, "Joe, you saved my life when you shot Hazelett. Think of it that way."

"I know. I'd do it all over if I had to. But I'll never be the same again. Now leave me alone."

13. Caravan to Montgomery

DUDE JUSTICE was tall and rangy, a man with steady gray eyes set in a strong, tanned face that seldom showed disturbance. He seemed to speak only when words were absolutely necessary. His reticence, together with a seemingly careless ease of motion, lent him a certain authority which few men challenged. It is doubtful that Dude Justice knew this, for he was not a man given to self-appraisal; rather his mind dwelled on business to the exclusion of almost all else. His loyalty to the Smith family was a matter of record, and now his resourcefulness was up for notice.

He rode up and down the long line of wagons, buggies, and surreys, on to the herds of cattle and horses, back to give some order to Friday Fance, to mend a break in the string of vehicles by hurrying a wagon or surrey ahead or to repair a broken wheel or axle. The grinding of wheels, the shuffle of teams and harness, the crying of Negro babies, often the strumming of banjoes and guitars, the voices of Negroes raised in spirituals, the crack of whips and shouts of drivers rang in his ears. The smells of dung, sweat, wheel grease, coffee and bacon on the fire were a part of any wagon train. He was used to these things. He expected sickness, a birth or two along the way, and, as slaves were valuable as well as unused to long winter travel, their welfare was a part of his responsibility. Beyond these things, decisions had to be made daily, sometimes hourly. Swollen streams, deep mud on the roads kept him busy in bad weather. The threat of Indians on the warpath and highwaymen kept him vigilant. Upon arriving in Natchez, the job of finding feed and pastures for the cattle and horses fell his lot.

Dude Justice felt somewhat relieved when Joe and Wesley caught up with the caravan. While he continued as before their arrival, the burden of decisions was shared by Wesley, whom he accorded the same sincere respect he had given the boy's father. Moreover, it was an earned respect, which grew out of the youngster's uncanny but mature judgment in handling affairs of the plantation assigned him by John Smith long before his death.

Dude did not ask about the meeting with Tobin, though Wesley told briefly what had happened. Justice had come to talk about ferrying the caravan across the Mississippi. The prices were too high, he said. The owner of the ferry was demanding three dollars per head for the cattle and horses, ten dollars for each vehicle, and fifty cents per person.

Wesley and Joe decided to call upon the ferryman, and when they entered his office they saw a large sign behind his desk:

Vehicles, including team	$1.25
Livestock, per head	.20
Persons, each	.10

When the owner laughed and said the sign was an old

one, that they could accept the prices or find another place to cross over to Vidalia, Louisiana, Joe called him a "damned robber." The big boatman came up with a swinging fist that opened the cut that Joe had suffered in the fight with Jack Spangler at Swartout. With blood covering his shirt front, Joe charged and finally succeeded in beating the man to the floor. A pitcher of water poured over him revived the man and he sat up, grinning despite the pain.

"Son," he said, "I've been whupped befo', but never by a better man. Them boat prices are just what yo' see on the sign there."

Wesley informed him they would begin loading at dawn next morning. He produced an inventory prepared by Dude Justice, and from this the loading sequence was determined. The ferryman suggested a certain number of livestock and vehicles for each boat crossing, the cattle and horses to be driven into the hold, the vehicles to the open deck. He could ferry the entire caravan before night-fall, he said.

At four o'clock next morning Wesley, Dude Justice, and Friday Fance were busily engaged in moving the huge caravan. The plan called for an orderly movement through the streets of Natchez so that another load would always be waiting at the water front when the big boat returned from the Louisiana side. Aunt Polly had been supervising the early breakfast preparations, and all hands were ready to move before the sun peeped over the flat rolling land behind the bluff. It was agreed that Joe and Dude would cross with the first contingent, taking Aunt Polly and her kitchen staff, and go into temporary camp, with Wesley and Friday Fance staying on the Natchez side of the river to supervise the loading.

Aunt Polly's surrey was approaching the long ramp to

the boat when she cried out to Wesley, "Now look heah, Mistuh Wes, I intends to go where yo' says go, but dis ole nigger is scared o' all dat water. Plumb sho nuff scared."

Wesley laughed and handed her a large handkerchief, saying, "Tie this over your eyes, Aunt Polly. And don't take it off until you reach land."

She obeyed him and was soon sitting blindfolded in her surrey. Wesley watched the big boat move out into the lazy Mississippi and grow smaller as it approached the Louisiana side. It had not touched land when his attention was drawn to a pair of fine bay mares and a bright new surrey. A start of pleasant surprise came with his glance at the occupants, Robert James McGowen, his wife and children.

Before the ferry returned from the opposite shore, Wesley and McGowen had decided to join their wagon trains and travel to Texas on a southerly route that would take them to Swartout on the Trinity River.

By noon of the following day the McGowen wagon train had crossed the river and the long caravan got under way. The McGowens rode in the lead surrey with outriders posted at frequent intervals to prevent ambush by highwaymen or Indians in the thick virgin forests of Louisiana. The long line of animals and vehicles moved steadily on, and after long days of wet, blustery Louisiana weather and ferrying the Sabine and Neches rivers, the big caravan wound down the muddy trail to begin the tiresome and difficult task of crossing the swollen, muddy Trinity on the little ferry that would carry them to the bustling town of Swartout.

Wesley prevailed upon McGowen to leave both caravans in his charge and proceed to the new home with his wife and children to spring his great surprise. With a promise to camp at McGowen's place after the crossing, Wesley and Dude Justice worked tirelessly all that day. At nightfall, when the last of the vehicles left the ferry, Wesley rode back to the temporary camp and paused to determine the source of hilarious laughter and loud talk somewhere among the Negroes. Then he saw Dude Justice approaching on foot.

"Glad you came, Mr. Wes," he said. "I need some help with Mr. Joe."

"Help with Joe?"

"He and some old acquaintance are on a tear, mean drunk. I finally got them to camp, but they've been threatening to shoot me and the niggers and just clean up the town in general."

Wesley followed Justice to one of the campfires and saw Joe's companion staggering toward a terrified group of slaves. He was waving a half-filled whisky bottle and yelling: "Sing louder, damn ye!"

The man was ex-corporal Spangler.

Unable to believe that Joe could strike up a friendship with this man, Wesley moved slowly to where his brother lay sprawled on the ground.

"What in heaven's name happened to you, Joe?" he demanded.

"Hi ya, Wes," said Joe after bringing his brother into focus. "Jus' havin' a little fun. Jus' a little fun. Me an' good ole Jackson got tired of fightin', so we jus'—jus' decided to be friends." Raising himself on an elbow, he cried, "Hey, Jackson, come over here an' meet my li'l brother."

Spangler obeyed. "Hi ya, li'l brother," he said, weaving back and forth as he eyed Wesley. "Have a drink with me an' Joe."

Wesley seized the bottle and flung it into the fire. "Get out, Spangler. Get out, right now," he ordered.

As Spangler muttered threats, Joe tried to rise and, failing, collapsed. Then the drunken troublemaker, who was becoming more of a menace with each meeting, lurched out of sight toward the town of Swartout.

Wesley had the Negroes wrap Joe in blankets and place him in a wagon. After ordering Sam to keep watch over his brother, he left for the McGowen mansion, his mind troubled by Joe's behavior. He slept little that night, for a question he could not answer kept rearing its ugly head:

Had the shooting of Hazelett done this to his brother?

Up at dawn the next morning, he went straightway to Joe and found him sitting with his head in his hands. Joe stared at him, eyes bloodshot, mouth drawn and sullen.

"Looks like you could attend to your own business, Wes. Now get away and leave me alone."

Wesley smiled and joined Dude Justice in getting the wagon train on the road to Montgomery. The livestock moved out first. When the buggies and surreys finally joined the procession of wagons, Justice rode the line for an hour, then drew his horse abreast of Wesley's. His silence was broken at last with a statement of concern:

"Mr. Wes, Mr. Joe hasn't been the same lately. Whatever it is, it's not good for him."

That was his speech. Justice spurred ahead after saying it, leaving Wesley staring after him.

Heavy clouds were rolling in from the northeast as they left the flat land of the Trinity River bottom and began the climb into the rolling hills that formed the divide between the Trinity and the East San Jacinto rivers. Before noon the wind shifted from east to south and on around to the west. In its gusty sweep rain fell in blinding torrents. Then a strong norther blew in and the rain began to freeze.

With the oiled canvas tied down securely on the vehicles and the horseback riders wrapped in their oilskins, they managed to make fair headway through the storm. Nightfall found them making wet camp on the Samuel Lindley plantation northeast of the town of Willis. Fires were finally started and the cold, weather-beaten travelers hovered over them, hungrily awaiting their supper. Wesley nosed his horse through the camp to see that everything was in order, and as he sat his saddle in the biting cold he wondered how Joe was faring after a long day of jolting over the rough trail in a springless wagon.

Seeing Aunt Polly standing at the rear of a wagon holding a coffee pot, he made his way to her, dismounted, and pulled the rear canvas back. There was Joe sitting in his blankets, eating hungrily.

His mouth filled with food, Joe smiled and mumbled a greeting. His eyes had cleared and he seemed himself again.

The meal finished, Joe said falteringly, "Wes, I'm sorry about last night. I just——"

"Forget it, Joe. Let's talk about something else."

As far as Wesley was concerned, Joe's drunken spree was relegated to the forgotten past. He wanted very much to know how Joe had fallen in with Jack Spangler, but now that the subject was closed, he was wise enough to wait until another time.

They awoke early the next morning to the appetizing aroma of food cooking over open fires. White smoke from the many blazes climbed steadily through the tall pines toward the stars. A pink glow in the east foretold the coming of a welcome sun that would warm the land and make their coming into their new home a happy and thrilling occasion. Before the sun peeped through the pines, the

teams were hitched and some of the vehicles were already
on the trail.

The brothers ate breakfast in silence. Joe looked sad and
preoccupied, and this worried Wesley. After handing his
empty plate and coffee cup to Sam, Joe got to his feet and
stood with his back against a tree.

"Wes," Joe began slowly, "I don't want you to even look
around until I've finished what I have to say." He groped
for words before continuing. "I'm still terribly ashamed of
what happened. Not ashamed of getting drunk as much
as it was of seeing myself compared to you. You're always
able to meet anything that comes up, while I have to feel
my way along, never certain whether I'm right or wrong.
I know if I stay with you, Wes, I'll never do anything but
hold onto your shirttail. Every time I let go of that shirttail I always do the very thing that makes the most trouble
for us both."

Wesley waited patiently, without once turning a glance
on his brother. He stared into the fire, wondering what
solution to the problem Joe had in mind.

"When we get to Willis this morning, Wes," Joe said,
"I'm going to leave. Pull away on my own. I'd like to take
Sam and his family, a few of the horses, a wagon and
buggy. I may write a draft for enough of the money we
have to start a store. Maybe as much as ten thousand dol-
lars, no more. Now before you turn around or say a word,
Wes, I want you to know I mean every word I've spoken.
I'm not going to change my mind."

Wesley continued to look sadly into the fire for long
minutes.

"Come sit down a minute, Joe," he said finally. His older
brother dropped down beside him. "You can't mean what
you said. And I can't even imagine what it would be like
without you. We've been together all our lives, Joe, and

you don't hang onto my shirttail. I hang onto yours. What about our fine new home in Montgomery?" His voice trailed off as tears welled in his eyes.

It was the first time Joe had ever seen his brother cry, but he was still determined to carry through with his plans. They mounted their horses and rode side by side in silence. Finally, as they moved up the long incline that led into Willis, Wesley turned in his saddle to face his brother.

"I know what we'll do, Joe," he said. "This is the answer we've both been looking for. Let's go on to Montgomery, and when I meet Major Tarbone in Houston I'll join the Texas Rangers, just as I've wanted to do all along. I don't want to run a plantation or a store, Joe. You do. See? It's as simple as that. You stay in Montgomery, I stay in the Rangers."

"I told you back yonder my mind was made up," Joe replied a little angrily. "I mean it. Do you understand?"

Wesley nodded, trying desperately to think of some argument that might prevail upon Joe.

"Besides," Joe continued, "you're not fooling me. You don't want to be a damned Ranger any more than I do."

"All right, Joe," breathed Wesley heavily. "If you are that determined, I can't stop you. But you are going to take your full share of everything—livestock, darkies, and money."

"I don't need any of the darkies except Sam and his family. And I don't intend to take over ten thousand dollars of the money," he growled. "I'll just take what I have to have to get started, no more. Now I'd rather we didn't say anything more about it." He put out his hand. "I'll miss you, Wes."

"Will I hear from you, Joe?" Wesley asked, taking his brother's hand.

Joe nodded, then turned his horse to go in search of Sam.

Wesley pulled his bay around and watched his older brother with a little smile. "He'll be back in a few days," he whispered to himself. "Because we need each other too much."

Later Dude Justice told him that Joe had turned back along the trail, taking Sam and his family, two of the wagons, a surrey, and three saddle horses. Wesley said nothing but slowly reined his horse and rode the line of march to a position at the head of the train winding its way toward Montgomery.

14. Heralds of the Future

WESLEY rode ahead now, scanning the country from each hilltop for a glimpse of his house. Expecting to see a half-completed mansion, and eager for just that, he raced on to the top of another hill and saw in the distance a long white house partially hidden by oaks and pines. It sat where he thought his place should be. Then he realized that it was his, that by some miracle Reuben Simonton had created a thing of beauty out of the lumber and steel and brick and stone Wesley had seen rising before leaving for Kentucky.

It was pretty in the winter sun, and he sat his saddle, staring, with strange emotions at work inside him. It was home, the beginning of a new life. He was both proud and humble. Bowing his head, Wesley sent up a silent prayer of thanks, in which he dedicated himself anew to Texas, to the welfare of Texas, to her people and his neighbors. He raised his head, feeling bigger and cleaner for those moments.

Another look at the gleaming house brought memories of Margaret Arnold. As if she, too, belonged there. Then a pang of regret was sharp as he thought of Joe. But Joe would return soon, for it could not be otherwise.

When he turned his gaze back in the direction of the wagon train, he saw Dude Justice coming up the hill at an easy gallop. He waited impatiently until the foreman was close before raising his voice with boyish enthusiasm:

"Look on top of that hill, Dude! That's the place!"

Touching the stallion with his spurs, Wesley left in a dead run for his new home.

Dude Justice smiled knowingly. At such times as this, when Wesley's joy seemed boundless, he wondered where the boy left off and the man began. Both were a part of the youngster, he reflected, which was as it should be. He saw Wesley's horse rise and gracefully clear the rail fence and, with scarcely a break in his headlong stride, race on toward the tall, flat-topped hill on which the great house stood.

Minutes later Wesley drew the big horse to a halt in the wide graveled drive and sat with admiration and amazement in his face. Here was his house.

Six tall white circular columns supported the roof of a veranda backed by a vista of french windows on the ground floor and equally spaced single-paned windows above. One hundred feet in length, the main house was flanked by a long one-story room at each end. The entire structure had been built of bricks made of white clay which firing had tinted a pleasing cream and pink.

Wesley was so absorbed in his study of the place that the appearance of a man and woman on the long gallery caused him to start. Recognizing Reuben and Bess Simonton, he leaped to the ground and cried his greetings on the run.

"How on earth did you do all this in such a short time?" were his first words upon reaching them.

"Wait until you look inside, Wesley," smiled Bess Simonton.

The big empty rooms were complete in every detail. The staircase, the halls, the gleaming white woodwork, the mantels—all, in fact, represented a dream, a plan, suddenly realized. The house awaited only the furnishings from The Oaks.

"The day you and Joe left for Kentucky," said Simonton, "I went to Houston and hired every available craftsman. Bess and half the people in Montgomery helped in a dozen and one ways"—he winked at his wife—"so you could give a big party as soon as you got settled."

"Party?" Wesley's face lit up. "That's a wonderful idea. Will you do the invitations for me, Mrs. Simonton?"

"Gladly. But to what place shall I invite the people, Wesley? Have you decided on a name?"

Wesley stared at the fanlight over the rear door of the broad hallway a moment. "Yes," he said with a little catch in his voice. "The Oaks."

They walked outside and watched the first surreys of the long caravan moving up the drive, Dude Justice in the lead. It was a pretty sight, standing there atop the hill and peering through gnarled oaks at the endless line of wagons and carriages, at the cattle and horses in Friday Fance's charge.

Then Aunt Polly alighted from her surrey with the aid of two strong slaves and shook her head from side to side. The whites of her eyes were prominent when she said at last:

"Mistuh Wes, I jest can't believe it's real. Is yo' sho dis ain't some trick o' my ole eyes, all dis finery down here in dis wild country of Texas?"

"Go touch it, Aunt Polly. It's real."

"Yassuh, but I'se gwine be 'stremely keerful, lessen I faints dead away."

Aunt Polly found The Oaks real, as did the people of Montgomery on the following Monday night. It was a big party, one the townspeople, the planters, and Wesley would not soon forget. In fact, Reuben Simonton remarked that for once the issue of annexation failed to dominate the gathering.

On the morning following the party Wesley departed for Houston and the promised meeting with Major Tarbone. He arrived at the Capitol Hotel that evening and engaged a room after learning that the Ranger occupied Room 219. Following his bath and change of clothes after a day in the saddle, Wesley rapped on the major's door.

With the booming "Come in," Wesley opened the door and saw the officer's hand on the butt of a big revolver in his gun belt. There was no apology, just a matter-of-fact statement:

"I never know who is going to come through that door, Wesley."

They shook hands and left for dinner at the Sixty-six Saloon. It was only after they were back in Tarbone's room that the Ranger spoke his mind.

"The way you handle a gun, Wesley, captured my notice and admiration. The way you handle yourself is what concerns me now. Although you have not told me in so many words, it's a simple matter of deduction that you went back to Kentucky to kill a man. Now——"

"Major," began Wesley, "that's——"

"Wait, son. Let me finish. The thing that interests me most is how this killing affected you. Answer me one question. Did it change your sense of values regarding human life?"

Wesley eyed the Ranger a full minute. "Major, I don't

know what it is to *want* to kill a man. I do know that I had to kill the murderer of my father. That's the end of my gunning for any man—unless it's in defense of myself or of someone I love."

Tarbone puffed a cloud of cigar smoke and peered through it in sharp scrutiny of his guest. "You said several times during dinner tonight that you loved Texas, Wesley. Let's suppose that you were called upon to defend Texas. What would you do?"

"My father believed strongly in the rights of the individual, Major. So do I. But I suppose you meant to ask what I would do if Texas was ever attacked. Right?" At the major's nod Wesley said, "I'd fight."

"I thought so. Just keep your gun clean and ready." Wesley did not ask why.

"Son," Tarbone went on, "you said you'd fight for Texas if she were attacked. Who other than puny, turmoil-ridden Mexico would ever attempt an attack on us except the United States? And the only reason she would ever attempt it would be because we left the Union. Texas is going to join the Union, Wesley, and then she is going to scramble around something awful in her effort to fight her way back out. Sam Houston is going to get us in the Union. God only knows who will get us out. Sam Houston is a great and capable man, but he is not a loyal Texan, he's a damned Unionist, and he'll never stop until he hands Texas over to the United States, lock, stock, and barrel. People who oppose him he hates with a passion. He hates me more than most, for I declare openly against him on his statehood question."

The Ranger paused to light his cigar.

"There are hundreds of men in Texas tonight," he continued, "who would kill Sam Houston in a minute if it were not for making a martyr of him. That would only hurry Texas into the Union, before she established any of her rights as a state."

Tarbone fell silent a moment. "Think about it, Wesley, and shape your politics. You can't dodge issues, son. And don't forget what I told you about your gun."

Although Wesley gave considerable thought to the Ranger's political views and puzzling advice in the short weeks following his visit to Houston, the responsibility of a big plantation in its infancy caused him to shelve all he had heard in a corner of his memory. There was much to be done in the weeks before spring planting. And then suddenly it was spring and long curving rows were turned in the black soil and planted in cotton, corn, maize, and peanuts. Vegetables sprang up in the garden, and under the guiding hand of Bess Simonton and other ladies of Montgomery the house was surrounded by colorful banks of spring flowers.

Wesley often wondered about Joe, where he was, how he was faring, and when he would return, as surely he must. Time eased the pain of their parting, and work was a balm for Wesley's loneliness. He and Dude Justice were constantly at their tasks. Before the young plants pushed up through the rich soil, they put the slaves to clearing more land.

Then one day Wesley received a letter from Lewis Traylor. He and Tom Weaver had sold the store in Paris and were transferring the money to the bank in Montgomery. This was good news, despite the fact that it broke the last physical tie with Kentucky. But there was more news—the land company had openly posted a reward for Wesley's capture, dead or alive. A reward of ten thousand dollars. Traylor urged him to take every precaution against people who might attempt to collect this blood money. He could be sure that such a sum would inspire adventurers to search him out.

Wesley frowned over the letter, wondering as he did so if any man could escape his past. He supposed not. The past was as much a part of a man as his present or future. In any case, he decided to heed the warning; ten thousand dollars was a lot of money.

He replied to Traylor's letter with words of gratitude and he urged Traylor and Weaver to come to Texas. Then he composed a letter to Margaret Arnold and enclosed an invitation to her parents to visit him in his new home.

Late in April he received a reply from Mrs. Arnold that evoked mixed emotions of sorrow and happiness: Eliphlet Arnold had died recently of typhoid fever, from which Margaret was just recovering. She was closing their Savannah, Georgia, home and returning to Haddom, Connecticut, but at Margaret's insistence they would visit him as soon as Margaret was able to travel.

Wesley eagerly awaited their coming. The pretty Yankee girl paraded before his mind's eye often during the month that followed.

Then one day as he approached the house for his noon meal he saw the house slaves removing bags from the Simonton carriage. Raking the stallion's sides with his spurs, Wesley charged up the hill, threw the reins to a stableboy and hit the ground at a run.

Seeing Mrs. Arnold and Bess Simonton, he composed himself and approached the veranda at a forced walk. Following Mrs. Arnold's greeting and a kiss on his cheek, he asked about Margaret and learned that she had been put to bed for fear of a relapse after the long journey. However, Mrs. Arnold led the way upstairs and, to Wesley's amazement, opened the door to his room.

Then he saw Margaret propped against a bank of pillows,

which framed her pretty face and honey-colored hair, and forgot all else as he returned her smile and peered deep into her brown eyes.

How long he held her hand in speechless admiration and wonder he did not know. Nor did he know when Mrs. Arnold left the room or when Aunt Polly entered. Polly's chuckle broke the spell.

"Lawdy me, Mistuh Wes!" Aunt Polly laughed until she shook.

Alone with Margaret, Wesley sat in a chair and looked at her again. "I'm so glad to see you," he said at last.

"I was beginning to wonder." Margaret's light laugh put him at ease. "But I've missed you too, Wesley, and I'm so glad to see you."

"Miss me much?" he asked, for something to say. Girls, especially Margaret, did something to his tongue and voice. She nodded, averting her face a moment, and he said, "I thought you never would get here, Margaret."

"It sure is hot in Texas," she said.

"Good for the cotton."

In the days that followed, Wesley and Margaret rode the fields where the slaves chopped the young cotton and over the pastures, pausing in the shade of big oaks where fine cattle browsed. Both were jealous of the early afternoons, time lost to each other by Margaret's strict schedule of rest. And later, as the days sped by, they looked sadly ahead to the Arnolds' departure for Connecticut. The Simontons and many other Montgomery people watched the romance blossom, and it was Bess who said to Wesley one afternoon:

"Why don't you do something to keep the Arnolds here, Wesley?"

"What?"

"You do want them to stay, don't you?" After his enthusiastic reply she said, "You just leave it to me. Have dinner for eight extra people at seven this evening, and we'll move heaven and earth to get Mrs. Arnold to stay."

A big smile spread across his face.

"Wesley Smith," said Bess, "how can you be man and boy at once?"

After telling the news to Margaret, who vowed Wesley didn't know her mother but that she would keep her fingers crossed for luck, Wesley told Aunt Polly, whose vow of secrecy he knew to be a prelude to a talk with Mrs. Arnold.

At seven the Simontons arrived with the Youngs, the Gays, and the Berkleys, old and respected families of Montgomery. Mrs. Arnold greeted them in her best mourning dress of black taffeta, though to relieve the sober drabness she wore a diamond necklace at her throat.

The dinner was gay and happy. Mrs. Arnold shoved her sorrow in the background and attempted to enter into the spirit of the occasion, for she realized that these fine people were trying to make her stay in Montgomery a happy one.

It was Bess Simonton who broached the subject. "Mrs. Arnold," she began a little hesitantly, "all of us here in Montgomery have come to think a great deal of you and Margaret, and we think you should stay on here because——"

"What Bess is trying to say, Mrs. Arnold, is this," Mrs. Young took over in straightforward manner. "Wesley Smith is living here in this huge, beautiful home all by himself. The boy is lonesome and needs companionship. We all came out here this evening to ask you, for Wesley and ourselves, to stay here and make this your and Margaret's home."

"Why, I don't know what to say," Mrs. Arnold replied. "I think that we should really go back East to my people where I can put Margaret in a good school. This is very sweet and considerate of you ladies and of you, Wesley, but there are so many things that might complicate matters."

Mrs. Gay took over the conversation. "Oh rubbish and fiddlesticks!" she exclaimed. "What can possibly be complicated about an attractive widow with a sweet and charming daughter like Margaret helping to keep a nice young man like Wesley Smith from becoming a regular hellion?" She pointed a slender finger at Margaret's mother. "I'm an old woman, Mrs. Arnold, old enough to be your mother, and I can't see anything complicated about your moving here. Unless you are more selfish than I think you are, you will admit that it will certainly be to Margaret's advantage to be reared in the South. That much we all know. Now I say move here and help this fine young man make a home out of this big pile of bricks."

There were tears in Mrs. Arnold's eyes as she replied, "You fine people have made me very happy tonight. Very happy."

When her smile fell and lingered on Wesley, he jumped eagerly to his feet and came to stand at her chair.

"Please, Mrs. Arnold," he said earnestly, "I've never known what it was to have a mother. I promise to do everything possible to make you happy in your new home. I'll make you glad you came here to live. Please say yes."

A moment later Mrs. Arnold spoke the single word that made Wesley Smith the happiest young man in Texas.

15. Politics and Comanches

THE Republic of Texas in the year 1845 walked a political tight wire. The big issue in the minds of Texans was the same as the paramount issue of the United States presidential election in 1844—annexation. Democrat James K. Polk of Tennessee favored the annexation of Texas and, aided by Andrew Jackson, won over the Whig candidate, Henry Clay. Before Polk was inaugurated, President Tyler, the incumbent, introduced the "Resolution for Annexation." It carried, and the invitation was thereby extended to the young republic to become the twenty-eighth state of the Union. It remained for Texans to decide which way they should go. The arguments were long and loud and bitter.

President Anson Jones of Texas, later called the "architect of annexation," was for preserving the republic. Sam Houston favored statehood. Houston and his followers declared that the alternative was bankruptcy for the republic; moreover, Houston proclaimed, the settlers living along what he termed the "western fringe" would be wiped out by the Comanches. With statehood, the United States would assume the national debt of six and one half million dollars and send thousands of troops to protect the settlers west of the Brazos River.

But Houston had changed sides. Before he came out openly for statehood President Jones believed the ex-president sincere in his opposition to annexation. Many of his personal friends in the city named after him were in doubt as to his real position, and they invited him to address them on the subject. Houston consented, and after a long harangue in which he vindicated his every move from the year he came to Texas, 1832, through his last term as president, he finally got around to the subject:

"I admit," he said, "that I have recommended that treaties of reciprocity be made with England, squinting even to the future extinction of slavery in Texas, when at the same time my only object was to turn public opinion in the United States in favor of annexation. I can justify myself by the suggestion of a very natural supposition.

"Suppose a charming lady has two suitors. One of them she is inclined to believe would make the better husband, but is a little slow to make interesting propositions. Don't you think that if she was a skillful practitioner in Cupid's court she would pretend that she loved the other 'feller' the best and be sure that her favorite would know it?

"If ladies are justified in making use of coquetry in securing their annexation to good and agreeable husbands, you must excuse me for making use of the same means to annex Texas to Uncle Sam.

"I can only rejoice with you, my fellow citizens, that we have arrived at a period when we are permitted to turn from the checkered past, and behold the bright and cheering future. That our annexation to the mother country is assured, there can be no possible doubt. I consider the benefit to be derived from the measure beyond the power

of language to describe. We have an extensive public do-
main awaiting the magic touch of the planter to call forth
its inexhaustible treasures. . . . Large planters and men
of capital have not heretofore had sufficient confidence in
the stability of our government to risk large investments
in Texas. Annexation removes the difficulty. . . ."*

Wesley and Reuben Simonton, who listened to the
speech, departed with admiration for the wily politician's
oratory but with no loss of their convictions. They continued to believe that Texas should remain a free and
independent nation.

In June 1845, President Jones was authorized by the
Congress of Texas to call a convention of delegates to meet
in Austin on July 4 to determine the course of Texas.

The Galveston *News* presented the proposition directly
to the people by asking why the Unionist faction was so
determined to push Texas into the dubious advantages of
statehood when so many of the Southern states were unhappy in the Union. "Why," asked the *News,* "should
Texas fear a war with Mexico? Certainly we should not
fear this enough that we will march down a road that will
lead only to bloody strife between the slave and anti-slave
states."

The citizens of Montgomery County held mass meetings and sent delegates to Austin, where all but one of
the sixty-one members of the convention voted for annexation. Then on October 13 the people of Texas voted
themselves into statehood. The war of factions was ended,
Houston the victor.

* This speech, quoted in part, was written by a Mr. Weeks, the
first shorthand reporter in Texas. The newspapers, all being
opposed to Sam Houston at that time, refused to publish it.
(Judge William Lewis' *Biographical Sketch of the Life of Sam
Houston,* Harold Steam Printing House, Dallas, 1882.)

Wesley had displayed unusual interest in the political battle. When it was over he asked himself, "What can a boy of sixteen do?" He had not yet learned the real power of diplomacy. He knew only the simple, direct approach to a problem. But if he could not settle affairs of state he knew how to operate a plantation. The results of the first year proved as much. The cotton yield exceeded his and Justice's expectations and the price was good. He had netted a tidy sum despite political defeat. In a measure, Wesley's financial success in that year of 1845 did much to offset the feeling that he would live to see Texas regret its choice of statehood.

There was Margaret Arnold also. In her company he forgot that the reward posted by the company that had sent the Tobins would be brought closer to home the moment the flag of the United States floated over Texas soil. Christmas with Margaret had been the gayest of his life, though the festive occasion had been dimmed at times by the realization that Joe might never return. Then on the twenty-sixth day of December, the anniversary of the shooting of Hazelett and Tobin, he felt again as he had a year earlier.

The year ended with a great celebration at the Simonton home. Eighteen forty-five became history on that starry night, and the future, whatever it held in store for Wesley Smith, seemed bright as he sat next to Margaret on the return trip to The Oaks—that is, until Mrs. Arnold advised that the tutor engaged to teach Margaret could also teach Wesley. He agreed so that he could be with Margaret, but asked that the classes be scheduled so as not to interfere with his work.

When on Monday, January 12, 1846, Miss Kent, an elderly spinster, began her work, Wesley could not put down the feeling that he had turned child again. He studied, however, and soon learned that, for all his avid reading and his knowledge of business, his education had been sadly neglected. Wesley took a great interest in the things of the past, for he realized that history had shaped the present and would continue to shape the future. He remained the realist who left the classroom for the saddle. The crops and the cattle were important.

On February 19, 1846, Wesley saw the Lone Star flag flutter down and the Stars and Stripes rise in the breeze as President Anson Jones retired in favor of J. Pinckney Henderson, first governor of Texas. Wesley had gone to Austin with the delegation from Montgomery over roads of the Republic. He returned over the same roads, but on the soil of the United States.

Shortly after the annexation of Texas, Mexico broke off diplomatic relations with the United States, and General Zachary Taylor was ordered to occupy the disputed territory between the Rio Grande and Nueces River, the latter claimed by Mexico to be the boundary between Texas and Mexico.

Following the declaration of war with Mexico on Wednesday, May 13, Major Tarbone came to The Oaks to enlist Wesley in his battalion of Rangers, to be attached to the American forces as scouts.

"I told you over a year ago, Major," said Wesley, "that I never intended to draw my gun to kill with again except in defense of my life, my loved ones, or for Texas. I don't think this war belongs to Texas, so I'm going to have to say no again."

"But, Wesley——" Tarbone began.

"I mean it, Major. I want no part of what looks to me like President Polk's land-grabbing war. Follow old Zachary Taylor's movements if you don't believe me."

The Ranger frowned in resignation. "I know how you

feel," he said. "I feel exactly the same way. I'm going to admit that I came here to enlist that gun of yours. It would be a tolerable comfortable feeling to have you backing me up in Wade's place."

"And you mean by that——" Wesley intoned a question.

"I mean that you are being offered the captaincy of Company A, Texas Rangers. Now, before you say no again, I want to tell you that it will be a hard rugged life, maybe too rugged for you. Besides, you'll have to furnish your own clothes, weapons, and ammunition. Texas furnishes your horses and pays you seventy dollars and found. But, as I said, it will probably be too rough for you."

"That kind of talk will get you nowhere, Major." Wesley laughed. "You've got to get the right kind of a war started before I'll go with you."

"Now Company A has been attached to General Taylor as his scouts," Tarbone went on, as if he had not heard Wesley, "because they are the best fighters and the most seasoned. That will be your command if you'll come with me."

Wesley rose from his chair on the cool veranda and leaned against one of the great columns, his back to Tarbone. He swept his hand before him in a wide arc as he gave his final answer.

"Major, what you see out there is mine. I've worked hard to make this place what it is, and if I quit it now everything my father left me could very well be lost. I don't even have Joe to lean on any more. My answer is still no."

The Ranger rose and extended his hand. "Very well," he said, "but you are going to have the opportunity to defend all this someday soon." He spoke prophetically as he gazed at the green fields and pastures. "I'll write you when I can, Wesley."

Wesley followed the war closely in the Galveston *News*, which he received every other day by stage. According to the paper, Major Tarbone reported to General Taylor during the latter part of June 1846 at Matamoros, Mexico, and on September 3 moved out ahead of the troops in the direction of Monterrey. On September 30 a news bulletin announced the fall of Monterrey after a short siege. Then the war seemed to go stale. General Taylor, after moving south to Buena Vista, was ordered into camp by his superior, General Winfield Scott.

About a month after the fall of Monterrey, Wesley received a letter from Tarbone, in which the Ranger expressed his utter disgust with the prosecution of the campaign. Nothing had been done since old "Windy" Scott had taken over, he said, and it looked to him as though "the balance of the war will be conducted by soldiers sitting on their lazy behinds."

Then, like a bolt from the blue, on Tuesday, October 13, 1846, the Comanches, who had been quiet all summer, suddenly went on the warpath. The uprising became general from the upper reaches of the Salt Fork of the Brazos down through the Edwards Plateau country and northeast to Mumford and Hearne. One party even crossed the Brazos at Mumford and pillaged the country as far east as Navasota, only nineteen miles from Montgomery.

Only nineteen miles from Margaret and The Oaks.

Luckily the settlers along the Brazos were prepared. They had seen the signs, and the scouts from several Ranger posts had witnessed the build-up for weeks. They knew the Comanches were making war medicine. The only thing they did not know was the exact time the savages would mount their attack.

Several days later Major Tarbone rode up the graveled drive of The Oaks. Wesley met him as he dismounted and, after greeting his old friend, invited him to sit on the veranda. The Ranger unfolded a copy of a newspaper and held it toward Wesley.

"Seen the bad news, son?" he asked.

"Yes, sir. Bad, isn't it?"

"It certainly is, but it comes as no big surprise. I don't trust the Indians, the Comanches in particular, but the white man is moving in on him mighty fast, and you just can't blame a fellow for taking care of his own. The Rangers always managed to get along with them somehow, but since the army moved in and started kicking them around they have been getting set for this war. Damn the West Pointers anyway! You can't tell them anything. They have to learn it all the hard way. And this time it will probably cost hundreds, maybe thousands, of lives."

Wesley waited for him to get around to his enlistment.

Tarbone settled back in his chair and lit one of his black cigars. "I didn't come by here to try to enlist you this time, Wesley. Company A is on its way to the Brazos. We've been outfitting in Houston and picking up a few new recruits."

"When are you moving out, Major?" Wesley asked casually.

The Ranger chose to ignore the question, though his grin reminded Wesley of a mischievous schoolboy. "Do you know," he said, "I believe I remember Wesley Smith saying something about being willing to fight for Texas. I wonder if he thinks the Comanches taking scalps and raping settlers' wives and daughters and burning out whole communities is good for Texas."

Wesley remained silent.

"One bunch of the redskins came pretty close to Montgomery, son," said the officer. "Only eighteen or twenty miles more and all that meanness could have happened right here." He waited for Wesley to answer.

"To be perfectly truthful with you, Major," said Wesley, "I don't want to leave Montgomery, but I'll make one sortie with you—without enlisting, mind you, and with the understanding that I'm going to be back in this house by Christmas."

"Pack a bedroll and plenty of ammunition, Wesley." Tarbone smiled. "We've just made a deal." He rose and extended his hand. "The company will pass your gates in about two hours. If you're not ready by then, you can catch us before we reach Navasota."

After Tarbone's departure Wesley went inside and told Margaret and the tutor that he would be gone several days. Next he searched out Dude Justice and after telling him all that had transpired instructed the foreman to take Margaret and her mother to McGowen's place on the Trinity if the Indians crossed the Brazos. Upon his return to the house he was met by Mrs. Arnold.

"Wesley, you are leaving to fight the Comanches, aren't you? While it's none of my business, I should think that job belongs to your friend and his Rangers."

"I appreciate your concern, Mrs. Arnold," he said. "Now, while I don't want to go, I must. The day I touched Texas soil I felt a sense of safety and security. I want to keep Texas that way, for you and Margaret as well as myself."

He got to his feet. "I love you very much, Mrs. Arnold." She rose and placed an arm about his waist. "I understand," she said. "Go, and may God bless you."

Outside, Margaret awaited him in the saddle. As Wesley approached she said, "I'm going to ride as far as the gates with you."

He was afraid to speak, for his heart was full. They walked their horses slowly down the drive, and for once the big stallion did not resent another horse traveling abreast. Sitting her sidesaddle primly, Margaret let one dainty toe emerge from her voluminous skirts and, at every step of her mount, allowed it to touch Wesley's boot. Her very presence had always thrilled him, and now her deliberate touch excited him as never before. Upon reaching the gates, he pulled the bay up and turned in his saddle.

"Margaret," he said hoarsely, "I love you. I love you more than you can ever realize."

"And I love you too, Wesley," she said wistfully. "I do wish you were not going away." She threw back her head and laughed, a little too gaily. "Hurry back to me," she whispered, then leaned toward him and kissed him full upon the mouth.

Before Wesley could take her in his arms, she turned her horse. Then she was racing up the hill, her long honey-colored hair flying in the wind.

Wesley wanted to follow her but thought better of it and spurred his horse through the gates. He did not dare look back, lest all resolve depart from him, but rode with a heavy heart toward Navasota.

16. Three Enemies

In that brief sortie under Major of Rangers Tarbone, Wesley learned a great deal that was not printed in Miss Kent's textbooks. One of the lessons the experienced Ranger drove forcefully home was the value of control over his mounting desire for righteous vengeance. Another was an attempt to bluff his way through a very serious game in which lives were at stake and an issue important to the whole frontier hung in the balance. Bluff in poker, whether disastrous or rewarding, remains a game of wits and temerity. One believes he can win and takes the chance. When facing the enemy in the field, it is often the same, though a serious leader debates the gamble in terms of blood instead of chips and considers his ability to back up the bluff if necessary. Here power implied must speak in strong tongue to offset the power missing. Such a game was not uncommon to the West; it was in a military sense something new to Wesley Smith, who found himself caught up in the middle of it.

Prior to that meeting with the Comanches, Wesley met another enemy. He had overtaken the troop about five

miles east of Navasota and was riding to its head in search
of Tarbone when someone in the ranks cried out:

"Hey you, Smith, come back here and speak to me
polite-like."

Wesley reined his horse short and peered intently at the
speaker, a big man with long, unkempt yellow hair under
a regulation slouch hat, army issue. The same cold, un-
smiling grin distinguished the face of Jack Spangler, an
enemy at the Sabine, and again at Swartout.

"When was the last time you saw my brother, Spangler?"
Wesley demanded.

"Hell and the devil! I haven't seen him since the night
we got pickled at Swartout. But that's neither here nor
there, bully-boy. I'm hoping a Comanche gets your goddamn scalp, and I'm hoping one don't—so I can take it
myself."

There was a note of comedy in the man's expression and
voice. Wesley laughed, said, "Sure, Spangler, either way,"
and rode forward to meet the major.

Tarbone greeted his young friend warmly, then gave
him to understand his status with the company was that
of an enlisted man; that, while discipline was strict so far
as the rules went, rules were few. However, Tarbone's
orders, together with those of his officers, were to be
obeyed without question at all times.

When they made camp that evening on the western outskirts of Navasota, Major Tarbone rode into town to in-
terview the citizens and determine the size of the war
party and the extent of damage. He learned that the town
proper suffered little or no damage and no casualties. But
reports reaching the town from the west were different.
Upon returning to camp that night, Tarbone climbed into
a supply wagon and called the men about him.

"I have been told by the people of Navasota," he said,

"that many of the settlers between here and the Brazos have been killed and scalped. Their womenfolks have been carried off to serve the pleasure of every Comanche who wants them. We have known for a long time that the bungling of the 'Yellowlegs' would cause just such an uprising, and now that it's here the damned cavalry is running around chasing its own tail, unable to find an Indian, except maybe a few old squaws and a few young ones."

He paused and spat in disgust.

He told the men that it was the job of the Rangers to put down the uprising before it spread to include the Apache nation; that in order to accomplish this they should search out the actual killers among the Comanches and return them for trial under the white man's law, leaving the others of the tribe wondering forever what had happened to them.

"That's the strategy, men. Doing it that way is our job. Now be ready to move out at daybreak."

The Ranger troop moved west on the morning of October 16, 1846. Although the trail was three days old, the signs all the way from Navasota to Mumford on the Brazos made pursuit easy. Buzzards told a grim tale of violence as they wheeled in high concentric circles over the land.

Tarbone dispatched a detail to perform the gruesome task of closing the wide-staring eyes and burying the nude and mutilated bodies. The first was a little girl of about ten with only a remnant of her once beautiful red-gold hair. Another who had been scalped was perhaps eighteen and still another was a pretty, mature woman in her middle twenties. The men and the older women had been more fortunate, for they had been mercifully buried in the ashes of their homes.

The Rangers, especially the old-timers, were accustomed

to death and violence, but these things turned their hardy stomachs. When they made a dry camp that night on the Brazos, near the spot where the little shipping town of Mumford had been, Major Tarbone realized it was going to be very difficult to control his men once they met the Comanches.

The troop moved out of Mumford early next morning. After a little more than an hour in the saddle Tarbone suddenly raised a hand high, the signal to halt. He held a quiet conversation with his captain, then rode back along the file of horsemen.

"We're almost in contact with a large party of Comanches, men. Now I want every mother's son of you to remember my orders. Unless I give the command there is not to be a shot fired. Understand?"

The men nodded and the major rode back to the head of the column.

They turned west from the river toward a little rise a half mile away. It stood in the middle of a large section of cleared land, which was flanked on the north and south by open woods and split-rail fences.

Just short of the crest, Tarbone again brought the troop to a halt.

"Ellisor, Temple, Woods, Smith," he called softly, cupping his hand to his mouth, "front and center."

Wesley and the three men reined their horses to the head of the column and halted near the major.

Tarbone pointed to fresh tracks and horse droppings, which suggested that the war party was very close, perhaps just over the rise. The major pondered the Indians' reasons for turning from the river, thinking and hoping that Federal troops might have been responsible. This being true, the savages might agree to a parley. If untrue, the Comanches might have chosen this ground for a battle. In event of an attack, Tarbone said, the company commander should take his men to the shelter of a bluff below the crossing and dispatch riders upriver for aid from the Federals, whom he hoped were riding south.

Then Tarbone touched a spur to his horse and rode slowly up the rise, Wesley and the three Rangers at his side.

As they topped the little hill, Wesley felt the hair rise at the nape of his neck and a shiver tingle his spine. There, not more than fifty yards away, were more than two hundred Comanche warriors drawn up in a wide semicircle along the lower contour of the shallow swale.

The Indians sat their ponies, silent, menacingly still, the only movement among them being the decorations of their vertically held lances blowing in the wind. In horrified discovery Wesley recognized the fluttering objects as scalps. Long tresses of golden hair and brown. Then he saw a lance held by a painted buck near the end of the line and he remembered the little girl he had helped bury.

As Wesley shuddered and forced his gaze from the awful sight, he caught himself in the act of reaching for the pistol at his thigh. He put down the impulse and straightened in the saddle to await Tarbone's next move.

The major slowly raised his left hand high, palm forward. This was a sign of peace. A big, lean Indian wearing a large war bonnet of eagle feathers stolidly raised his arm and with a grunted command touched naked heels to his pony and rode slowly and majestically forward, two braves on each side. They halted directly before the white men and eyed them in silence.

Tarbone deliberately waited out a full minute before solemnly advising that he desired a parley. The chieftain grunted his approval, and Tarbone drew his horse alongside the chief to begin the parley.

The Ranger made it clear that the Comanches had violated the white man's law and that those who had killed white people must be turned over to him for punishment.

Not once did he deflect his glance from the piercing eyes of the chieftain as he spoke of the many United States troops that would arrive soon. These soldiers, he said, would not only demand the surrender of the Indians who had murdered white people but would engage the Comanches in a running battle of annihilation.

The other's unblinking eyes hardened. Tarbone seemed caught up in his own bluff.

"The people of Texas desire to live in peace with their Indian brothers. I have never lied to a Comanche. Now give me permission to point out the guilty braves of your party and leave with them."

The chieftain's face remained inscrutable for some time. Then his eyes seemed to flash defiance, though this expression faded into what Tarbone later said he thought was debate and indecision. But the suspense was not to the Ranger's liking. The stakes were too big. He was greatly outnumbered, and he knew that a Comanche victory here would serve as a spark to inflame the minds of every savage west of the Brazos.

The decision of the bonneted leader came as a surprise to Tarbone. The Comanche turned his horse and pointed to the long line of painted warriors. Then with a gesture of peace he led the way down the knoll.

Although suspecting trickery once beyond the aid of his troop, Tarbone could do nothing but follow the Comanche chief. This he did, doing his utmost to hide his growing fears behind a calm and determined countenance. This became more than difficult, however, when he reached the hideously painted savages. But it was more important to his own safety to act out the big bluff now than it had been minutes past.

He rode down the line of horsemen and pointed out the Indians whose lances displayed the scalps of whites. At a signal from the chief these braves fell in behind the major—eleven in all. Bringing them to a halt before the chieftain, Tarbone said to the latter:

"You must command these men who made war on white women and children to follow me. When we depart, you are to ride far to the west so the soldiers who will soon arrive cannot capture and hang all of your party. But you must go in peace and keep that peace."

Tarbone was thinking that now was the time the feathered chieftain would raise the eerie battle cry. It did not come; instead, a command in the Comanche tongue was addressed to the prisoners: they should go with the white man. As amazed as he was relieved, Tarbone decided to move at once. He paused and raised his hand in a farewell salute to the chief and reined his horse alongside the prisoners.

Wesley and the three Rangers who had ridden escort came forward and disarmed the savages. They were careful to remove the scalps from the discarded lances and fasten them securely to the waistbands of the Indians for the purpose of identification at the forthcoming trials.

"Major, sir," Temple said during this interval, "this redskin don't have no white scalps. These is both Mex."

The major rode back to where Temple stood and closely examined the gruesome objects.

"You're right, Temple," he said. "They are Mexican, all right. Turn him loose."

He took the Indian's lance from Temple and held it out to the warrior, who sat his pony stiffly, looking straight ahead. When Tarbone advised that he was free to go, the big brave drew himself erect on his pony and said:

"Me thank. Me remember."

He wheeled his pony and trotted over the ridge to join his fellows.

"Hurry it now," said Tarbone as the Comanche rode out of hearing. "Get those devils fast to their ponies. We've got to move out before the chief decides to liberate the prisoners or before the cavalry gets here and tries to take them away from us. We don't want them tried in New York."

He swung into his saddle and waited impatiently while the men rapidly lashed the prisoners to their ponies and attached lead ropes. Once the troop was moving toward the river, Tarbone sent word to Wesley to move from his position near the rear of the double file up to ride with him.

"You've had a fine lesson in Indian behavior today, son," he said, beginning to laugh nervously. "And, for that matter, so have I. It's beyond me why that chief ever let us get away with this. I'm still just a little shaky inside and I promise you I'll never try that trick again. You just can't tell what a damned Comanche will do."

Wesley looked bewildered as he eyed the Ranger. "Major," he said, "I don't know much about Indians, but wasn't the chief as guilty as these men? After all, he is the chief, and he probably gave the order for murder."

"Probably. But if you're suggesting that we should have taken him too, you've got a lot to learn. Yes, sir, son, a lot to learn. As I said, you just can't tell what a Comanche will do."

"Or a Ranger," Wesley replied, looking straight ahead.

Once the prisoners were delivered in Navasota, discipline in the Ranger camp relaxed somewhat. Wesley was reminded around the campfire of the menacing glances Jack Spangler had given him on the trail, for the ex-corporal continued to study him as though he were looking for an excuse to pick a quarrel. The opportunity came when Wesley spoke of returning to The Oaks for a week. Spangler spread his evil grin across his face and asked the major's permission to accept Wesley's invitation to visit in Montgomery. Wesley's quick denial of issuing the man an invitation caused Spangler to leap up in feigned insult and drop a hand to the butt of his revolver.

But Wesley's hand was quicker, and his pistol pointed steadily at the other's belt buckle, causing Tarbone to jump up and put himself between the pair.

"Put those damned guns away!" he roared. Then he turned on Jack Spangler. "You have many good qualifications as a Ranger, Spangler, but you're a damned fool to try to outdraw that youngster. Just mark my words if you want to live."

Wesley rode toward home, aware that one day in the future Spangler would force him to use his gun. It might be next week, next month, or ten years later, but unless someone else destroyed the man first, trouble was inevitable.

Margaret Arnold met Wesley on his return and drew him away from voluble Aunt Polly. Smiling, she asked if her brave Indian fighter had killed the whole war party singlehanded. She rode with him that day over the fields and seemed jealous of the time he gave Dude Justice, which pleased Wesley. Then upon their return to The Oaks she placed the mail that had accumulated in his absence before him and, with a rustle of petticoats, left the room.

One of the first letters bore a New Orleans address. Opening it, he saw the name Marion Nagle and recalled the night on the Mississippi steamboat when he and Joe witnessed the poker game and uncovered the dishonest gambler who had placed Nagle's life in jeopardy. And now the man who in return had presented Wesley with six diamonds wrote as follows:

My dear young friend—

I am writing you at long last, for now I can repay in small measure the kindness you did me two years ago.

It is common knowledge in the circles in which I move that a price of $10,000 has been offered for you dead or alive. Let me hasten to inform you that your enemies have learned where you reside and are even now on their way to Texas to make an attempt toward the collection of that reward.

The man who will try to shoot you down is a gunman of note known as LaRue. I intend to follow him to Texas and will try to be not too far behind when he arrives. Other than the circumstances which promise to bring us together again, I am delighted at the opportunity of seeing you in the not too distant future.

My very best regards to you and your fine brother.

Your obedient servant and friend,

M. Nagle.

Wesley stared for long minutes into the roaring fire. After two years they were still after him. A determined bunch they were. He thought of going back to Kentucky and trying to find the one man behind this persistent plot against his life.

"No," he whispered finally, "I'll let them come to me."

Promising himself to be more careful, he suddenly crumpled Nagle's letter. About to throw it into the fire, he changed his mind, smoothed the letter, and put it carefully away.

The week's leave from the Ranger troop passed all too soon. There was work to do and there was Margaret

Arnold, now an integral part of his life and The Oaks. For days he and Dude Justice burned the Diamond Six brand into the left hips of calves, though not once did he look at the brand without thinking of the reward posted against him and of the warning of his friend, Marion Nagle.

The time for parting with Margaret came again, though she was reluctant to let him go once they reached the gates. This time she slipped out of the saddle and held her mouth up for his kiss. How long they held each other, neither knew nor cared. Then she was riding away and he was turning his horse in the other direction, toward Navasota again.

Keeping him company on the way, all pulling against Margaret and his peace of mind, were thoughts of the Comanche, enemy of Texas, the personal enemy Spangler, and last though not least the man named LaRue. Three enemies, three very real and formidable threats against his life.

17. For Texas and Self

FOR six long weeks Wesley rode and camped with the Rangers. The campaign took them into the land of the Comanches, across the Edwards Plateau, up the Brazos River and down the Colorado, with never an Indian in sight. Life in the saddle was hard. A man grew lean and wiry and touchy. He flared up at a word, and when trouble was averted he wondered at his own irritable frame of mind.

Wesley met the leering grin of Jack Spangler over the campfires and in silence glared back at the troublemaker with a dare in his eyes. He reached the point quite often where the prospect of settling this thing between them seemed nothing less than a pleasure, though at these times the discerning ex-corporal appeared content to whiplash Wesley with half-smiles and veiled glances, but never a word.

The troop rode on, searching, anxious to meet up with Comanches if only to break the monotony of useless days in the saddle and cold weary nights in the open.

Then one night when the late moon rose cold and dim

over the dry camp up the Salt Fork of the Brazos, a sentry slipped into the camp of sleeping men and roused Major Tarbone. Wesley listened and suddenly felt a rippling of nerves up and down his spine. What he heard was soon verified by strong smells on the prairie wind.

The officers swiftly and silently alerted the men, and within minutes all their horses were ringed about the still-warm bedrolls and each Ranger held his rifle across a horse's withers. They waited a good half hour, the men silently damning the Indians, the U. S. Cavalry, the Mexicans, and the cold, in the order named.

The hoarse, deep howl of a timber wolf was answered by another in the distance. One of the older Rangers turned to a man next to him, saying in a whisper, "Did that sound right to you?"

Tarbone and his captain walked silently around the circle of men and horses, whispering orders to every second man: "Get off your feet and rest a little if you can. They won't come at us until it gets light. Hold your reins so your horse won't run off."

Just before daylight the air grew colder and a heavy overcast rose from the north. As the gray, dismal dawn broke with a promise of sleet and rain, they saw the Indians. They came in single file and in platoons of perhaps twenty, their ponies picking their way almost daintily through the tall grass. As the light grew stronger, the Rangers were able to see the hideous faces smeared and striped with blues and yellows and reds, all overlaid with a predominance of the Comanche death color, black. From many of the lances scalps fluttered like banners in the strong, biting north wind, and over the shoulder of each brave hung feathered arrows in buckskin quivers. A few of the warriors carried painted shields of heavy buffalo hide which were capable of deflecting, if not stopping, a pistol bullet.

The advance group was less than two hundred yards away when Major Tarbone suddenly swung up on his horse. After cautioning his men not to fire, he rode a short distance from the circle of Rangers. Standing high in his stirrups, he held up his hand in a gesture of peace. Immediately the Comanches, even those still far out on the prairie, leaned low on their ponies and raced toward the Rangers.

Tarbone turned his horse and, to show his contempt for the charging Comanches, rode unhurriedly back into the circle.

"Hold your fire!" he cried, dismounting. "They'll swing away and circle. Every man and horse to this side."

With the other men who had formed the leeward half of the circle Wesley led his big stallion across the bedrolls and ammunition boxes and stood with the horse at his back. Wanting to give his bay as much protection as possible, he dropped the reins and placed his rifle across the rump of another animal between him and the oncoming horde.

The Comanche leader suddenly swung to the left and began winding the entire party into a big wheel. Tarbone advised that they would grind closer and closer and chew relentlessly into the defenders' position, risking only a few warriors at any time to the white man's fire. As predicted, the chief made another turn to close the rim of the wheel and drew his warriors at top speed past the Rangers at a distance of about seventy-five yards.

Suddenly, from every Comanche throat burst a horrible throat rip. Wesley felt as though he had been struck in the pit of his stomach with a bullet. The sound was intended to terrify and stun the enemy, and in this instance Wesley admitted its efficacy. A nausea actually assailed him.

The savages completed their great circle. The leader brought them closer, with the grinding edge of the wheel less than fifty yards away before the chief sat straight on his pony and let the first arrow fly. It struck the ground flat and flew broadside against a horse's leg, making him flinch. This was the signal for each warrior to loose an arrow as he raced past.

"Begin firing!" ordered Tarbone. "Be sure of your mark. Don't waste ammunition. We may need every round."

To his immense relief, Wesley felt the sickness of his stomach depart. He let a savage face swim just behind his sights for an instant, squeezed the trigger, and watched the enemy fall heavily from his pony, roll over and over in the tall grass, and lie still. As he reloaded his rifle, Wesley saw Jack Spangler, his face wreathed in the characteristic devilish grin, fire a gun that lay nonchalantly across his horse's withers. When the shot unseated a Comanche, Spangler yelled with delight and began to reload rapidly. The odds against them did not seem to worry Spangler. He was happy if he could kill.

The wheel rolled closer and closer until the rim was no more than the length of a wagon tongue away. The Rangers were now engaged in the kind of fighting they knew and understood best, close combat with pistols. And, in spite of the rain of arrows, their aim was deadly. Suddenly the chief gave an imperceptible signal and the Comanches wheeled their ponies across the cold prairie in full retreat.

"Shall we follow them, Major, sir?" asked Captain Thomas in a shout across the perimeter of the defense circle.

"Hell, no!" Tarbone yelled back. "That's just what they want us to do."

The noise of battle had subsided instantly, and now the quiet that fell on the prairie made the Rangers fully cognizant of the freezing, dreary day ahead. Captain Thomas made the rounds of the men and reported to Tarbone casualties of one dead and four wounded, one horse killed and several others struck by the flint-tipped arrows.

While the camp was being reorganized and a burial detail named, Wesley saw Jack Spangler slip into the tall grass, where an Indian had rolled off his pony. Curious, he followed, thinking that, like Spangler, he might find some piece of Indian battle equipment to keep as a memento of the encounter.

Wesley was some ten yards behind Spangler and peering into the tall grass when a movement between him and the ex-corporal caught his eye. He looked up to see a savage raise an arm to throw a tomahawk at Spangler's back. Almost in the same instant Wesley fired. The heavy slug struck the Indian's left shoulder and spun him completely around, but not in time to do more than deflect the tomahawk's aim. It struck Spangler high in the right leg, bringing a cry of pain and surprise. Wesley's second shot struck the Comanche under the left shoulder blade and he was dead before he fell.

Spangler wrenched the tomahawk from his leg and glared at Wesley.

"Well, well," he sneered. "So the brave Mr. Wesley Smith saved Jack Spangler's life. Damn you, I hope you're happy, for I'm not. Not by a damn sight, Smith, 'cause I don't want to owe you a thing when I take your scalp."

Still sneering, he limped away, leaving Wesley eying him in amazement.

The wounded were attended to while several of the men

built a fire and cooked a welcome meal of jerked venison, beans, corn pone, and coffee. While they ate, one of the seriously wounded men died. As the cold grew more intense and the icy rain began to slant sharp and heavy on the freezing north wind, they buried him in a shallow grave beside his companion. Tarbone spoke a prayer and the Rangers heaped a great mound of stones to mark and protect the final resting place of two loyal Texans.

The Rangers placed their three wounded companions in the supply wagon, covered them with thick buffalo robes, and swung up into cold wet saddles to continue a ceaseless patrol.

On Wednesday, December 16, 1846, the weary troop went into temporary camp at Brenham, a large, clean settlement of German immigrants, newly arrived in Texas. Tarbone gave them leave of twenty-four hours to buy supplies and take whatever relaxation this frontier community offered. It was here that Wesley early next morning took leave of Major Tarbone and his Ranger friends and rode toward Navasota and The Oaks. Late Saturday afternoon he entered the drive of his home. As Margaret ran to meet him, he vaulted from the saddle and folded her in his arms. He was home for Christmas just as he had promised.

The day after Christmas, Tarbone arrived. As Wesley welcomed him, he detected in the Ranger's grave expression business of a serious nature. When they were alone Tarbone came directly to the point, saying:

"The company is back in Houston for a time, Wesley. But that's not why I'm here. Jack Spangler came to me with a story likely to interest you. He said that while he hated your guts he didn't want to see you killed by a hired gunman. It seems that some high mogul of the company that offered the reward for your hide came to him and tried to make a deal. Wanted him and some of the other Rangers to kill you."

"Where is this man now, Major?" asked Wesley. "I think maybe I had better talk to him, don't you?"

"Now just sit straight in your saddle," said the Ranger. "I know where the fellow is. He's staying at the Capitol Hotel and we can get to him any time we want to, but let me bring you all the way up to date on the thing. I told Spangler to go back to this man and make a trade whereby he would get the ten thousand dollars as soon as he killed you. Now, Wesley, Spangler is going to bring this fellow out in the open for you. Then he's your meat. Do what you please with the sonofabitch. If it was me, I'd kill him, but that's up to you."

"When will Spangler make his deal?" asked Wesley.

"You start for Houston tomorrow. That's Sunday, and there won't be many people traveling. Get to Cypress Creek not later than noon. Pull your horse out of sight and wait. Spangler and Temple will be along shortly, and the man with them will be the fellow who wants you dead or alive. He's going to have ten thousand dollars on him. Spangler wants it split between you, him, and Temple, but Temple won't have any part of it and I know you won't. Anyway, from that point on it's your game. If you don't kill him, I think I will, since I just don't take kindly to people like him."

"You've changed just a little from what you preached to me a couple of years ago, Major."

"Hell!" the old Ranger roared. "Bastards like him ought to be killed."

Wesley produced Marion Nagle's letter and handed it to Tarbone, who read it carefully before saying:

"This all makes sense now. I helped old Marshal Bender jail a fellow named LaRue a couple of nights ago. Charged

him with being drunk and disorderly. He's still in jail. As
to this man Nagle, I spotted him at the time we arrested
LaRue—he was buying the drinks for LaRue. But this
thing is more complicated than that." Tarbone laughed
heartily. "Listen, son, LaRue couldn't pay his fine. Had
no money on him. He's the gunman and he's still in jail."

Perplexed, Wesley said, "Then who is the man Spangler
and Temple will bring to Cypress Creek?"

"The man with the money. The big mogul who prefers
you dead, son, that's who he is."

Wesley's eyes narrowed. "So the land company is coming to me," he said almost to himself. Then he looked at
Tarbone. "I'll be there, Major."

He was. Noon Sunday found Wesley sitting on a sand
bar of Cypress Creek a few yards downstream from the
West Montgomery Road crossing. His horse was concealed
farther down the creek.

It was nearing one when he saw three riders approaching from the direction of Houston. He soon recognized Rangers Jimmie Temple and Jack Spangler. Although he could not quite fathom the latter, and certainly
he did not trust him, he doubted that Spangler would be-
tray Tarbone for fear of his own worthless life.

The third rider was a big, hard-faced man of perhaps
forty, black-haired, with sallow skin. As the trio moved directly toward the crossing, Wesley observed the man's
close-set eyes and heavy black brows. By his appearance
he seemed wily, vicious, and cruel.

The weather being unusually warm for December, the
two Rangers removed their coats and hung them across
their saddles before leading the horses to water. The
stranger remained in his coat, but as he stood waiting for
the Rangers he pushed his coat back and jammed his
hands into his hip pockets, exposing a small revolver in a

holster under his left armpit. Wesley felt a queer hatred and resentment toward this man who was trying to buy his life just as he had bought the expensive hat on his head.

Temple and Spangler led the horses back from the water and looked curiously at the big man.

"We better get off the trail," Spangler said. "Your sitting duck will be along pretty soon."

This was a signal for Wesley to move silently up the bank of the creek. He slipped behind a big oak leaning over the stream and waited until the three men moved closer and tied their mounts. Then, as they prepared to sit on the sand, he jumped down the sloping bank of the creek and covered them with his pistol.

The two Rangers raised their hands, but their companion stood rooted to the spot, too startled to move.

"Keep your hands away from your guns," Wesley warned Spangler and Temple.

"If you hadn't got the drop on us——" Temple spoke up, winking slyly at Wesley.

"Shut up!" Wesley barked savagely.

Unable to trust Spangler, Wesley managed to put Temple between him and the ex-corporal, never once removing his eyes from the land-company man, whom he addressed next.

"What's the matter with your hands?"

"Hell, any fool can see I'm not armed," the man replied angrily, raising his hands shoulder-high.

In his cold, gazelle-like eyes was murder, and Wesley saw it. The man waited for either an advantage or an even chance. He stood out a minute of outward calm and resignation, though he appeared too calm and resigned. His brand of acting, while superb in a way, reminded Wesley of the stillness of a snake coiled to strike.

"Mind if I smoke, young man?" he asked.

"Go ahead."

As the man reached casually for the cigars exposed in an upper waistcoat pocket, his eyes on Wesley, he turned slightly. Then suddenly he produced a small revolver and pointed it at Wesley.

Temple's cry of "Look out!" was unnecessary. Wesley's big Colt roared almost with the warning. The heavy slug literally blasted the little gun from the man's hand, continuing down the inside of his index finger to tear flesh and bone from a badly mutilated wrist.

Then another shot sounded and the man's knees suddenly buckled. Eyes glazed, he fell face up, dead. It was then that Wesley saw Jack Spangler, a smoking pistol in his hand, grinning as he contemplated with pleasure his handiwork. Spangler raised the barrel of the gun to his lips and blew the last wisp of blue smoke from it. Then with a little flourish he holstered the weapon.

Wesley took the steps separating him from Spangler. "Thank you, Spangler," he said, putting out his hand. "I appreciate what you just did. I couldn't bring myself to kill——"

"Hell and the devil! Don't thank me for killing the dirty sonofabitch. You've probably been thinking how you saved my life from that damned Indian over on the Brazos. Now start thinking about me saving your worthless neck. Just figure we're even."

He turned away from Wesley, his grin exposing the white of his teeth against a tanned face. In a few moments he was back with the horses. As they proceeded to lash the dead man across his saddle, Wesley saw Spangler slip a heavy wallet from the man's coat and place it inside his shirt. In this manner Spangler collected the ten thousand dollars for killing a man.

There was another episode to the affair, which the major related to Wesley later: Tarbone found Marion Nagle waiting patiently in a buggy near the county jail. Without glancing in the gambler's direction the Ranger walked into the jail about three o'clock in the afternoon and released the hired gunman. Since he guessed the outcome of the meeting between Wesley and the black-haired man in Wesley's favor, he was ready to wrap the whole problem up in one package and be done with it.

As LaRue walked rapidly away from the jail in the direction of the livery stable, Nagle followed him in the buggy, and Tarbone in turn mounted his horse and shadowed both men from a safe distance.

He felt certain that the gunman would ride toward Montgomery in an effort to collect the reward offered for Wesley's death. He also believed that Nagle would follow the gunman. He was correct in both assumptions. LaRue walked directly to the livery barn and presently rode rapidly to the northwest, down the West Montgomery Road.

As Tarbone neared the ford on Buffalo Bayou he came upon Nagle's team tied at the side of the trail. The buggy was empty. Then he heard several shots from a small-caliber revolver and he spurred his horse in the direction of the ford.

Nagle walked away from the edge of the water as Tarbone rode up, and came to stand at the side of the Ranger's horse. He extended a small gun.

"I'm afraid I just killed a man, Major. It was in self-defense. I am your prisoner, sir."

Ignoring Nagle's pistol, Tarbone reined his horse down to the edge of the water and took a cursory look at the dead LaRue, whose stilled hand held a big pistol. Then the major rode back to where the gambler stood and said:

"Thank you for helping me stop this man, Mr. Nagle.

He was a bad egg and I congratulate you on still being alive."

Nagle smiled and pocketed his little pistol.

"However, I'm going to have to hold you," Tarbone said with mock gravity. "Long enough for you to have dinner with me and Wesley Smith."

Before Nagle completed his reply, they saw Wesley, Spangler, and Temple fording the shallow bayou, leading the horse burdened with a dead man.

While Tarbone listened to the full account of the land-company official's death, Wesley stood with Nagle, viewing the body of gunman LaRue. Finally, after he learned how LaRue had been trailed and killed, he turned to the gambler and extended his hand.

"I can't quite express the gratitude I feel, Mr. Nagle. But I want you to know that you have more than evened the score. I am in your debt, sir."

"You are not, my young friend," Nagle replied. "The way I see it, the hands have been played out and the chips are still about even."

18. Mistress of The Oaks

WESLEY SMITH bridged the next three and one half years of his life in a single sentence: "As the years passed, The Oaks knew times of plenty and drought." As his story unfolded, however, certain events that involved his friends as well as the progress of Texas came to light.

One of these concerned Major of Rangers Tarbone, and another the patient enemy and riddle, Jack Spangler.

The war with Mexico reached several stalemates, owing to the brand of politics played by the wily Santa Anna, President of Mexico, and the vacillation of the United States War Department. All the while the depredations of the Comanches continued. Although the U. S. Cavalry insisted it had the situation well in hand, Texas was forced to put more and more Rangers in the field in order to protect her people. Fifteen hundred extra Rangers kept Tarbone behind a desk directing operations in which he would have preferred to participate during the year of 1847. In these forays against the Indians, Jack Spangler so distinguished himself through daring and ability that before the Mexican War ended and the Comanches settled down he was elevated to the rank of lieutenant, Company A, Texas Rangers.

It was during these times that George T. Wood, in 1847, became the second governor of Texas. His first message to the legislature was a demand that the debt of Texas "must be paid. The honor of the state must stand without a blemish." Nor did he quibble on the Indian question; instead he spoke strongly, saying that the Indians "must be pursued, hunted, run down, and killed," that Texas should offer a liberal bounty for their scalps, that if the Federal Government could not handle the situation Texas could. His demand for Texas Rangers for frontier defense won the support of Senator Sam Houston in Washington.

Because of this support, however, Wood was classed as a "Houston man" by the rapidly growing anti-Houston faction and was voted out of office after only one term. Peter Bell became the third governor of Texas in 1849 and inherited the boundary dispute between Texas and New Mexico, then at its height. When the United States threatened to take the land, Bell called a special session of his legislature, who supported him to the extent that he threatened to send Rangers to Santa Fe and run the Federal authorities off Texas land. Washington decided to compromise, and the United States bought the vast territory that extended far west and north to the present state of Wyoming. Thus Texas was able to pay the debt of the former republic. As a consequence, Governor Bell declared by proclamation the last Thursday in March as Thanksgiving Day.

The determined governors of the new state typified the people whom they served, a people who wanted what was justly theirs and who were ready to fight for it. They had come from all states in the Union, had pioneered and won over the wilderness and Mexican oppression during the years since Stephen F. Austin established the first colony of Americans on the lower Brazos. They were people like Tarbone and Wesley Smith, and there were Spanglers among them.

But as Wesley Smith said in bridging the gap from 1846 to his twenty-first birthday in 1850, The Oaks had known times of plenty and of drought. The plantation prospered, and in the good years Wesley acquired large landholdings around the town of Willis. After living under the threat of Indians, gunmen, and a ten-thousand-dollar reward on his head, he was at last free to plant and reap, to become excited over the prospect of a railroad from Houston to Palestine, in East Texas, and thence to St. Louis, Missouri, that would transport his cotton to Eastern markets and save him the trials and expense of driving his cattle to Galveston and New Orleans.

Wesley had never given up the search for Joe. Often he ran down rumors, only to discover them false. The only one that seemed to contain any semblance of truth concerned a Smith and his Negro Sam who were traveling to California. Though Wesley planned often to go in search of his brother, he never quite found the time to do it.

On Thursday, June 6, 1850, Wesley Smith turned twenty-one. The day marked an important milestone in the life of the youth who for years had coped in manly fashion with adult problems. And Mrs. Arnold, Margaret, and the Simontons thought the occasion of his attaining his legal status as a man merited a celebration. They invited friends and neighbors by the scores, and by midmorning of June 6 guests began arriving in buggies, surreys, by stage and on horseback, from Willis, Danville, Houston, Swartout, Montgomery, and plantations near and far.

Wesley stood with Margaret in the spacious white doorway of The Oaks, welcoming his many friends. His face lit up with pleasure when Major Tarbone and Captain Thomas arrived. Following the midday feast at long tables in the shade of the oak trees, the children slept on quilts and the young ladies retired to the upstairs rooms for rest preparatory to the big dance that evening. The men gathered on the lawn and veranda to smoke cigars and talk.

When conversations turned to issues of the day and every man seemed intent on carrying his point, Tarbone winked at Wesley and said, "Within the next hour we'll kill off all the Indians in Texas and spit in the face of every land-grabbing politician in Washington."

He predicted rightly.

The political situation was acute. The South was crying secession, and statesmen were frantically trying to appease both the Northern and Southern factions. California had applied for admission to the Union in 1849 as a free state, and the matter of slavery or anti-slavery was debated for the territory acquired from Mexico. Early in 1850, Henry Clay had presented a resolution of compromise. Even the Texas papers had advised the people of the South to stand up for their rights before concluding with grim predictions of war should the North enlist the new Western votes in Congress against the slave states.

Wesley listened as the men argued the right of a state to withdraw from the Union. As conversations became more heated and the Negro servants were kept busy serving ices and drinks, Wesley began to wonder if any of his guests would be sober by evening. He had no sooner made a wish that the ladies would emerge and take their menfolk in hand than he saw Margaret and a group of women approaching the men. Relieved, he continued to study Margaret.

Suddenly, like discovery, he remembered that he was twenty-one and that the time had come to do something he had put off for years. Without further ado, he drew Margaret aside and asked her to join him in the library as soon as possible. She asked if something had gone wrong and was told that an urgent matter required their immediate attention. Unmindful of the state of bewilderment in which he left her, he went straightway to the library and removed a small box from the desk that had been his father's. He had no sooner placed it in his pocket than Margaret entered.

With curiosity in control of her expression, she said with a gentle scolding on her lips, "Wesley, I can't politely neglect our guests for long. What is it that's so important?"

Wanting to blurt forth, "Marrying me, that's what," he found his tongue paralyzed.

Then he tried desperately to form just the right words. He had thought of his proposal of marriage to Margaret many times, but with no idea that it would be difficult, especially since they had both lived under the same roof for years and their conversations had been built on the premise that they would eventually be married. But it was not easy. Finally he took the little box from his pocket and raised the hinged lid, disclosing one of the large diamonds Marion Nagle had given him, in a mounting of yellow gold. The very sight of the ring confused him still more, though he was determined not to allow this opportunity to pass.

"Margaret," he began doggedly, "when I was in Houston the other day I had this made for you. It's something I want you to——" He stopped, speechless.

"Why, darling," she exclaimed, "it's beautiful! Do you want to put it on my hand?"

All his tenseness left him as he took the ring from the box

and slipped it on her finger. Then he asked her to sit down.

Margaret slipped into a chair, still holding his hand, and Wesley went down on one knee before her and said in a trembling voice:

"Margaret, sweetheart, it seems that I've loved you all my life. And—and now that I'm a grown man—well, now I can ask you something that I've waited forever, it seems, to ask you. Will you marry me tonight?"

"Tonight? Heavens no, Wesley Smith!" Suddenly aware of his crestfallen look, she smiled tolerantly. "Wesley, I don't mean that I don't want to marry you. I sincerely believe we were intended for each other. But Mother would never consent to our marriage without the proper announcement."

Wesley swallowed hard and grinned. "Of course, Margaret. Of course. I was just—well, I've waited a devil of a long time."

"So have I, darling. But since we'll be married a long time let's make it a great occasion." Then she said, "You talk to Mother, tell her we want to be married here at The Oaks next Christmas Eve night. If she gives her consent, and we both believe she will, ask her to make the announcement when the dancing begins this evening. Will you, Wesley darling?"

Then she moved to his waiting arms and gave him her lips. After long minutes she pushed him away. "Please! I simply must go now. What must our guests think of me?" She walked to the door, paused to look back at him, then said, "Wait here. I'll send Mother as soon as I can locate her."

When she lingered another moment, her happiness shining through, Wesley said, "You know, Margaret, you don't act at all surprised."

"It's because I'm not," she replied. "But I'm mighty proud."

Neither Mrs. Arnold nor Aunt Polly showed surprise at what everyone had for years considered inevitable. Only Wesley appeared dazed. When Mrs. Arnold announced their engagement to the crowd at the dance that evening and his friends responded with hearty congratulations, he continued to ask himself if such a wonderful thing was actually true.

The months between the announcement and Christmas seemed the longest of his life, despite the fact that crops and cattle kept him busy that summer and fall. He drove cattle to New Orleans and took his cotton to Houston and Galveston. Margaret and her mother visited Houston often to shop, causing Wesley to wonder at all the fuss and bother that always attended a wedding.

During the week before Christmas, guests began to arrive from Haddom, Connecticut, New Orleans, Savannah, and other distant cities. Bess Simonton quartered them in the fine homes in and around Montgomery. Then the tradespeople arrived with boxes and bales of decorations, foods, liquors, and no end of dresses. On Sunday the big house seemed a complete shambles and Wesley wondered if it could be made ready for the wedding in time. Then, under the skillful direction of Mrs. Arnold, Bess Simonton, and the ladies of Montgomery, Aunt Polly and her brigade transformed the mansion into a holiday wonderland.

On the evening of December 23, Mrs. Arnold insisted that after the wedding rehearsal Margaret should not see Wesley until time for the Christmas Eve ceremony. But when the attendants departed that evening Margaret and Wesley wandered hand in hand about The Oaks, coming at last to the big dining room where the many fine wedding gifts they would cherish all their lives and hand down to their children were on display. There was a handsome silver-and-gold water pitcher from the friend of Wesley's father, Henry Clay. The beautiful tea service was from Mrs. Susan Spiller. All about were presents from wonderful friends, including Lewis Traylor, Tom Weaver, and the McGowens.

They left the house and strolled to the front lawn, where they paused and listened to the slaves singing far down the hill. Neither of them spoke for a time, but stood with an arm about each other's waist and watched the late moon rise above the distant trees and cast its pale light on the fog streamers between them and the fields below. They held jealously to every moment of the enchanted evening until the voices of the slaves faded and the lights in the cabins along Lake Creek winked out one by one. Then they said good night.

He remained at the foot of the stairs, his admiring gaze following her every upward step. At the landing she turned and waved a hand. Then with a gay and delightful little laugh, her petticoats rustling, she disappeared from sight.

It was Christmas Eve of 1850. The household stirred to life with the first light of dawn, and Aunt Polly began to hurl orders to her staff of domestics long before the many ladies arrived to take over The Oaks.

According to custom, Margaret was supposed to remain in her room all that day, without any contact whatever with the man she was to marry. As the morning advanced and the ladies moved up and down the stairway exclaiming over the bride, the gifts, and the wedding gown, which had been old and beautiful before Margaret was born, Wesley soon discovered that the house was not the place for him that day. By word, glance, and gesture the women, even Aunt Polly, made it plain that he was in the way.

He spent the long morning in the slave quarters, going from cabin to cabin with gifts and candies. It was as in the past a pleasant job, one heretofore performed with Margaret at his side, but for some reason that he could not put a finger on he hurried through it. Then, aware that he had the afternoon on his hands with nothing to do, he had his stallion saddled and rode across the bare fields until almost sundown.

A strange feeling of weariness assailed Wesley as he dismounted, causing him to realize that doing nothing whatever beyond killing time constituted the hardest work he had ever encountered. He supposed also that the tension of the day contributed greatly to his physical fatigue.

Once in his room, he bathed his face and fell across the bed. When he opened his eyes and discovered that night had fallen, he leaped up, wondering if he were about to miss his own wedding. Then a match flared up and a man was touching the flame to the lamp wick. A moment later the man replaced the lamp chimney and turned to extend a hand.

Wesley uttered an exclamation of joy and rushed to embrace his old friend Reverend Milo Walker of Paris, Kentucky, who had come a long way, he said, to marry Wesley and Margaret.

"It was at Mrs. Arnold's invitation, young man. And I assure you of one thing, you will be well married on this night, Wesley."

As Wesley dressed, Major Tarbone, his best man, came swinging in. Although the major looked neat and dapper in his store clothes, something seemed to be missing when he walked. Wesley jokingly remarked that the old Ranger had worn his heavy pistol so long that the weight of it taken off his hip had unbalanced him.

Wesley could not have asked for a prettier setting for

his wedding. Flowers were banked high, and under the soft light of many candles the big parlor crowded with friends took on the dignity of a sanctuary. As Wesley and Tarbone marched slowly toward Milo Walker, who stood tall and white-headed against the background of flowers, Wesley felt that this occasion was but a prelude to a happy and successful marriage.

Beyond this profound hope and prayer, he was caught up in the events preceding the ceremony. The wedding music and the appearance of Margaret in exquisite silks and old lace, then the lovely woman who was about to become his wife was standing at his side—all evoked waves of happiness in him. Then Reverend Walker was saying the marriage service. Though Wesley missed nothing of all that was said, he stood a little overcome by the very simplicity and beauty of the ceremony. Almost in a daze he slipped the ring on Margaret's finger.

With this, the minister raised his hand. Wesley listened intently to the sincere petition:

"O Almighty God, may it please Thee to send Thy most bountiful blessings on these, my friends, Margaret and Wesley Smith. Help them always to keep their ideals high, their minds and souls and bodies strong and clean in Thy sight. Make this a Christian home, Father, for all the years of their lives. Make their lives long and useful and let there be happiness and prosperity ever with them. Bless their friends, their loved ones and their servants. And, merciful Father, I beseech Thee, keep the tyrant's sword forever away from this door. Amen."

Aunt Polly, from her secluded corner of the big parlor, sounded a muted "Amen."

As Wesley turned to face his radiant bride and claim a kiss, he heard the murmur of whispers rising to fill the room and wondered briefly if any of his friends disapproved of the ending of a prayer he thought fitting and beautiful.

He and Margaret planned to go as far as Houston that night, spend two days there, then take a boat to New Orleans. Major Tarbone had offered an escort of Rangers from Montgomery to Houston, and they had gratefully accepted. Their valises and bags had been put in the surrey and now, with the reception less than an hour old, Major Tarbone had the vehicle waiting on the front drive. There he and a half dozen Rangers awaited the arrival of the bride and groom.

Margaret and Wesley in traveling clothes met at the head of the stairs. Margaret waited for her bridesmaids to gather below, then threw her bouquet. This custom completed, she and Wesley dashed down the steps and into the waiting surrey amid generous showers of rice.

When the Negro coachman touched the whip to the horses and the surrey leaped forward, the awful clatter of cans and boxes and old shoes tied to the rear axle vied with the cheers of well-wishers. Then, with Major Tarbone and his Rangers in escort, Margaret and Wesley began their great adventure into the happiest month of their young lives.

Upon their return to The Oaks late in January of 1851, Wesley decided the time had come to put his land near Willis into cultivation. After sending to Kentucky and Virginia for tobacco seeds, he moved Friday Fance and several slave families to the Willis plantation.

Marriage had not only given Wesley a most welcome responsibility but had caused him to study closer the political situation afresh in order to determine as best he could the economic future of the South. Even in her present era of prosperity the South lay under a cloud of uncertainty. The abolitionists' efforts were renewed with the

Compromise of 1850, after which talk of secession died. As Wesley and other observers saw it, the future of the Union could be sorely threatened by abolitionist propaganda, for while the national question was purely a matter of slavery or anti-slavery as it touched the economy of the nation, the rabid Northern factions were bent on creating a great moral issue. They searched for accounts of abuse of the Negro and resorted to not only truth, but the truth enlarged for the sake of sensationalism. Many were sincere and honest. Many were not. But regardless, they kept the crusade alive.

Men of foresight argued that the end was inevitable, that the industrial North and the agricultural South were fast taking divergent courses, that the two could not long live together as an undivided nation. But what was the solution?

Wesley often asked himself this question. The answer was not to his liking, for he could see no compromise between peoples who did not think alike. In Washington, yes. But as against public opinion, these compromises were merely scraps of paper waiting to be discarded.

However, an answer of a sort did come to Wesley one evening in October of 1851. He was seated in the upstairs sitting room with Margaret when finally his thoughts came into the open, breaking the thoughtful silence between a husband with a newspaper and a wife quietly sewing clothes for their forthcoming baby.

"It's the only thing for me to do. The sooner the better."

"What on earth are you talking about, darling?" Margaret asked, lowering her sewing.

"Why"—he grinned sheepishly—"I suppose I was just talking to myself. But I was looking far ahead into the future. The paper here," he said, holding the Galveston *News* up for her to see the black banner of two words,

SECESSION NEWS, "says there will be a war between the states one of these days."

"Why should people have war, Wesley? Seldom does war accomplish anything other than bringing sorrow to the people on both sides. Think how awful this war would be. Brother against brother. My husband fighting my father's people and my people fighting me and mine."

Wesley agreed, but told her that memories of horrible facts seldom checked the zealots.

"I've seen this coming a long time, dear," he said. "Mr. Clay's compromise may serve to stall it awhile, but it will still come. The Yankees may be right about the slaves. But that won't be their reason for bringing war about. I think they want to hurt the South, ruin it if they can. I don't mean all Northerners. We both know good solid people that have come to Texas from Pennsylvania, Ohio, Indiana, and other Yankee states. These people know the problems we have. But up North the politicians preach that we are cruel to the slaves. We are not, and for two reasons. If they can't credit us with the moral reason, then they should realize that it's bad business to mistreat valuable property."

Wesley got up and walked to the window. "You know, Margaret, for many long years it has been considered a kindness to the savages from the dark continent of Africa to bring them to the Southland and clothe and feed them in a Christian environment."

"How charitable, Wesley dear," Margaret replied, holding a teasing smile in check. "Is that your reason for owning so many slaves?"

Whirling, he eyed her. When she laughed merrily he grinned and said, "You talk like the damn Yankees." When she reminded him that she was a Yankee from Connecticut he added, "The sweetest one that ever lived."

He moved to her and sat on the floor at her feet.

While tousling his hair playfully, she said, "Wesley Smith, I do hope you're just imagining trouble. You forget that you and all Texans gave thanks on that Thursday back in March of this year of 1851, on Texas' first Thanksgiving Day."

"Not I, sweetheart. I'm thankful for you and for our child you're carrying, for the good crops this year, for the tobacco crop at Willis that was good enough for me to build barns and sweathouses. No, I didn't forget.

"But just to be on the safe side of the ledger I am going to raise more and more cattle every year. Then, if the darkies should be freed, Dude and I can do most of the work with very little help. We may not make as much money—maybe we'll make more—but at any rate we'll be independent of the freed Negroes at a time when things will really be rough for the South."

That night Wesley penned a letter to his father's friend, Henry Clay, and addressed it to Ashland, Lexington, Kentucky. The message was a request that Clay sell him as many as thirty bulls from his fine herd of Hereford cattle. He wrote another letter to Tom Dixon of Brenham, asking for as many two-year-old heifers as Dixon could get together.

"Let me get these cattle going," Wesley thought aloud, "then to hell with the Yankees. If they free the slaves, they still have to eat and I'll have beef they'll buy at my prices, not theirs."

On the following day Wesley began to prepare for the influx of cattle. When his plans became known, after thirteen hundred more red cattle had accepted the Diamond Six brand, many of his friends declared he was wasting a lot of good cotton land in pasture. Why was he doing this?

"Just looking ahead," Wesley replied.

Then one afternoon in November, Aunt Polly sent a house boy to find him. Upon hearing the news, Wesley threw down the Diamond Six branding iron and raced for the house. Aunt Polly met him with a gruff command:

"Now git a hold on yo' sef, Mistuh Wes. Dat baby gonna be borned this very afternoon, and they ain't nothin' yo' can do but wait."

Wesley waited most of the afternoon of Tuesday, November 25, 1851. He smoked too many cigars and imbibed more bourbon than ever before as he paced back and forth in his study. Becoming a father was a new experience. The waiting became an ordeal before Dr. Young, ably assisted by Mrs. Arnold and Aunt Polly, delivered the Wesley Smiths' first-born. As they brought the child into the world, she gave vent to her first tiny yell, which reached Wesley's ears and caused him to hit the stairs in a run.

He was halfway up the stairs when Mrs. Arnold appeared in the door of Margaret's room. Wesley paused, his eyes questioning and begging for some assurance that mother and baby were all right. Mrs. Arnold smiled and said:

"Congratulations to the father of a beautiful daughter."

For a moment he could only stare at her. Then he was asking about Margaret.

"She is doing as well as can be expected, Wesley. Now you must wait a little while before going in to see her. In the meantime, you may congratulate me upon becoming a grandmother."

Wesley raced up to her and took her in his arms. Laughing happily, they waited until Dr. Young appeared and said the father could now see his wife and child.

With eyes sharp and curious, Wesley entered the room.

His glance fell on Aunt Polly, who sat in a rocking chair by a window with a small blanketed bundle in her arms.

"Heah comes dat papa o' yours, chile, plumb scared to death," she chuckled. "But yo'all gonna make his eyes pop wider than they is now, 'cause you dat pretty, honey love."

Seeing Margaret, Wesley went to her and knelt by her bed. She smiled and drew his face down to hers and kissed him, then pushed him away.

"Don't you want to see your new daughter?" she asked. As he nodded and rose, Margaret laughed and said, "Don't put the Diamond Six brand on her until she's weaned, sweetheart."

Wesley held her hand a moment, then said huskily, "I'll put the brand on a thousand more head of cattle just for her, darling."

Then he walked toward his own child. Looking down at her, he felt great waves of thanks and happiness flooding his heart. Forgotten were cattle and business and all grim predictions of the future. The Oaks and Diamond Six had a new and demanding mistress, and he, Wesley Smith, was by far the proudest man in all of Texas.

19. Secession and War

THERE WAS a stir over the land and expectancy in every face. Wesley detected it in the expressions of his neighbors and friends, in the eyes of his family and his slaves. It was freighted with the excitement of a people rising to what they believed a just cause. It was secession. The slow grinding of fate had produced a thing long overdue, a break that in Wesley Smith's opinion was written in the stars.

It was by no means a welcome event, unless one could drive from his mind's eye the panorama of the war sure to follow, of brother shooting brother. But in the eyes of every realist it was the inevitable culmination of political errors patched and repatched and worn threadbare.

"It had to come," Wesley said to the group of planters seated on his veranda. "The election of Lincoln proved it, and South Carolina, God love her, pointed out the proof."

"Right," agreed Reuben Simonton, "and so did Louisiana, Florida, Georgia, Alabama, and Mississippi."

"And now Texas," said Robert McGowen.

The gathering on that warm February day of 1861 was

just one of many since the fall election. However, this meeting was more significant, since the inevitable had finally come to pass. On the ninth of that month Jefferson Davis, the late senator from Mississippi, whose efforts for final conciliation had been unsurpassed in Washington, had been inaugurated at the Alabama state capitol in Montgomery as President of the Confederate States of America. A new nation had come into existence with seven states banded together, the last being Texas. While Texans had yet to approve by vote the ordinance of secession in order to make it official, there was no doubting the sympathies of her people. Still, the situation looked grave from any angle.

A planter slowly lowered his glass and raised his voice. "Secession," he said, "is a damned serious thing."

McGowen took the cigar out of his mouth. "I agree, Jim. All of us do. But we also agree that oppression is a damned sight worse. If the Black Republicans in control of Congress have their way we'll stay in the Union to take the toe of their boots in our faces. We've tried compromise and every legal means to settle the slave question. But the North doesn't want it settled because it wants to use that as an excuse to cripple the South's prosperity. Every Southern state has its own grievances. Texas has hers. But when all's said and done, our reasons for action are basically the same as those of South Carolina, Florida, or Mississippi."

The men realized that all McGowen said was true. Federal troops had failed miserably in the prosecution of the Indian wars in Texas. Governor Runnels had been forced to send Rangers to the aid of the "bluecoats." When Sam Houston had been elected governor in 1859, he too pleaded with the United States for troops to put down Indian raids. The United States chose not to listen. And now Sam Houston was begging the people of Texas to stay in the Union. He was outnumbered. He refused to sanction the three charges made by Texans at the convention of January 28 in Austin when the secession ordinance was passed:

1. The North had violated the Constitution by using the power of the United States Government to oppress the slave states.

2. The Federal Government had failed to protect persons and property on the frontier.

3. The Northern states had violated the compact between the states.

The men looked up at the flag flying over Diamond Six. It was the Lone Star banner of Texas. They had heard Wesley say, "There will be another flag, my friends, the flag of the South. And when it comes I'll fly it. And I hope my children and their children will continue to fly it over Diamond Six."

"That's the way to talk, Wesley," said a young planter enthusiastically. "If it comes to a shooting war, we'll outshoot them."

The sentiments of the men on the veranda of The Oaks symbolized those of men all over the South. Gravity, doubt, and apprehension were met with feelings of pride, confidence, defiance, and some jubilation. A cause had become uppermost in the minds of Southerners. They believed they had been mistreated, that their states' rights were being wrested from them. They sincerely believed also that if war with the North became a fact they could in a short time put the enemy to rout.

War tension gathered from day to day. Fearing an Indian outbreak, the Texas Rangers were again alerted, and Wesley began to expect a visit from Major Tarbone.

On Saturday, February 23, Texans numbering 60,826

went to the polls and approved the ordinance of secession by an overwhelming majority. Many of the counties showed no dissenting vote. Opposing secession were San Antonio, Austin, and other smaller towns in West Texas.

On March 16, Sam Houston was removed from the governor's office because he refused to take the oath of allegiance to the Confederacy. Edward Clark became governor and set to work to mobilize the great resources of Texas for the prosecution of the war. There was no longer any doubt. The break had come, and a shooting war was inevitable.

Wesley knew he was a part of it. He would rise to defend his family, land, state, and cause. He had known this before his first child Irene was born, again when Wesley, Junior, and Owen came into the world. He looked back over the years, some lean, some prosperous. He had planned for what was now at hand. If the Negroes were freed, he would not have to depend on them for needed labor. He had gradually turned away from cotton to cattle, many cattle. He felt he would leave them in good hands.

Wesley had written Major Tarbone of his desire to serve Texas and had received his orders to report to Houston, where he would be sworn in as captain of Company A, Texas Rangers.

On the day of his departure his family joined him in the parlor. There were no sad farewells, for he had paved the way for a pleasant leave-taking. Not even Aunt Polly dared show a tear. He kissed his children, held Margaret close a long time, then walked out of the house and on to where Dude Justice awaited him.

"Dude," he said, "listen to me. If Texas is invaded, I want you to take my wife and children to safety. Then I want you to come back and scatter the cattle in the palmetto flats on the San Jacinto. Kill every horse we own, even my stallion. Understand?"

"I understand. I'll do it."

"And as long as the war stays away from Montgomery, raise everything you can to help the South."

Dude Justice promised and took Wesley's hand in pledge.

In Houston a few nights later, Major Tarbone walked with Wesley to the railroad station at the foot of Main Street. Having just been sworn in, Wesley was ordered to take the Houston & Texas Central cars to Brenham at once. There he would assume command of his company.

As they stood near one of the two dimly lit cars awaiting the train's departure, the major said, "I've lived a rough and violent life, Wesley, but have always managed to keep my violence on the side of the law." He paused to puff his black cigar back into life.

"I knew that day on the Sabine," he continued, "that I was taking a glimpse of myself as a youngster when I observed the way you stood up to those ruffians who tried to rob you and your brother. I've told you several times, son, that you have the makings of a killer. Now, for the duration of this damnable war, I want you to be a killer. A merciless killer of every man who makes any attempt to injure Texas or any part of the South."

He again paused to puff on his cigar, and when he resumed his conversation his voice had softened.

"Your orders for the present are to patrol the areas marked on the map I gave you. Feel free to vary from this as circumstances require. You may be needed almost anywhere, so be certain and telegraph me at every opportunity. Wish I were going with you, but I have been attached to General Sibley's staff and I'll probably have to sit on my tail behind a damned desk through the whole war."

A trainman cried, "All aboard," and as several late arrivals hurried into the cars, the little potbellied locomotive wheezed and coughed into action.

Until this moment Wesley had not realized the full impact of war. As he sat in the dim flickering light of the car, smoking his cheroot and listening to the rhythmic click of the wheels grinding over the rails, he was suddenly very lonesome and homesick. Before, when as a Ranger he had left Margaret, it had been with the understanding that he could return at his own pleasure. Now that was changed. He had the responsibility of the command of a group of fighting men with whom he must move and prosecute a specific segment of this war.

By sheer power of will he forced all thoughts of The Oaks from his mind and snuggled deep in his greatcoat. He slept until the train rolled into the little station at Brenham shortly after daylight. As it ground to a halt, Wesley peered out of the window and saw Jimmie Temple and another Ranger leaning against the railroad station.

The two men smiled as Wesley stepped from the coach and moved toward them. Then they threw him a belated salute. "Lieutenant Spangler sent us in to meet you, Cap'n," said Temple. "We're camped just outside of town."

Spangler again. Wesley said nothing but thought a great deal.

Breakfast was on the fire when they entered the Ranger camp. As soon as they had eaten, Wesley called the officers to his tent.

"At present," he told them, "our orders cover certain patrols marked on this map. But our real job, as long as this war lasts, is to kill as many enemies of Texas as we can, be they red, brown, white, or black. We want to keep the Comanches as peaceful as possible, and this should not be too difficult since the Indians hate the sight of a yellowleg. I want every one of the men to work hard at making friends with the Comanches. That's all, except that we will move out for Austin in thirty minutes. Dismissed."

A minute later Wesley looked up from the map he held and saw Jack Spangler still sitting on a wooden foot locker, gazing at him intently with the familiar expanse of white teeth in the middle of his sun-blackened face. His eyes were drawn into a hateful stare as he sat facing Wesley, and the smile that bared his even teeth seemed treacherous and mirthless.

"What is it, Lieutenant?" Wesley demanded.

"Just a word to set your mind at ease on a little matter, Captain," Spangler said. "The first time you saw me I was in a Yankee uniform. Well, to set the record straight, I hate Yankees even more than I hate you."

Wesley met his glance squarely and smiled. "That's damned interesting to know, Lieutenant. As for hating me—well, I can live with that, I reckon. But I want to set you straight on a thing or two. You don't really hate me. You hate the things I have—home, family, land, and slaves—because you are not willing to make the sacrifice necessary to get them for yourself. No, you don't hate me, you're jealous. But enough; we understand each other, Spangler. You just remember that you're sworn to defend Texas and the South. As long as you keep that faith, we'll get along. That's all Lieutenant."

Spangler's face sobered and his lips formed a tight, thin line. He rose, threw a perfunctory salute, and shouldered his way through the tent flaps.

Wesley sat in deep thought for several minutes. Spangler was a troublemaker and killer. He was also a good Ranger. If only there were some way to bring the man around to rational behavior. But how? There was no answer to this, and besides, the troop was ready to move.

The trek to Austin was without incident, though the company had scarcely made camp when Wesley received a telegram from Major Tarbone ordering him to report to General Sibley's headquarters for a very important assignment. Before nightfall Wesley learned just how urgent the matter was.

When Texas Rangers under the command of Captain McCulloch demanded the surrender of San Antonio on Tuesday, February 16, 1861, Major General David E. Twiggs, in command of the Department of Texas, gave up without a struggle supplies worth $1,500,000 and all military posts in the state. In men alone, he surrendered approximately one tenth of the United States Army. However, an undetermined number of Federal troops had withdrawn from San Antonio and New Braunfels when secession seemed assured and had supposedly marched for the safety of the Territory of New Mexico.

General Sibley had learned of the troop movement and, fearing a possible attempt to capture the capitol of Texas, he dispatched Ranger Company A to intercept the Federals should his surmise prove correct. Following a hard eighty-mile ride the Rangers had learned by telegraph on the nineteenth that all United States troops had surrendered. Only the detachment from New Braunfels, numbering around one hundred and fifty men, had not been apprehended.

And now that intelligence had established the fact that the missing Federals were quartermaster troops in possession of rifles, ammunition, and supplies the Confederacy needed, and that they were moving into Indian country, their capture was imperative.

This was Wesley's assignment, and he led his company out of Austin early next morning.

Company A was making camp for the night at Dripping Springs when a party of nine Comanches suddenly appeared out of the post-oak brush. Wesley saw no war paint and decided they constituted a hunting party. Spangler, however, raised his rifle.

Hastily pushing the muzzle down, Wesley said, "No. They seem friendly."

Their leader raised a hand in the open-palm salute, and when Wesley did the same the Indian rode up and said:

"Me Red Cloud, son of chief. Me remember you." Facing Temple, he said, "Me remember you."

Temple squinted the eyes in his leathery face and shook his head slowly. "Cap'n, damned if it ain't the young buck the major turned loose years ago—the one with the Mex scalps. Remember?"

Wesley did. "Temple, talk to him and find out what he wants."

After the usual "gobble-gobble" talk, the old Ranger turned to Wesley.

"He says he knows where the yellerlegs' supply train is camped, Cap'n. And that ain't all—he says the Yanks are passin' out rifles to the Comanches and teachin' 'em how to shoot 'em. But you can't tell, maybe it's an Injun trick, since he's passin' up a shiny rifle just to tell us."

"And maybe it's not a trick, Temple. The Rangers saved his life once. Ask him how many guns have been given to the Indians."

"A whole passel of 'em, Cap'n," the Ranger soon replied. "Sounds to me like he's tryin' to say more'n a hundred."

Realizing how this endangered the lives of white settlers, Wesley searched for a quick remedy to the situation as Temple and Red Cloud continued their powwow. "Temple," he said at last, "we've got to get those rifles before any more of them are passed out. Ask him if he will help us."

"That's pretty dangerous, Cap'n," drawled Temple, "but you're the boss."

He put the question to the Indian, who signaled his companions to ride into camp. Then, to Wesley's amazement, he saw that the entire party was armed with Sharps rifles, U. S. Army 1859 issue. The powwow continued for a short time before Temple turned to Wesley.

"You may not like this, Cap'n, but Red Cloud says that if they can take soldier scalps he can have fifty braves with us by early mornin'."

Wesley felt himself shudder inwardly. God, what a decision to make. The guns had to be taken, that much was certain. With several hundred savages armed with rifles, the slaughter of the settlers' families would make bloody history. Most of the men of these families had already answered the call to arms. He had to keep faith with them and do everything he could to protect their families and their homes. But to allow the Indians to take scalps? He turned to Temple again.

"Ask him, Temple, if——" he began. "No, wait. What do you think we should do?"

"Hell, let 'em do it, Cap'n," the grizzled old Ranger snorted. "It's no better'n the bastards deserve."

"You're right, Temple," Wesley said thoughtfully. "It's a crime against civilization to arm savages for slaughter. But for us to be a party to these Indians scalping white men is no better. No, I won't agree to it."

Temple argued that they would probably lose the quarry if they refused to humor Red Cloud, that they would also lose the aid of more than fifty Indian fighters.

"And, Cap'n, you know damn well it'll save the lives of a lot of women and children."

Wesley nodded. "I know. Hell, I know. But, Temple, I'd live with it the rest of my days. However——" As he eyed the Indians he thought of something, a savage's love of horses, mules, and mule meat.

"Temple, ask them which they prefer, the horses and mules of the yellowlegs or their scalps."

Soon Temple said, "Cap'n, the bastards want both." When advised that a choice of only one would be allowed, the Indians decided at last in favor of the livestock.

Then Wesley told Temple to order the Indians to lead the way for a scout of the Yankee camp. "And tell him to have his braves ready to attack at daylight tomorrow morning." When this was done, Wesley added, "Tell them to leave those rifles here and to bring all the others they can find when they come back in the morning."

Temple spoke again. Without a word the nine braves threw the guns to the ground, then sat their ponies passively, waiting for the Rangers to mount and join in scouting the enemy camp.

They rode almost due south for two hours before Red Cloud held up a warning hand and pulled his pony to a halt. He and Temple held a subdued conversation with Wesley, and then the three men rode silently into the gloom of the trees along the rocky Blanco River. After less than two hundred yards, the Indian halted his pony and slipped silently to the ground. Wesley and Temple followed, leaving their horses tied to a low-hanging limb. The three men began to move silently through the black woods, the Comanche in the lead.

They came out of the timber without being challenged and stood on a sand bar a hundred yards downstream from the Yankee camp. To all appearances the "bluebellies" were little worried about being discovered, for there were three big fires burning along the river's edge and Wesley could see many of the soldiers walking in the firelight, all unarmed. Their rifles were stacked in an orderly row around the perimeter of the rough circle formed by some twenty wagons. This loose circle of vehicles was the only precautionary measure employed by the Yankees against attack. Wesley was sorry now that he had bothered to enlist the assistance of Red Cloud. He and his Rangers could take this detachment of Yankees easily.

The Indian chief whispered something to Temple and disappeared into the timber. After half an hour he was back. He reported that he had found only two soldiers on guard around the entire camp and that they were not alert. Indeed no part of the camp seemed alert. Wesley and his companions continued to watch for another hour. They saw no sentry or patrol enter or leave the circle of wagons. The Yankees were satisfied that the Indians would not attack at night, and they had no fear of Rangers or Confederate troops being within striking distance. The camp slept.

They followed Red Cloud back through the timber. Upon reaching their horses, the chief gave a low bird call. Presently the hunting party appeared and, with a grunt to Temple and Wesley, he led them off to the west.

The Rangers made a dry camp, posted sentries, and slept until a pale glow began to streak the eastern sky. Then they rolled their blankets, made coffee over a shielded fire at the bottom of a dry wash, and looked to their rifles and side arms.

Just as they stepped into their saddles Red Cloud appeared silently out of the dawn with a large group of warriors at his back. The Rangers and the Indians rode to the edge of the timber and dismounted. The chief designated several of the braves to hold the ponies, and Wesley ordered three of his oldest Rangers to attend their horses. Then the party began a stealthy, silent advance upon the Yankee camp.

It was almost full daylight when they closed the distance between them and the sleeping soldiers. Wesley found himself with a Comanche moving on either side of him, and as the light grew stronger he could see their hideously painted faces. The sight was appalling and his thoughts raced back over the years when as a boy he had helped bury the scalped and mutilated victims of this same nation of savages.

One of the two sentries had been called in, probably for his breakfast, and the other had leaned his rifle against a bush while he took a plug of tobacco from a pocket and began to cut a chew. Wesley saw the big Indian at his right rise swiftly. The only sound was the sickening thud of a stone ax against the man's skull. The soldier slipped silently to the earth, and the savage who had killed him bent down to the body. His knife flashed twice, making two half circles; there was a slight tearing sound as he jerked the trooper's hair upward, and the bloody trophy was free as the dead body fell back to the ground. The Comanche held the grisly hair up for all to see, then with evident satisfaction quickly attached it to his waistband with a thong of rawhide.

Wesley wanted to retch. He shuddered. Then his anger flared. He raised his pistol to put an end to the violator of the agreement. Expediency held him, however, for to kill the savage would not only warn the soldiers in blue but turn his Indian allies into sudden enemies. Caught thus, he could do nothing but proceed as planned.

With the sentry out of the way, Wesley rose and stepped almost to the edge of the timber opposite the Yankee camp. "You in the camp!" he cried. "We are Texas Rangers and have you surrounded. We call on you to surrender and we want your answer *now*."

He put angry emphasis on the last word.

There was complete silence in the camp for several moments and then a rifle was fired from behind one of the wagons. The bullet smashed into a tree at Wesley's side. The shot was a signal for a concerted rush by the soldiers for the stacked rifles, but before they could disengage the swivels by which they were stacked and bring the guns to bear, the Rangers and the Indians had rushed the wagons and were among them.

The Rangers fought silently, though the Comanches yelled louder and louder as they streaked through the camp. Wesley had fired all the shells from his revolver and had jumped to the doubtful safety of a small boulder to reload when above the sounds of the conflict he heard a tremendous explosion. Something seemed to slap him hard on the side of his face. As he instinctively threw himself to the ground for protection, a blue-clad soldier fell from the back of a nearby wagon and sprawled across him, dead. Then he saw Jack Spangler standing close by, smoke curling from the pistol in his hand, and he knew the lieutenant had this time really saved his life.

"Close, wasn't it?" yelled Spangler, grinning as he turned again into the raging battle.

Fifteen minutes after the attack was mounted the fight was over. The largest part of the enemy troop of some one hundred and fifteen men had retreated behind a hastily erected barricade of boxes and crates. Their fire had been deadly until these breastworks had been disposed of. After that every time one of them raised his head for more than a snap shot, a Ranger's bullet searched him out.

The sight of the Comanches further terrorized the

troopers. They raised a white handkerchief on a bayoneted rifle and asked for a parley. It was granted, and their commanding officer, a major, came forward to meet Wesley. He asked what treatment he and his men could expect if they surrendered, and Wesley assured him safe conduct to the military prison at San Antonio. Beyond this the Ranger gave no promise.

This officer had been issuing guns to the Indians, knowing they would be used on women and children of Texas, and Wesley felt no compassion for him. The major, not realizing Wesley's anger, grew belligerent before the parley had progressed far.

"It is beyond my comprehension," he stormed at Wesley, "that even you Texas scoundrels would stoop to enlist the aid of savages. Just look at that red heathen! There's a soldier's scalp hanging at his belt! Scalpers, by God!"

Wesley slapped the man hard across the mouth with open palm.

"Shut up, you murdering bastard," he said between clenched teeth. "You're a fine one to talk. Hauling wagonloads of guns across Comanche country to arm the Indians, knowing they'll use them to kill our women and children. Well, I'll tell you this, mister, just one more little word out of you and I'll let you get back of your goddamned barricade and we'll kill every last mother's son of you. Now do you want to surrender or not? It doesn't make a continental damn to us, for we'd rather kill you than feed you."

"We surrender," the officer replied with dispatch.

There had been thirty-nine soldiers killed, three Rangers, and nine Indians. The major was ordered to name a burial detail, and the men named began to dig on the high rocky bank of the Blanco while the Comanches strapped their dead to their ponies and prepared to depart with all the enemy mules and horses.

Wesley laid a friendly hand on the shoulder of Red Cloud and said, "Temple, tell the son of a great chieftain we thank him. And tell him I want the buck who scalped the sentry to be severely punished."

"Me your friend," Red Cloud said through the interpreter. "You my friend. Will punish brave."

Then Wesley asked that the mules and horses be used to convey the wagons to San Antonio. They would be returned to Red Cloud's band. When the Indian assented, Wesley asked him to gather all the rifles he could find in the hands of Comanches and deliver them to him two weeks from this day at a spot they agreed upon. The Indian gave his word and departed.

A search of the wagons disclosed twenty-six cases of government-issue Sharps and thousands of rounds of ammunition, enough to arm two hundred and sixty Comanches. For the first time Wesley thought he had done Texas a real service.

The trip to San Antonio was uneventful but slow with the heavily loaded wagons. On the afternoon of the fifth day they rode into Fort Sam Houston and handed their prisoners over to the military authorities. Then Wesley gave his Rangers twenty-four hours for well-earned fun and relaxation. He retired to the Menger Hotel, where he ate an early supper and went to his room to write a long letter to Margaret and his family. He minimized the dangers and hardships of Ranger life and dwelled only on those things that he and Margaret and their children knew and loved.

True to his promise, Red Cloud collected many of the rifles issued to his people by the United States troops and on the appointed day he awaited Wesley on the upper reaches of the Blanco with eighty-five breech-loading

Sharps. When the Rangers in turn delivered the horses and mules pledged by Wesley, the Comanches showed surprise, for it was a new experience to find a white man who kept a promise to an Indian.

20. Under a Flag of Truce

WHILE the people of the South laughed at Lincoln's proclaimed blockade of the long Southern coast, issued in April of 1861, and rallied to defend the cause, Wesley's Rangers continued to ride the frontier. The spring rains gave way to hot, sultry weather and still the Rangers kept up the ceaseless and fruitless patrol. Little or no news of the progress of the war reached the troop. Wesley did learn that Governor Clark had responded to the first call of the Confederacy for troops with eight thousand men. Rumors that Galveston was being blockaded by Federal gunboats, that a mighty Confederate warship had been outfitted in New Orleans and put to sea under Raphael Semmes, that President Jefferson Davis's stoppage of cotton to Europe would force England and France to intercede in the South's behalf reached the Ranger camps with other bright and grave bits of news. But of one thing they were assured: a full-blown shooting war was in the making.

The first major engagement of the war came on Sunday, July 21, 1861. The Battle of Manassas, called the Battle of Bull Run by Northerners, resulted in a signal victory for the South. When the news reached Wesley, he and his troop participated in the widespread rejoicing and, as other true Confederates, predicted an early end to the war. And since the Comanches were showing no inclination to make war, Wesley wired Tarbone requesting a leave. The Major complied by giving him one week. Leaving his men at Brenham, Wesley lost no time in riding for Montgomery.

The Oaks seemed unchanged as he rode anxiously up the winding gravel drive. There were his cattle in the green pastures and there were his crops in the summer sun. And ahead, Margaret and the children were waiting with open arms. He had been gone from home a long time. He was tired of the saddle and camps and food prepared in the open, and he was wondering what one week of luxury would do to him.

He found Aunt Polly sick and worried about the war. She had dreamed that a great horde of Yankees had descended on The Oaks and freed the Negroes. Her big worry was that her people, once free, would starve. Wesley's arrival cheered her immensely, though it was not until he scoffed at her dream and told her that he wanted her to live long enough to help raise his children's children that she became the dominating Aunt Polly again.

Many of his friends and acquaintances had enlisted and gone to help fight the war, "to win it before the winter of 1862." The people at home flew the new flag of the Confederacy and predicted the fall of Washington before the crops were gathered. There were those, however, who asked why Generals Johnston and Beauregard had not pursued the Federals at Manassas and taken Washington when it was in their grasp, and why General Lee, Davis's adviser, seemed reluctant to fire on the flag he had served under in Mexico and Texas. Was Lee still loyal to old

Winfield Scott, Lincoln's military adviser? But for every
critic there seemed a hundred jubilant supporters. The
conduct of the war had been perfect, said the majority;
the proof was victory, the rout of the Northern armies
in Virginia.

When Wesley's leave came to an end, he looked west,
in the opposite direction from the real theater of war. He
felt isolated, useless, and upon his return to Brenham
and a meeting with Tarbone he asked to be released in
order to join a fighting unit in Virginia.

The major flatly refused. He told Wesley that while his
job with the Rangers might appear unimportant and tiresome in the face of rousing news from the battlegrounds
of Virginia, the defense of the Texas frontier was highly
essential to the progress of the war. The West was another
front, he said, and to expose the supplies of war in demand by the Confederacy to ravaging Indians, forgetting
the lives of settlers, would be tantamount to striking a
blow against the South.

Wesley knew this was true. However much he despised
the thought of more months of riding the long, tiresome
patrols, he did not argue further with the major.

As it happened, Tarbone's logic was justified in the
year of 1862. Francis R. Lubbock, who succeeded Clark as
governor of Texas on November 7, 1861, inherited Indian
trouble. The tribes, not only the Comanches, began to
make raids on the settlers, and soon Lubbock found himself with a two-front war on his hands. The Rangers were
alerted. They chased the redman here and there, but always another raid took place in a remote section of the
state. Since the Rangers could not be everywhere at once,
Lubbock met the problem by proposing that the counties
between the Red River and the Rio Grande, numbering
twenty-five in a line, each put one company of twenty

men in the field at a salary of $500 a year for each man and $750 for each captain. They were called "on-the-spot Rangers," and their worth against the onslaught of Indians was soon manifested in deed, for they augmented the regular Ranger force when Texas needed them most.

Farther west, General H. H. Sibley and his Texans captured Fort Craig in New Mexico Territory and marched on to take Santa Fe in an endeavor to win the West, including California, for the Confederacy.

All the while Wesley and his men found their hands full against the unpredictable Comanches. Seldom did he return to The Oaks, and when he did on short leave, he found that the people were beginning to feel the effect of blockade by the Federal Navy. Scarcities of luxuries were followed by rising prices. Then medicines and boots and clothing became scarce; even salt. The blockade runners could not meet the demands of the people. It seemed that the Federal Navy was slowly but surely tightening the economic screw on the Confederacy.

It was in April of 1862 that the Federals struck almost in unison beyond the east and west borders of the state and turned the hopes of Texans into ashes. Near Santa Fe, General Sibley's army was defeated by General Canby's troops from Colorado and forced into a disastrous retreat for the Lone Star State. Then, of graver consequences, Farragut's Gulf squadron ran past the forts on the Mississippi delta and captured the city of New Orleans. With Texas practically cut off from the Confederacy, a new fear began to dominate the minds of Texans: Invasion.

Dude Justice recalled his promise to Wesley, to scatter the fine cattle in the palmetto flats and take Margaret and the children to safety. He felt that the time to do this was drawing near. He said nothing to Margaret or Mrs.

Arnold, though the latter, close in touch with affairs of Diamond Six and a great help to Justice, asked what he would do in the event the Yankees came.

"Exactly what I promised Mr. Wes, ma'am."

Then he acquainted her with Wesley's wishes in the matter.

"Let's hope it doesn't come to that," she said, producing a letter from Wesley. "But if it does——"

She stopped in midsentence to survey The Oaks. It stood white and pink among the big green oak trees. Down the hill fat, sleek cattle ate the rich grass and stood in the shade of trees. The scene was too quiet and peaceful, too much in contrast to war and thoughts of war. And yet there was talk of a possibility of a campaign against Texas out of New Orleans. When one considered that Texas was the Confederate arsenal and storehouse of the West, it was only natural to assume that the Federals would try to stop the flow of goods. However, Mrs. Arnold had heard that the tyrant General Butler had his hands full in New Orleans. She fervently hoped so.

Dude Justice finished reading Wesley's letter, then looked at Mrs. Arnold. "He says he might get home in October, but if not we're to sell the cotton and invest the money in Confederate Bonds again."

"Did he say anything about an expected invasion?" she asked.

"Only that sooner or later the Yankees would try it." He grinned. "And that putting a foot in Texas and keeping it there were two different things."

It happened sooner than Wesley expected. On October 4, 1862, a Union fleet appeared at Galveston and garrisoned the city after shelling it.

In Brenham with Company A in rest camp, Wesley received the news by wire. He could hardly believe it

at first, though when the unhappy incident was confirmed
he began to worry about a full-scale invasion. Thinking of
Margaret, his children, and all at The Oaks, he wired
Tarbone for another leave. The major came in person and
told Wesley he was needed now more than ever but to
go and report to him in Houston not later than November first. Then he said:

"Galveston has been a thorn in Yankee flesh for a long
time, Wesley. They knew there could be no real blockade
of the Texas coast as long as the Confederates controlled
Galveston. But that's just a start, son. Just a start. We have
news that Federal General Banks—he's the one that Stone-
wall Jackson chased ragged—is planning a campaign to
invade Texas with an army of some thirty or forty
thousand troops from New England within the next three
months. He'll spring it from New Orleans to Galveston and
roll through East Texas where the crops are best—if he
gets a foothold in Galveston."

"If?" Wesley replied, somewhat dejected. "Seems they've
got that foothold waiting for him."

Tarbone looked hopeful as well as wise and secretive
when he said in conclusion, "So it seems, Wesley. But we'll
just wait and see."

It was a long lonely ride to Montgomery. Wesley looked
back over the year at the defeat of Sibley, the fall of New
Orleans, and now the capture of Galveston, and wondered if his world were slowly collapsing around him.
A world he and Joe had ridden into eighteen years earlier,
the Republic of Texas. He recalled the issue of annexation
and the predictions attending it—Texas would see the
day she would fight to get out of the Union. It had come
and with it trials, trouble, war, death, and invasion.

Once his land and house came into view Wesley felt
better. And his family and friends did much to relieve

his feeling of dejection. Days in the open among his slaves and cattle caused the war to retreat in his mind far beyond a distant horizon. He kept busy days and sat with Margaret and the children evenings. October sped by on wings he could not slow, and November found him once again in Brenham, looking unhappily forward to dusty trails, chill nights in the open, and all the discomforts of winter.

There was trouble to quell in this place and that, and Company A rode out to perform its duty. November brought rain and muddy trails. The nights were cold and the campfires seemed devoid of warmth or cheer. The men growled and glared at one another, though when Comanches came at them they struck back with the calm efficiency of a crack fighting unit. They were just that, Wesley reflected often. All they desired was the assurance of action. This he was unable to give them until the day his dirty, dog-tired troop rode into Millican, and then only vaguely. But it was enough.

Wesley went immediately to the telegraph office to report a job done to Major Tarbone. The reply that flashed over the wire minutes later evoked surprise and no end of questions:

"Report to me in Houston posthaste with troop and full gear. Use train."

Thinking, wondering if the Federal invasion of the Texas mainland had begun, Wesley tensed until he trembled all over. His family, land, and home would be at the mercy of the invader. But if the message meant action, he and his hard-bitten Rangers would respond with cheers. And the words, "posthaste, full gear," surely meant that the opportunity to fight the Yankees was at hand.

He turned immediately to the stationmaster's office, where, after learning that a train would leave for Houston within three hours, he produced Tarbone's urgent message and demanded two cars, one for his men, the other for horses and gear.

Long before time for departure all equipment, horses, even supply wagons, had been loaded. With the prospect of fighting instead of more thankless routine patrols, the men decided to celebrate. Wesley let them drink until they boarded the car, whooping and yelling. Then he and Lieutenant Spangler moved down the aisle of the coach, tossing whisky bottles out of the windows and warning the more boisterous of the lot to quiet down and sleep in order to appear sober before the major the next morning.

When the train reached the station in Houston shortly after sunrise, Tarbone boarded the car and shook hands all around. He told Wesley he was placing his troop under officers of the Confederate Army for a few weeks of rigid military training.

Wesley eyed his old friend closely. "Look here, Major, these men came here expecting a good scrap. Don't you think they should know what's back of all this?"

"Hell, Wesley, what I think has nothing to do with it. All I can tell them, or you, is that they'll get all the action they want, maybe more. The general will see to that."

"What general?"

"The new commander of the Confederate military forces in Texas. I reckon you've heard of General John B. Magruder."

Wesley showed surprise. "You mean 'Prince John' Magruder?"

"I do. The man who outfoxed the Yankees by marching a couple of thousand men around and around until they looked like twenty thousand and convinced the enemy it was time to retreat. That's him, son. He arrived in November. All I can tell you is that he's organizing an expedition. You and your troop and every man we can round up who's able to fire a gun is to be a part of it."

His curiosity growing in leaps and bounds, Wesley asked if Magruder might be thinking of going after General Banks in New Orleans.

"Let's just say, Wesley, that what he plans is likely—if successful, mind you—to slow old Banks to a right damn happy standstill."

"Thanks, Major." Wesley grinned. "I think I know the what, where, and why of it now."

"Sure! Sure! Now go tell every Tom, Dick, and Harry. Say it out loud so some damned Yankee spy can hear and point every cannon on the Gulf right in our faces."

Wesley could not keep a straight face. "Maybe the Sixty-six Saloon would be a good place to start, eh, Major?"

Tarbone laughed with him, though he sobered quickly and eyed Wesley speculatively for a full minute. "You better come with me, Wesley."

The Ranger took him directly to General Magruder's headquarters and introduced him to Colonel J. J. Cook, whose regiment was the Arizona Brigade, and Major P. C. Tucker of the general's staff, then said, "This is the Ranger captain I was telling you about. Good head on him. What's more, he's got a sharp eye and a tight lip."

Before Wesley departed he learned to his amazement that, despite the Federal capture of Galveston in October, a Confederate cavalry force remained entrenched at Fort Eagle Grove on the island three miles west of the city of Galveston; that these men entered the city almost every night by way of the Gulf beach, where sand dunes concealed them, and rendezvoused at Schmidt's garden, a picnic park at Twenty-first Street between Avenues N and O, and left the city for the fort and Virginia Point before daylight. Food supplies for these men were sent regularly by a subsistence committee in Houston under a flag of truce.

Wesley then heard his orders: He was to join the bearers of food supplies, visit the city by night, learn anything of military value, and report regularly. Just in case something happened to him he should select a man from his troop to accompany him. And since he would be just one of many employed in this manner, the warning given all civilians should be remembered: Carry nothing on paper, for if he were caught with tangible evidence against him he might be treated as a spy.

Wesley departed, pondering the lax security measures of the Yankee occupation forces as well as the hazards and opportunities of his new assignment. Then he was debating in his mind the choice of a man to accompany him. When it narrowed to Temple and Spangler, he decided finally on the latter. Though unscrupulous, Jack Spangler possessed the necessary qualifications for the job.

Several days later Wesley and Spangler, among others, left Virginia Point under a flag of truce and crossed on the railroad trestle to the island. Wesley saw in the distance the five Federal warships anchored in the harbor. They sat with heads of steam on, ready to give chase to any blockade runner or to meet any attack by land or sea.

Spangler broke Wesley's meditation with, "This is a hell of an assignment. I'd rather be shooting the bluebellies than riding under a damned flag of truce."

"Just be patient," Wesley replied.

Spangler spat in disdain.

Wesley and Spangler continued on toward Fort Eagle Grove, a colony of tents, and mingled with the cavalrymen until nightfall. Then they slipped along the screen of dunes and made their way with the Confederates cautiously, single file and widely spaced, into the city.

At Schmidt's garden, Spangler joined a group and left the picnic park while Wesley listened to talk about the Yankee defense of Galveston. For the main part the enemy strength was on the water. The ship *Harriet Lane* was said to have been Farragut's flagship before he took over the *Hartford*. Heavily armed with a four-inch rifled Parrot gun on point at the forecastle, a nine-inch Dahlgren swivel forward of the foremast, two eight-inch Dahlgren Columbiads, two twenty-four-pounder howitzers, cutlasses and small arms for ninety-five men, the paddle-wheel steamer left no doubt as to her ability to deal death and destruction. And her master, Commander John Wainwright, the men told Wesley, was ready to do just that. Supporting the *Harriet Lane* were the steamers-of-war *Owasco, Sachem, Clifton,* and *Westfield.*

Shortly past midnight a gun went off several blocks away, and after an interval one of the ships fired several shells into the city. Wesley learned later that a Federal sentry had been mysteriously shot to death. The Confederates scattered at the time, however, and assembled again only after the Yankee patrols returned from a search of the city to their barricades at the foot of Twentieth Street.

As the food party rode back to Houston the next day, Spangler seemed quite pleased about something. He produced a sack of real coffee, stolen from the "Yankee bastards," he said, though he did not reveal the contents of a wrapped package inside his coat.

"Honest-to-God coffee, Cap'n." He grinned. "It'll sure beat the potato-coffee we've had to stomach lately." Then he said, "You know, I've been thinking we could slip in and take the island away from the Yankees."

"You forget the ships, Lieutenant," Wesley replied. "And the barracks on Pelican Spit."

"To hell with all that!" Spangler snarled. "I want to kill the dirty—— Yankees."

Wesley and Spangler made three trips with the food parties before Christmas of 1862, and each time a Federal soldier was shot. On each return trip to Houston, Spangler brought some stolen item the blockade had made scarce to Texans, as well as an unidentified package under his coat. Suspecting Spangler of participating in the shooting of the bluecoats, Wesley decided to keep an eye on him on the next visit to Galveston.

Wesley realized that he had thus far brought back little if any information not already in the hands of Magruder's staff. However, he was ordered to continue as before, eyes and ears alert for any news whatever. Meanwhile he awaited his next trip with thoughts of Margaret and his children in mind. When his loneliness for The Oaks became almost unbearable with the approach of Christmas, he went to Major Tarbone with a request for leave during the holidays. The Ranger sent him to Confederate Major Tucker, who flatly refused; because, he said, the big assault was near at hand.

Observation made the fact plainly evident. Great stores of powder and arms had accumulated at the foot of Main Street in Houston. Barges were constantly on the move downstream with cotton bales. The general's staff, even "Prince John" himself, consorted with steamboat captains and marine men, often riding the steamers and cotton barges down the bayou. Captain Henry S. Lubbock, of the steamboat *Bayou City*, took aboard a brass thirty-two-pounder rifle cannon, and the *Neptune*, a river boat, was armed with a pair of twenty-four-pounders. Artillerymen practiced aboard these vessels as well as Captain Lawless's *John F. Carr* and the *Lucy Gwinn* under Major McGee. Atop all this activity, Confederate troops ashore drilled constantly. So did Rangers and civilians too old to stand the trials of regular army life.

Among the latter, affectionately called the "feather-bed regiment," Wesley recognized his old friend Robert Mc-Gowen of Swartout, his white hair blowing in the December wind. When the short drill ended, Wesley approached him. McGowen looked up, then threw his rifle to the ground. With his arms about Wesley, he said:

"Thank God for the sight of you, lad. You and I have run a thousand miles to get away from the Yankees. Now all we own may depend on how well we fight them."

There were men from Montgomery and Willis and Danville in that "white-haired" company, several of whom had scoffed at orders to return home and raise food for fighting men. They could shoot, Magruder's officers had learned, could shoot straight and fast and true.

Wesley heard from these men that Magruder, despite all the conflicting tales about him, had brought fresh hope to Texans. He had about him that air of Southern dash and extreme politeness to friend or enemy that had earned him the sobriquet of "Prince John, the most elegant of Confederate generals." He drank a great deal, it was said, and entertained on a lavish scale. Rumor said he had been relieved of command in the Virginia theater of war because of his merrymaking. Another item, true or false, presented him as the one man in Jefferson Davis's opinion likely to save the storehouse and arsenal of the Confederacy—Texas—from the enemy. In any case, Mc-Gowen and the others agreed that he was not the type of general who would sit out the war doing nothing. For their money he would send "Damnyankee Banks back to New Orleans with his tail 'twixt his legs" the minute he came.

Wesley was listening to more about the gallant general

when a soldier asked for Ranger Captain Wesley Smith. "Major Tucker requests you report at once, sir," he said when McGowen pointed to Wesley.

"Christmas Eve gift, lad." McGowen smiled. "And when you write home send my best wishes of the season to your wife and family."

Wesley returned the greeting and made his way to head-quarters, where he received orders to carry food and gifts to Galveston next morning, which was Christmas Day. There was also a letter from Margaret. As he read it, his desire to return to The Oaks seemed a hundred times greater than before.

He could see Margaret and the children gathered around the big tree, and, almost, he heard the laughter of Bess Simonton and Aunt Polly. The fields would be brown and bare this time of year, but soon the winter plowing would begin and the rich black loam would fall away from the plowshares, leaving them shiny and bright. But most of all, it was Christmas, and he should be home to pass out gifts to the children and visit the slave quarters loaded with gifts and his pockets bulging with candy. Instead—

"Galveston," he said in a growl.

Accompanied by Spangler, Wesley reached Galveston with a heavy load of food and delicacies. The Confederates and Yankees seemed to forget they were at war this day. They met at the edge of town with glad tidings on every tongue, drank together, and laughed and sang. Some of the Federals talked of their homes and families, their eyes misting full. "I'll tell you, Reb," one said, "I'd trade you this sand dune and the states of Texas, Louisiana, and Arkansas for just one look at New England."

"A trade, Yankee. And after we whip hell out of you Northerners, I'll collect."

So it went that day, Wesley listening and watching, Spangler fraternizing but with a mean gleam in his eyes. Then late in the afternoon a Federal ship arrived with troops. That night Wesley learned that two hundred and sixty-five men in blue, Companies D and I of the 42nd Massachusetts Volunteers, sent to bolster the occupation forces, were barricaded on Kuhn's wharf at the foot of Twentieth Street. At last, he thought, he could return with useful information.

On the return to Houston on the twenty-sixth, Spangler again carried a wrapped bundle under his coat. As before, Wesley wondered what it was but kept his silence. Once in Houston, he forgot about Spangler and made his report. This time Major Tucker thanked him warmly for a piece of valuable information and left forthwith to present it to Colonel Cook, who returned with a map of Galveston and asked several questions.

Outside, Wesley looked up into the starlit sky and then at Company A's campfire in the distance. He walked aimlessly for a while, then moved to where Temple and several other Rangers squatted with coffee cups in hand. As he came within earshot of the group he heard something that caused him to stop and listen. Temple had just said Spangler was very drunk.

"I've seen drunk men before," Temple continued with a shudder. "That ain't what made me sick, boys. It's what I saw in the lieutenant's tent. Four of 'em swingin' above him like——"

He stopped short and looked up at Wesley, then covered his embarrassment by pouring coffee for his captain.

"What did you see, Temple?" Wesley asked.

"Nothin'. Not a thing, Cap'n."

Wesley slowly lowered his cup to the ground, rose, and

made his way to Spangler's tent with lantern in hand. Entering, he saw in the pale light the grisly things Temple had mentioned. A sickness came upon him and he turned his head a moment in order to dispel the feeling. He knew now what Spangler had concealed under his coat on the return trips from Galveston. Four Yankee scalps.

Looking down at the lieutenant sprawled out in a drunken stupor, Wesley put down the impulse to drag the man to his feet and beat him within an inch of his life. He called a Ranger and ordered him to pour hot coffee down Spangler until he sobered, then to send for him.

An hour later the Ranger reported to Wesley, who entered the tent again and dismissed the guard. Spangler sat on a wooden foot locker, his yellow hair hanging down over his puffed face. To his credit, he straightened upon seeing Wesley and threw the hair out of his eyes.

"I'm listening, Spangler," Wesley said, pointing to the gruesome objects dangling in the lantern light.

"I don't have to explain anything," the lieutenant said defiantly. "I joined this damned outfit to kill Yankees. What you see is proof that I did just that."

Anger flared in Wesley. Before he realized what he was doing, he had jerked Spangler to his feet and slapped him hard across the mouth with the back of his hand. As the man stumbled back, his hand fell to his pistol, but Wesley was faster and Spangler dropped his hand from the gun.

"You ought not to have hit me, Captain." The familiar mean smile flashed across his face. "No, you oughtn't to have done it. I'm going to kill you for that, Captain. No hurry, but I'm going to kill you."

"Any time you rake up the guts to try, I'll be ready, Spangler. But I won't turn my back on you long enough for you to shoot me down your way. Now you listen to me.

"If it wasn't that we need every gun we can get, and if

it wasn't for the disgrace you'd bring to the Rangers, I'd drag you before General Magruder. He'd have you shot like the wild animal you are. But we'll take this matter up later, rest assured of that. Now clean yourself up and bury these damned things. Understand me?"

There was no reply, just a leer of defiance.

Wesley's voice rose to a shout: "Answer me, damn you!"

With no change of expression, Spangler muttered, "All right, Captain."

Wesley backed to the tent fly, not once removing his eyes from Spangler. Outside, he walked to the campfire and told Temple and the men to say nothing about what they had seen and heard, then moved off into the night to think. Somehow he felt that a little of the dirt in Spangler's soul had rubbed off on him. As much as he despised the Yankees, he felt an apology was due them for crimes committed under a flag of truce. However, his hands were tied. He could do nothing. Frustrated and sick, he tried to remember that this was Christmas.

21. Assault on Galveston

THE movement began on Wednesday, December 31, 1862. Houston bustled with activity all that day as men and guns and shouted orders moved toward the south. Companies marched and mule teams strained at cannon. Confederate regulars, Texas Rangers, and disciplined civilian volunteers, each with rifle and pistol, moved by land for Virginia Point, all a part of Magruder's army. By water, the steamboat *Bayou City*, with twelve artillerymen from Company B, Cook's regiment of the Arizona Brigade, and sixty riflemen sharpshooters, Robert McGowen of Swartout one of them, led the gunboat procession. Heavily armed and manned, the *Neptune*, *John F. Carr*, and *Lucy Gwinn* steamed after her for the head of Galveston Bay.

Plans had been carefully laid. The assaults by land and sea were timed to the wee hours of New Year's morning. It was imperative that the bay squadron and land force each attain its objective as timed. Otherwise the whole plan would be doomed to failure. Magruder had made this clear.

Wesley at the head of Company A, Rangers, had ex-

plicit instructions. Upon reaching Virginia Point, he was
to maintain quiet and order, light no fires, and remain
alert to the order to move. A noisy approach meant there
would be no New Year's celebration of victory. Each
Ranger had heard these instructions from his captain.
Spangler promised a fulfillment of orders.

Darkness fell and the long line of troops moved forward
to Virginia Point to sit in wait for the new year of 1863.
Ahead, Confederate messengers from Fort Eagle Grove
on the island brought information regarding positions of
the Federal fleet. The *Harriet Lane* was anchored at the
western entrance of the channel leading to sea off Thirty-
first Street, the fires in her boilers banked. The ships
Owasco, Sachem, and *Clifton* rode anchor along the three
miles of city waterfront with light heads of steam, all capable of navigating. The *Westfield,* under a full head of
steam, sat the harbor entrance, ready for patrol duty or any
blockade runner. In brief: vigilance ordinary.

With no light but the stars overhead, Wesley stared
across the water at Galveston. Sprawled on his back, Temple was bemoaning the fact that he could not light a cigar,
and Spangler was speculating aloud on the celebration
the Yankees had in mind. The men munched cold food,
raised their heads when the time of night rippled along
the line.

Ten o'clock. Eleven.

The water of the bay scarcely rippled. A fish thwacked
the surface, a man coughed softly, and another laughed.
No sound crossed the arm of bay from Galveston. The
lights played in the upper bay, and someone said they
emanated from the boilers of the Confederate gunboats.
Evidently this was true, for one of the Federal ships
began to steam up toward Pelican Spit. Information from
the staff ran down the line: She was the *Westfield.*

At twelve the order came to move.

The men got to their feet, aware that another year was beginning. They asked in silence what lay ahead, victory or defeat for the South? As the troops began to move toward the railroad trestle over the shallow water, the *Westfield* came to a sudden stop at Pelican Spit. She had probably run hard aground. The surmise rippled hopefully up and down the Confederate line of march. Then the fires of the Confederate flotilla were seen moving north again instead of south, and the men were asking silently if something had gone wrong. What Magruder was thinking, Wesley didn't know. He could only imagine the general's feeling of the moment. There was no halt in the march, however, and soon Company A was absorbed in the long gray column creeping noiselessly across the railroad trestle in the advance on Galveston.

There was much to do before the concerted attack began. Perhaps Magruder expected a miracle, thought Wesley; or else he underrated the Federals. The march continued until all men were walking the sand of the island. Although silence was the order of the hour, the movement of so many men and their supplies seemed at close range enough to alert every Yankee on the island. The crunching of feet and the creaking of supply wagons continued. The artillery was moving in behind them and the stealthy advance on the earthworks around the city brought them closer by the minute to the guns of the *Owasco, Sachem,* and *Clifton.* By two o'clock Company A seemed right under the muzzles of the terrible Dahlgrens. The earthworks were occupied and the heavy guns rolled up to be manned. Under the expert direction of the general's staff, the batteries were posted to sweep the channel, ships, and barricades. The time: three o'clock.

Though not a Yankee appeared the wiser, one could

never tell. With everything in readiness, guns planted and manned, Colonel Cook's force of five hundred men began their advance toward the Kuhn's-wharf barricade with scaling ladders. Magruder led his men toward the corner of Twentieth and Strand.

Wesley and Company A crept toward the wharf. The last order was to hold fire until Magruder gave the signal. It seemed all too quiet to Wesley. If the Yankees had celebrated the New Year, they had long since brought it to a close. Nor had so much as one enemy sentinel moved their way. Wesley's scalp tingled just the same as he searched the shadows for one. When a man emerged from around the corner of a stone building, he tensed. The figure moved on with a whispered word of cheer—the Yankee gunboat *Westfield* had definitely stuck her nose into Pelican Spit. She was helpless.

The men accepted this bit of good news, but as the waiting stretched on and on they began to ask in whispers: Where were the Confederate gun boats? Wasn't three o'clock the time they were due? Or was it later? It was then approaching half-past three.

Jack Spangler sat on a ladder's edge, hunched forward, rifle in the crook of his arm. Temple stood stiffly alert, ready to raise his rifle and blast away the moment Magruder gave the signal. In the dim light Wesley studied his men. A calm, disciplined unit, he admitted, thinking of their many meetings with Comanches. An enemy was to them just an enemy, something to destroy or capture, and the strength of the Yankee in no way intimidated them. It was just as well, he decided.

Something white darted across the street, and Wesley started. Temple's rifle butt was suddenly at his shoulder. Though it was only a cat, it caused pulses to quicken and men to strain their eyes forward in an attempt to pierce the opaque night.

Wesley's thoughts were back at The Oaks, when a movement up ahead jerked his mind rudely back to Twentieth Street in Galveston. A sharp cry of alarm sounded down at the wharf, and he saw a stab of light as the door in the barricade opened an instant to allow a Federal sentry entrance. They had been discovered. The game was up.

The seconds ticked on into the past and still no signal came to open fire. Wesley was wondering what was detaining the Yankee fire, when a shot rang out behind him.

Magruder! This was the signal to open fire on the fleet and barricade. Almost in the instant Colonel Cook's booming voice sounded the charge. Scaling ladders moved forward as the Confederate batteries thundered in the night and hundreds of rifles barked sharply to punctuate the yells of the charging Southerners. The wave of regulars in gray and Texas Rangers surged ahead until they were massed into a tight target. When the 42nd Massachusetts Volunteers began to pour a withering fire into the ranks of the attackers, Wesley yelled at the top of his voice:

"Up with the ladders!"

Spangler shouted in his ear: "They're too goddamned short! A hell of a——"

The order sounded to retreat. Wesley gave ground with the men, firing with each backward step. The barricade seemed to spit fire in constant flashes. The thud of bullets in the dirt and the singing of lead on its way were augmented by cries on every side of Wesley. A gun flew into the air as a Ranger or a man in gray fell. A lad from Brenham who had ridden a dozen sorties under Wesley hunched forward and reeled over, his fall forward slowed by Temple, who got in the way. Little Carl had seen his last fight. But there was no time to mourn him and the

others who had fallen; the Yankees were making a living
hot hell out of the foot of Twentieth Street. Cries of "Take
cover!" were futile to the men bunched in the avenue of
fire.

A Union ship some three hundred yards distant had
opened up with Parrot guns and Dahlgrens in pivot. Her
eight- and nine-inch shells exploded in the midst of the
attackers now in full retreat.

Wesley took cover in the doorway of a stone building
until a shell struck close and showered him with rock and
dust. Dashing to another doorway, he looked back in time
to see a shell explode at the spot he had stood only seconds
before. He had never been under such deadly fire in his
life, and he was praying to escape death as he ran like a
deer for the corner ahead.

Once the wall of stone separated him from the *Owasco's*
galling fire, he tried to rally what was left of Company A.
Spangler was doing the same. Temple was alive, and then
there were others. Before the tally could be made, Wesley
looked around and saw General Magruder just as he gave
the order to withdraw the entire force.

The order momentarily stunned Wesley. After all the
blood and carnage and valor, failure seemed a bitter dose.
The Federals had scored a signal victory. As he stood there
with his gun barrel too hot to touch, a cheer lifted from
the Confederate ranks. Seconds later Major Tucker's
courier cried out to Magruder:

"Our gunboats are coming, General!"

The battle on the water was commencing. The Federal
ships, now unable to blast away at the land, moved out,
leaving the barricades minus the support of heavy guns.
Magruder instantly went to work reorganizing his forces,
deploying troops and artillerymen into positions for assault

on the barricade. Cannon were brought up to even the score.

The bay flashed and roared as the *Bayou City* steamed up with her sharpshooters behind cotton bales. Something had silenced her thirty-two-pound rifle cannon, though she charged on and rammed the *Harriet Lane* before she could get up sufficient steam. The *Neptune* struck her on the other side of the wheelhouse, careening her just as the *Bayou City* struck again. The combined efforts served to render the Federal guns useless at close range even as the ceaseless fire from Confederate sharpshooters raked her decks.

With the *Westfield* helplessly aground and the *Harriet Lane* beaten, Magruder ordered the latter boarded by his aide, Major Tucker. Day was dawning when this was done. Soon it was reported that her commander, Jonathan Wainwright, had been killed.

At 8:45 A.M. Commodore Renshaw of the *Westfield* with three officers and seventeen men got into a boat after laying a powder train to the ship's magazine. When it failed to explode they boarded the ship again. They had no sooner reached the deck than the *Westfield* blew up. All hands were killed.

Then the Federals *Owasco*, *Sachem*, and *Clifton* steamed toward the harbor entrance, and Magruder looked in vain for anything to stop them. The *Bayou City* was rammed fast to the *Harriet Lane*, and of the river boats only she had the power and men aboard to give chase. As the *Owasco* steamed out with a flag of truce at her masthead, she opened fire on the *Harriet Lane*.

Federal troops under the command of Isaac S. Burrell at the barricade on Kuhn's wharf surrendered that afternoon. Even with the garrison in his hands, General Magruder refused to strike the United States flag over Galveston. That could wait, he said. The idea of flying the enemy colors was to invite any Federal ship into the harbor for certain capture.

The Federal losses were lighter than Magruder's in the land and sea encounter; only seventeen Yankee officers and men were killed and forty wounded. Almost four hundred surrendered. The recapture of Galveston had been realized. To the South the New Year's Day victory was a good omen for the year of 1863. To Texans, who had regained their major port, the successful assault lessened the threat of Banks's rumored thrust from New Orleans. But of greater significance to the Confederacy, the Federals lost not only their foothold in the Southwest but the springboard from which to launch an invasion of the state of Texas.

Following the surrender that day, General Magruder told his men that they had contributed daring and valor to the element of surprise, that in doing so they had successfully engaged the enemy in one of the fiercest naval battles of the war. Their deeds on this day were a credit to the Confederacy, he declared, adding that they had proved themselves worthy rangers of the sea as well as the land.

22. Appointment with Destiny

ABOUT FOUR O'CLOCK that afternoon the prisoners were placed aboard a train that would take them as far as Alleyton on their way to the prison camp at San Antonio. Under a guard made up mostly of Rangers, the train rolled into Houston amid a rousing welcome for the victors.

Discipline had necessarily been relaxed on the return journey. Other than the guards who rode the prisoners' cars, the Rangers and Confederates created a celebration of their own. Whisky had been confiscated in Galveston and brought aboard. The men drank and cheered and sang, and the officers watched without interfering. By the time the train reached Houston many of the men were roaring drunk on Yankee whisky.

Wesley left the train and searched the cheering crowd for Major Tarbone. Finding him, he demanded leave to return home. Tarbone did not argue, but smiled and volunteered to look after his men.

"Thank you, Major. Now I'll tell you something. The whole lot of them have been drinking heavily."

"How many are drunk, Wesley?"

"All that lived through the battle," Wesley replied, moving off.

While shouldering his way through the crowd, Wesley collided with Robert McGowen. Delighted to see his old friend, he proposed dinner at the Sixty-six Saloon and, if McGowen was returning to Swartout next day, that they get an early start. In accord on both points, they marched arm in arm toward the Capitol Hotel. After engaging rooms for the night and indulging in the luxury of a bath, they met at the appointed time in the saloon and sat down at a table to relive the happenings of the last twenty-four hours.

McGowen grinned as he massaged his right shoulder. "It's been a long time, lad, since I fired a rifle that fast and long. But I'm lucky. I had just left the big brass thirty-two-pounder when she burst. On the fourth firing. It killed Captain Wier and several others. But we were almost on the *Harriet Lane* and there was no time for us to grieve. We had to shoot."

He looked sadly at the table. "I reckon it kept our minds off the tragedy."

Wesley understood, for he had been unable to so much as pause when Little Carl of Brenham went down.

Then the waiter brought drinks and they turned the conversation to happier channels. Both were anxious to reach their homes and they talked for some time about crops, the land, and the prospect of an early end to the war. The blockade had tightened and the Confederate dollar bought less than before. Atop these things, they both agreed that without foreign intervention on behalf of the Confederacy the industrial might of the North could not fail to win in the end.

"Sure, Wesley," McGowen said. "No matter how we try to get on a cheerful subject, we always return to grim facts we'd both like to forget." He paused there to flash a smile across the table.

"Lad, we had better not take our troubles home with us. Besides, we seem to forget today's victory."

Their food arrived and they ate in silence for a time. Although whisky had warmed them, memories of the pre-dawn fighting of that day robbed them of its cozy effect. For some reason Wesley thought of Joe, wondered where he was, if he had gone to war. He experienced the grim satisfaction of knowing they were on the same side. Then he was seeing Spangler's tent again, the grisly objects hanging there on Christmas night. He resolved to clear his mind of morbid thoughts.

"I hope Dude has cleared more land for pasture," he said.

McGowen looked up. "You know, Wesley, although you're probably right about less cotton and more cattle—the slaves may be set free even in our time—I just can't for the life of me turn away from cotton. I reckon I was raised to it."

"I don't say I'm incapable of making a mistake, but as I see it——"

Wesley broke off suddenly. His eyes narrowed some-what and remained fixed on a man who had just pushed through the saloon doors. He was Jack Spangler, and he stood surveying the place.

Wesley knew Spangler had seen him, despite the fact that he gave no indication of it. As the Ranger lieu-tenant shouldered his way to the bar, McGowen looked up at Wesley.

"You were saying——?"

Wesley began where he had left off. As he talked, he noticed that Spangler had engaged one of the bartenders in close conversation, that the bartender glanced at their table as he poured into Spangler's glass. Soon the man walked around the end of the long bar and directly to Wesley's table.

"Are you Mr. Robert McGowen?" he asked.

"Yes, I am McGowen. Why?"

"The big blond feller, down the bar a ways"—he pointed —"wants you to come over and let him buy a drink."

McGowen's brows lifted and fell in a puzzled manner. "Isn't that man your lieutenant, Wesley?" Turning abruptly to the barman, he said, "Thank him for me, but say that—— No, wait. I'll tell him myself."

As McGowen rose, Wesley instinctively placed a detaining hand on his friend's arm. Then, thinking better of it, he forced a smile and said, "Better make it short, Mr. McGowen. He can be mean when he's drinking."

"So I've heard," said McGowen with a laugh.

Rising, he walked toward Spangler, who slouched against the high mahogany bar and eyed McGowen from behind a leering face. Not quite sure just what Spangler's game was, but suspecting it to cover something else, Wesley rose in a casual manner and sauntered toward the bar. He reached it a few steps behind McGowen, who was saying in a friendly manner:

"Thanks for your kind offer, Lieutenant Spangler, but I've had my quota for the night. Some other time."

Spangler's eyes flashed and his hateful grin spread wider as he pinned McGowen with a steady, direct glance. "So," he said. "So! Why, you old lying sonofabitch, why don't you come out and say it? You think you're too damn good to drink with me, don't you?"

Suddenly he raised his glass and flung the whisky in McGowen's face.

With the liquor burning his eyes, McGowen took a

blind backward step and threw his coat back in a reach for a handkerchief.

"Keep your hand away from that gun!" Spangler yelled, dropping his hand to the .44 hanging low on his thigh.

Wesley, who stood a little apart from the pair, noticed that when Spangler's hand came up with the pistol his eyes were not on McGowen but squarely on him. He knew in that instant that McGowen was merely a pawn in Spangler's game for vengeance.

In that split-second interval between watchfulness and action, Wesley realized with startling clarity what he had known all along, that it was a duel to the death between him and Spangler. It made no difference that each had saved the other's life on occasion; they had been singled out by destiny to meet as they were now.

Catlike, Wesley bounded out of the sights of Spangler's pistol just as it roared. The heavy slug tore past him and buried itself in the far wall of the saloon. His own gun answered twice, and the bullets thudded into Spangler's chest just as he began to thumb the hammer back for his second shot.

There was a sober look of fright and bewilderment on Spangler's face, and, his right arm lifted high enough for him to place his pistol hand on the bar. Then some muscular reaction caused him to stand on tiptoes before he began to collapse. As he fell, his thumb released the hammer of the .44. The gun exploded, shattering his own whisky bottle before smashing into the handsome mirror behind the bar.

Then Spangler fell, burying in the sawdust the hateful grin that reappeared on his face.

Wesley shoved his gun back into his holster and slumped into a chair. "I would appreciate it if someone would get Major Tarbone for me."

23. The Yankee Wagon Train

EVERY TIME Wesley returned to Margaret a gladness filled his heart. The very sight of her eased the tensions of war and drove the unpleasant happenings of the trail—combat and blood and all personal conflicts—into a distant corner of his memory. The return to her after the recapture of Galveston and the shooting of Jack Spangler was no different. He took her in his arms and felt the cleansing effect of her touch.

That first night home, Margaret and the children kept him busy relating his experiences at Galveston. McGowen spoke of the things that had happened to him, though he was careful to omit any mention of the Spangler affair. When at last the children were sent off to bed and Robert McGowen grew sleepy, Wesley and Margaret retired to their room as happy as young lovers.

Wesley's homecoming demanded a party, Margaret advised, and early next morning she began preparations. Scarcities brought about by war and blockade created a problem, though she was too happy to have her husband home alive and unharmed to dwell on them. The guests arrived by early evening and were met at the gates by the aroma of beef cooking over the pits. Real coffee was also a rare treat and made up for the absence of imported wines and other missing delicacies. For a time the war seemed forgotten, though it was too much a part of everyone to remain a banished subject. After much talk about the progress of the war on all fronts, Bess Simonton said she had just received a letter from Reuben.

When the demand to hear what he had written was not to be denied, Bess said, "Well, I'll read parts of his letter. Some of it is intended only for me." Then she began with, "Now, Reuben says:

" 'We have the Yanks on the run, darling wife. Not so much because we are better fighters, but because we have a cause, more to fight for. We enter battle knowing that we are defending our rights as citizens against an aggressor. We must fight to remain free men. As I have wondered so many times why the people of the North think they can change our way of thinking by either legislation or force of arms, I am now wondering if Abe Lincoln's government actually hopes to solve a problem as big as slavery by a simple proclamation that says the slaves are free. . . . We have high hopes that General Lee will solve our problem this year. Then I can come home to my dear wife and eat Aunt Ellen's cooking once more. I never intend to leave Montgomery County again after the war is over——' "

Bess wiped a tear from her cheek and hesitated. "I'm sorry," she said in a broken voice.

A silence gathered in which all who had listened shared her feeling of the moment.

"Bess," said Wesley after the group had dispersed, "when I think of all the husbands and fathers and brothers fighting away off up there, I feel ashamed of my part in this war. I may have looked over a gun barrel at as many Yankees, but I have not been called upon to make the personal sacrifice those men have."

"Wesley Smith," scolded Bess, "you make me tired. We all know what you did to the Yankees in Galveston. But for men like you, they might be in Montgomery tonight. We all know what good you and your Rangers have done among the Indians. Those savages might have wiped East Texas off the map. So you just hush that kind of talk."

Wesley smiled and turned the conversation to other channels. But he still censured himself for letting other men fight his battles.

Several days later Wesley received a long letter from Major Tarbone. He urged Wesley to concentrate on food production on every available acre. The Confederate soldiers were hungry, and food was the most important thing he could furnish now.

Wesley went to work with determination when the cold, rainy winter turned into sunny spring. Crops were planted and a Diamond Six was burned into the red curly hides of nearly two thousand more Hereford calves. If it was humanly possible, Wesley told Dude Justice, he would produce enough beef to feed every Confederate fighting man. This, in a measure, would repay them for the sacrifice they were making for him.

In July of 1863 the Galveston *News* advised that Lee had joined the Federals in a great battle in a little Pennsylvania town called Gettysburg. To Wesley and others, Lee's penetration of the North was encouraging. Surely the South was on the way toward winning the war.

A few weeks later Wesley and Margaret rode the stage to Houston, in order to be on hand Monday morning when the scarce articles were placed on the jobber's shelves. As they entered the city they came upon a large gathering of elderly men standing in front of the little frame building that housed the Houston *Telegraph*. Carriages and buggies ranged along the street, all filled with women and children. As he and Margaret stepped down from the stage, Wesley asked why the people were gathered here. He was told that Lee was retreating, that evidently the Confederates had not won at Gettysburg. And Grant had finally captured Vicksburg.

Wesley turned to Margaret and held her arm as they crossed the street to the hotel. As soon as they were shown to their room, Wesley, with studied deliberation took off his coat, hung it on the back of a chair, then removed his gun belt and put the big weapon on the marble-topped dresser. This done, he sat down heavily on the side of the bed and put his head in his hands. Margaret knew how disturbed he was over the tragic news, for her own heart was heavy. She sat down beside him and placed an arm about his shoulders. Finally Wesley raised his face and said painfully:

"Margaret, the South just can't lose this war. The people up North don't understand us, and their politicians don't want to. If they win, we'll feel their heel for a long time. And they'll grind it deeper than any foreign invader, because there's hate now—on both sides."

He rose suddenly, letting her arm fall unheeded from his shoulder. "I'll be gone for a little while, darling," he said softly. "I must see Major Tarbone tonight."

Moments later Margaret was alone. Although she understood Wesley's feeling of despair, she too felt it and needed him then. She rose and tried to busy herself. Then with a sob she fell across the bed and cried until finally sleep claimed her.

Long after midnight Wesley stumbled into the room and tried to light the lamp at their bedside. "I've been drinking, Margaret," he said, "but I'm not drunk, just tired. Very tired."

He sat on the edge of the bed and took her hand in his. "Somehow, no matter how many cattle I ship to our soldiers, I can't bring myself around to believing I'm doing my share in this damnable war." He lowered his gaze to her upturned face and saw the curious look in her soft eyes. "So it boils down to the fact that a man must live with himself."

"What are you leading up to, Wesley?"

"That I just can't sit idly by, Margaret. I'm leaving soon to fight the Yankees again."

"I—I've been expecting it, Wesley," she said, her voice close to breaking, "and hoping you didn't have to go. I'm selfish, darling."

"So am I, Margaret. But——"

"Where are you going this time, Wesley?"

"To the Territory of New Mexico. You know the rumor of the big shipment of gold from California to save the Federal government from financial ruin. Some reports have it going by ship around Cape Horn, others place it on the overland route. Still other rumors have it divided and hidden among supplies aboard ships and prairie wagons. Maybe it's all rumor, but there's talk of a big Yankee supply train out of California, so I'm taking my Rangers out to look for it, to take it if we find it."

Though Margaret said nothing, she lay awake long after Wesley fell asleep. She prayed for his safe return from another dangerous mission and for the end of a terrible war that took him away from her.

A week later Wesley joined his Ranger company in San Antonio, where Temple and his men were outfitting for the long trek into Apache territory. At the Alamo he received his orders from General Sibley and set out for the territory the Union had wrested from the Confederacy, a vast dry and barren land that actually belonged to neither the blue nor the gray but to the most ferocious Indians on the continent. Not one enemy but two, Wesley reflected as he led his troop toward the Pecos River and on northwest for the upper swing of the Rio Grande.

In order to travel with minimum encumbrance, the old heavy supply wagons, called schooners, had been discarded in favor of three light wagons. As a result, Company A reached Horsehead Crossing on the Pecos in record time and, meeting with no resistance at this great Comanche stronghold, moved on at a fast pace. The Indians followed, rode ahead, and flanked the troop, but always in the distance, melting away with the approach of the white man. When the Comanches fell behind, Temple warned that the hard-hitting, merciless Apaches lay ahead. Wesley realized that Temple knew the Indians of the Southwest. Often he wondered if the faithful, leather-faced Ranger wasn't part Indian himself.

On Wednesday, September 9, 1863, the troop was moving generally northward after having skirted the southern jut of the San Andres Range at El Paso. Ahead lay the Spanish village of Mesilla, a junction for overland travel from Arizona and California and the road up the Rio Grande for Santa Fe. The adobe buildings along the river baked in the hot sun. To the east the mighty spires of the Organ Mountains lifted almost straight up out of the desert, as if to stand guard over Mesilla and the little town of Las Cruces.

Wesley sent Temple and another Ranger ahead to scout the settlements and the converging wagon roads farther upriver. Hours later the patrol rode in, hot and dusty, to report no sign of Yankee soldiers but prints of numerous horses and wide-tired wagons, indicating a movement of cavalry troops and a wagon train of considerable size. The movement was upriver.

"Maybe six or seven hours ahead of us, Cap'n," Temple replied to Wesley's questions. "But the way the ground was tore up, I'd say there was really a passel o' men and wagons. My guess is a thousand men and fifty to sixty heavy schooners. Damn heavy, Cap'n."

As Wesley pondered the situation, pitting the large number of troops against his small band, Temple said:

"Probably the Yanks needed a army to escort the train through Apache country, Cap'n. Fact is"—he paused to bite off tobacco and work his mouth—"we run across sign of a party of Apaches who seemed to be keepin' tab on Mr. Yank."

"What are you getting at, Temple?"

"Just this, Cap'n. With a little help from the heathens, we might wear them Yankees to a frazzle. Seein' as I'm pretty well knowed by the Apaches, I might make a few trades and promises and talk 'em into joinin' us."

Wesley studied Temple sharply.

"I know what you're thinkin', Cap'n. But old Temple can take care of hisself. With a little firewater and a mule for their bellies, seems I got fair persuasion on my side."

"How many men would you need?"

"None. Just me. And if them signs don't fool me and if I can strike up some pals in the Apache camp, I'll be back sometime tomorrow."

Wesley finally consented. Watching Temple ride off leading an old mule with several quarts of hard whisky strapped to its back, he wondered if in his eagerness to capture the wagon train he was sacrificing Temple to a horrible death at the hands of the Apaches. As the day lengthened, he stared at the spires of the Organ Mountains painted in sunset golds and continued to wonder about it.

When Temple rode into camp late the following afternoon, Wesley wanted to shout for sheer joy. He met the scout and waited for a report, but Temple was in no hurry. Finally he began with almost an apology:

"I just hope I done the right thing, Cap'n. Got the devils pretty worked up before I passed the rotgut around. Course, the mule was roastin' and the bastards was relishin' the entrails. But the chief wanted more than I took along. He demanded all the horses the yellowlegs was ridin'. 'Now see here,' I says, 'you promise me only fifty braves and you want all them horses. I'll give you a hundred head, no more.' We dickered some. He asked how many was in our troop and I told him. Then I knowed he was figurin' that fifty braves had us outnumbered nearly two to one, that he couldn't lose no matter how things turned out. Fact is, I didn't want more than fifty of the treacherous devils. You just can't trust an Apache too far."

Wesley nodded approvingly.

"Now, Cap'n," the old Ranger went on, " 'twould be my idea to move into our meetin' place with our Injun pals tonight, just to be sure how many of his braves he plans to bring tomorrow."

Wesley was more concerned with the Yankee odds against them. He knew Temple was right in not wanting a large force of Apaches, but he also knew that he was not going to let the Yankee wagon train get away if there was the remotest possibility of stopping it. If this train was from California and there was gold in those wagons, if they were successful in taking it, its capture might well determine the course of the war, for England and France desired gold as much as scarce cotton.

"To hell with the odds," Wesley said. "We've had the odds against us all the way in this damned war."

As he turned to go into his tent, he said to his lieutenant, "Give the order to move out at sundown. Be sure the men get their supper early."

By midnight the Rangers had moved quietly into a dry camp on the bank of the Rio Grande, some fifteen miles north of Las Cruces. There they settled on their blankets while Temple and three picked men moved in a big silent circle around the camp to search for any signs of a larger Apache gathering than agreed upon.

In the north the clouds piled up threateningly, and long before daylight the sky was bright with continuous flashes of lightning. Heavy claps of thunder rolled down the river, giving promise of flooded arroyos along the winding trail upstream.

As Wesley lay on his blanket and watched the lightning and listened to the heavy cannonade of thunder, he tried to imagine what the officer in command of the wagon train would do. Temple had told him of several treacherous fords the Yankees would have to negotiate, and he was hoping rains would make these crossings impossible.

At daylight the Apache chief rode into the Ranger camp with fifty fierce-eyed, bandy-legged bucks, the meanest-looking Indians Wesley had ever seen. They built fires after surveying the camp and the Rangers and began cooking two big white-tail deer they had brought with them. Although they appeared to be peaceful enough, the Rangers kept their firearms close at hand. While the Apache was much smaller in stature than the Comanche, he had shown the white man that he was twice as cunning and fierce as the plains Indian. He traveled light and fast, struck, scattered, and ran. He looked cruel, was cruel. It was in his piercing eyes and square, unyielding face. But as an ally, he was the greatest fighting man America had ever produced. The word "Apache" meant hate, and he fought with hate uppermost in his mind. But he was known to hate all men, and he was therefore treacherous.

At nine-thirty Temple rode in with his scouts and after a short exchange with the Apache chief he reported that everything seemed in order for the move upriver.

Wesley outlined his orders to Temple, who passed them on to the chief. The approach was to be quiet and no attack was to be mounted until Wesley gave the word. Then the procession got under way. With Wesley, Temple, and the Indian chief leading, the Apache warriors following, and the Rangers bringing up the rear, they took the trail leading into the hills up along the Rio Grande.

They traveled fast since it had not rained this far south. Temple told Wesley the Yankees would more than likely be at the first ford ten miles away. Long before noon they covered the distance. Halting the group, Wesley sent Temple and the chief forward to locate the train. In an hour they were back.

"The damn fools are camped down on the river on a big shelf, Cap'n," Temple reported. "If it rained up the river like I think it did, we'll really have them in a trap."

He went on to explain that there was only one narrow cut down to the river from the west side of the stream and that the river was already so swollen that crossing it was next to impossible.

"It's gonna be a helluva lot higher, too, Cap'n," Temple said. "And if they got even half sense they'll get off that rock pronto. Else they'll drown."

After Wesley gave the order to begin the advance in strict silence, they moved quietly into a position covering the one narrow opening that led down to the river.

Being so far removed from civilization and with such a

preponderance of manpower at his disposal, the Union officer in command had foolishly neglected to post sentries. This made the blocking of the narrow road a simple matter. The Rangers carried large rocks and boulders while the Apaches looked disdainfully on and stacked them across the opening to the river, leaving a passageway just wide enough to accommodate a wagon.

When the barricades had been built to a height of about six feet, Wesley held a short conversation with Temple before moving to the edge of the rocky bluff overlooking the river. Carefully parting the tangle of brush along the rim, he surveyed the scene below him.

There were, he estimated, approximately twelve hundred men, a like number of horses, and, within the range of his vision, more than fifty wagons. All of the vehicles were covered with government-issue wagon sheets stretched tight across the curved wooden staves.

Even though they had the Yankees in a trap, the odds were still twenty to one in favor of the soldiers. However, Wesley refused to think of this. Instead, he thought of the possible gain. The many wagons contained supplies that could be sent to the Confederate soldiers at the fighting front. Perhaps there was a wagon loaded with gold. If so, it would bolster the defense of the South, perhaps spur the longed-for aid from England and France.

His mind made up, Wesley eased back from the bluff and deployed his forces along the best protected side of the cut and placed a small group directly behind the barricades. Taking a half dozen men with him, he returned to the bluff.

"I want every one of you to pick a soldier in different parts of the camp," he ordered, "and when I fire I want every man of you to do the same."

The soldiers on the shelf below, oblivious of the nearness of an enemy, milled lazily about while the Rangers silently knelt and picked their victims. Wesley drew a bead on the chest of a big officer who was striding among the soldiers to his left, and squeezed the trigger of his rifle. Immediately the man pitched forward on his face. Six other Ranger guns roared and half a dozen more soldiers followed him to the rocky ground in various parts of the camp.

"Listen to me, Yankees," Wesley cried. When every soldier on the ledge froze, trying desperately to locate his position, he said again, "Listen to me. Don't go for your guns or we'll kill every last damned one of you. Stand where you are."

As the soldiers stood stock-still, momentarily confused, awaiting a command from their officers, Wesley cried, "All of you officers come to the back of the wagon standing nearest the water. Hurry it up."

Several officers, one of them a colonel, stalked toward the vehicle. Then suddenly, by some unseen, unheard signal, the enlisted men made a concerted rush for the shelter of the steep riverbank and disappeared from the sight of the Rangers, leaving only a handful of enlisted men and officers at the rear of the wagon nearest the river. Forgetting the enemy officers standing by the wagon, Wesley decided to deal with the soldiers who had sought shelter under the bluff on which he stood.

"Here, you men," he ordered his Rangers, "roll those rocks over the bluff. We'll get them out of their damned hole in a hurry."

There were many round and jagged rocks strewn about, each weighing from fifty to a hundred pounds. As the Rangers began rolling and pushing them over the edge of the precipice, a mighty cry went up from the rocky shelf. The cavalrymen scattered over the wide expanse of the lower bank, many of them diving into the swirling waters of the swollen Rio Grande, only to be pulled down by the foaming river, now rising rapidly.

Several hundred of the blue-clad troops rushed for the narrow cut that led up from the river, while others mounted horses and rode roughshod over them in their wild, fear-crazed attempt to escape the unseen enemy. But the defenders of the barricades were ready, and a crashing volley from rifles, together with speeding Apache arrows, stopped them in their tracks. Many were crushed under the stampeding feet of charging horses that fought their way up the rocky slope. But the horses brought their riders directly into the path of arrows.

One wild-eyed young rider fought and slashed his way up and through the narrow pass and with a final rush cleared the rock barricades. As he passed, an Apache grasped the pommel of his saddle and swung up behind the terrified trooper. They disappeared into the brush. Seconds later the Apache rode back alone with the soldier's blood smeared about his already hideously painted face and chest.

The Indian chief saw the warrior as he returned to the fight, and the gory sight put an end to all restraint. Above the noise and confusion of the slaughter, he gave the signal and the Apaches charged. A bloodcurdling cry echoed back and forth between the steep walls of the canyon below, causing the hair of every white man to stand on end. Knives flashed as the Apaches, now fighting as a mounted group, the way they knew best how to fight, went tearing down the pass and turned their ponies onto the shelf over which the storm water from the Rio Grande was now beginning to spread.

Now that they could actually see and come to grips

with an enemy, the troopers steadied and began to fight for their lives. The Apache charge carried through a small group of cavalrymen who could not reach their horses. Armed with long bayoneted rifles, these men held the butts of their guns against the rocky earth, bayonets chest-high to the flying ponies, taking a toll of horses. The defenders quickly dispatched the Apaches, who rolled off the dying animals.

"The damned fools!" Wesley cried in disgust as he watched the remaining warriors come to grips with the soldiers.

One volley from a group of rifles sheltered behind boulders killed all but one of the remaining Apaches. As Wesley watched, the lone warrior raised his arm and hurled a knife. An officer bent double and plunged face-down into the angry water now running a foot deep through the wagon spokes before a dozen rifles sent the Apache tumbling from his pony.

Suddenly it grew quiet. Not a voice was raised. Not a shot was fired.

"Are you ready to surrender now?" Wesley shouted. "We give you this last opportunity, so make up your minds quick."

"Who the hell are you, anyway?" an officer demanded.

"Texas Rangers," Wesley replied. "And we don't give a damn whether you surrender or not. If we don't get you, the river will."

Presently the Yankee answered with a question: "What are the conditions?"

"Good treatment and safe conduct to the military authorities at San Antonio."

Without any pause for consultation, the Federal soldier said, "We are your prisoners, Ranger, provided you are able to identify yourselves as Rangers."

"Here is my identification," Wesley replied, tossing over the edge of the cliff the silver star Captain Wade had worn so gallantly.

"Tell us how to proceed, Ranger."

"Send the wagons up first," Wesley commanded. "Two at a time, and only one driver in each wagon. And if you value your life, return my badge."

Soon the wagons began the arduous grind up the steep slope. Each was searched and the drivers disarmed. Then came the troopers, mounted ten to a group. The Rangers tied them to their saddles with their hands behind them. By sunset, the prisoners were all disarmed and ready to begin the long trek back to San Antonio.

Of the twelve hundred cavalrymen who composed the supply-train escort, less than five hundred survived. Owing to the deadly aim of the Rangers, the murderous weapons of the Apaches, and the deadly hoofs of the terrified horses, there were comparatively few wounded men to care for. These, some fifty in all, were loaded into the wagons, and the detachment's medical officer was ordered to care for them.

Before assigning burial details, Wesley and the Union colonel, who had requested that he be put on his honor, walked down the narrow pass to be sure no wounded men remained on the bloody shelf. As they neared the end of the narrow defile Wesley saw that one of the wagons had not been sent up. It was the one that had been nearest the water's edge, and now the river was washing high on the bed of the vehicle.

"Why was that wagon left behind, Colonel?" asked Wesley sharply.

"Why, I don't know, Captain," the colonel replied.

"Lieutenant Temple," Wesley shouted up to the bluff, "send a four-up and a driver down here. Quick."

They could not force the team to back into the swirling water far enough to get it hitched to the wagon. A heavy rope was tied to the end of the wagon tongue, but before it could be hitched to the doubletree behind the team the vehicle began to roll slowly backward. Then it disappeared with a splash in the swirling torrent.

"Now, Colonel," snapped Wesley, "I want to know what was in that damned wagon you were so anxious to keep away from us. Was it gold?"

"Just rifles and ammunition, sir," the colonel replied, staring at the spot where the wagon disappeared, "which you Rebels will never be able to use on us."

"Be that as it may," Wesley said, studying the man in blue closely, "I'm not inclined to believe you."

Suddenly he drew his pistol and shoved it against the colonel's stomach. With his face close to the other's he said, "I ought to kill you, and the fact that I've given my word to see you safely to San Antonio won't stop me if I find out you've lied to me. This is your last chance to live, Colonel. Now what was in that wagon?"

"Rifles and ammunition," the colonel replied with no fear in his voice or expression.

"Where is the gold shipment from California? And don't tell me you haven't heard of it."

"Yes, I've heard about it. Some say it went by clipper ship. I don't know."

No amount of questioning or repeated threats could change the Yankee's story. Finally Wesley holstered his pistol and made a wry face. "Colonel, I'll tell you this much," he said. "If there was or is gold in that wagon, you are a bigger hero to your side than all the Grants, Shermans, and the rest of your generals. For if we got our hands on the reported gold shipment, the South would push your armies into Canada."

The colonel merely shrugged as he said he was anything but a hero.

Following another glance from the Union officer to the raging water, Wesley said it was time to join the troop and get on the road to San Antonio.

The march was slow and without incident, despite the fact that twenty-five men were spread thin to guard twenty times their number. The Federal troops seemed relieved that their part of the war was over, and they gave the Rangers no trouble. After the first night on the trail their bonds were removed and, although they were carefully guarded, the enlisted men were given camp chores to perform under the direction of their own officers, and the colonel was allowed to share Wesley's tent.

On the afternoon of Sunday, October 4, 1863, the Rangers marched their prisoners into the stockade on the grounds of the Alamo and delivered them and the captured supplies to the Confederate Army of Texas. As Wesley turned to depart, the Yankee colonel said:

"Captain Smith, I wish to thank you for the fine treatment accorded me and my men. You have been most generous and I hope that I will be able to repay you someday."

As Wesley eyed the colonel, a tight little smile tugged at the corners of his mouth. "If you want to repay any kindness I might have done you, Colonel, just write old Abe Lincoln and ask him to call off his dogs and leave the South alone."

24. In Defense of Home

WESLEY wired Major Tarbone of the capture of the wagon train and asked for orders. The major responded sooner than expected: Wesley should make a forced march to Alleyton, where the company would take the train to Houston. Wondering what inspired this, Wesley began the march that very day, despite the weariness of the entire troop. Late that night they made a short dry camp near Seguin, where they drank deeply of captured Yankee coffee over a fare of canned beef and dried apples. At eleven on the following night the saddle-sore Ranger company rode into the sleeping village of Alleyton, just thirty-one hours after leaving San Antonio.

The troop pulled up at the little depot where Wesley found the stationmaster taking a message ticking over the wire. Wesley found a chair and sat down just as the monotonous clicking of the instrument ended. The operator then turned to Wesley, who identified himself, and read the message he had just received: Company A, Texas Rangers, and all gear were to be hurried by train to Houston.

The telegram was signed by one of General Magruder's staff.

Within the hour the baggage, horses, and gear were loaded and the trail-weary men piled into their seats for welcome rest. Wesley was shaken from a sound sleep by the bump of the locomotive as it coupled to the cars. He looked at his watch under the dim oil lights then fell asleep again. He did not open his eyes until dawn, when one of his men roused him with a cup of steaming coffee in hand and said they were pulling into Houston.

Wesley gulped the hot liquid and, as the train ground to a stop, he saw Tarbone. When the troop emptied out of the cars, he approached the major and shook his hand.

"No gold in that shipment, Wesley?"

After hearing the story of the Rio Grande encounter, the major responded to Wesley's questions with:

"First of all, your family is well, doing as good as can be expected in these times. As for the war, we beat the living hell out of the Federals down at Sabine Pass last month. A young lieutenant named Dick Dowling, with only forty-seven men defending the little breastworks called Fort Griffin, whipped over four thousand Yankees, captured two of their gunboats and three hundred and fifty of the bluebellies. Never even had one of his men wounded. However, since we lost at Arkansas Post early in the year there has been a gradual infiltration of Federals. Now the enemy is spreading out over a wide area, burning homes, barns, warehouses, everything they can put a match to. They have already destroyed a lot of fine homes along the upper Trinity, and it's going to be up to you and the Home Guard to stop them. The last raid they made was around Palestine. Two days before that they stormed through the country around Athens, burning

every building they came across and killing everyone who
got in their way."

He stopped suddenly and lit one of the few excellent
cigars he had been fortunate enough to come by in these
days of scarce luxuries.

"Where do you intend to send us first, Major?" Wesley
asked. His heart was in his throat, for the invader was
close, close to Margaret and The Oaks.

"Give your men six hours' leave. No drinking. Then
have them meet you at the West Montgomery Road
crossing on Buffalo Bayou at noon," the major replied,
disregarding Wesley's question. "We'll go to the office
now and have a look at the maps you'll want to follow."

Wesley issued the necessary orders, and he and Tarbone hurried to the little office on Fannin Street, near the
Sixty-six Saloon. They entered the office and Tarbone
closed the door, motioning Wesley to a chair.

"While the report is not confirmed yet Wesley, the raiders are supposed to be closer than I told you. We heard
indirectly that they made a raid on the town of Crockett
last night and that they were moving through the farms
near Huntsville soon after."

Wesley felt his heart tighten. He was suddenly sick
and cold. He tried to speak, but the words would not
come. "Oh, God," he prayed under his breath, "don't let
the Yankees come to Montgomery." Finding his voice, he
said, "Major, do I have to wait here until noon? I want
to go by The Oaks anyway, so may I go on and meet my
men there?"

"Get on your way," said Tarbone. "Temple will meet
you at The Oaks as soon as they can make it. I'll have them
leave as soon as they can feed and get their gear ready to
move."

Wesley half ran all the way across town to where the

horses were penned in a pole corral. The guard helped him catch and saddle his horse, a deep-chested gelding, and ten minutes after leaving Ranger headquarters he was well on his way out of Houston and traveling fast in the direction of Montgomery. He held the bay to a long lope the animal could maintain for hours on end and guessed that noon would see him at The Oaks. He almost made it, even after pausing in Montgomery to warn the people there of the close proximity of the Yankees. He turned his lathered mount into the gates of The Oaks at a quarter past twelve.

Margaret saw him racing up the hill, and she and the children stood on the white veranda to welcome him. As the laboring horse raced up the drive, Wesley said a prayer of thanks for being able to live in Texas with his loved ones, so far removed from the heavy fighting that had swung back and forth across the states of Virginia, Alabama, Tennessee, and Georgia. The Northern soldiers who swept in scattered bands across Texas had no supply trains to keep them in food, clothing, and ammunition, and thanks be to God, they would learn that Texans would make it difficult for them to live off the land.

As always, Wesley's homecoming was a joyful occasion. As he lay on the big parlor sofa with his head pillowed in Margaret's lap with the children all about, a feeling of contentment crept over him. Forgotten were Yankees, war, blood and strife, and cold rainy trails. He was home. Home.

Soon Mrs. Arnold entered to welcome him home. She was followed by Aunt Polly and many of the servants, who found some excuse or other for entering the parlor.

"I don't want to frighten any of you," he said to Mrs. Arnold after careful deliberation, "but I believe it would be safer for you and Margaret to stay on the other side of

Montgomery with Bess Simonton for a few days. There's a small band of Yankees in the vicinity."

"Oh, Wesley," said Margaret, "I must tell you this. Betty Irvine's father and brother were both killed at the battle of Arkansas Post. And that fine Spiller boy—you remember him—well, he was wounded and captured but managed to escape. He came home about a week ago."

She took Wesley's hand in hers. "And, darling," she continued with a brave smile, "we knew the Yankees were coming, but Mr. Justice and the men are somewhere between us and them. He sent us a note only last night, saying he would keep a rider ready to warn us if they got too close."

"And what would you have done," he asked with admiration in his eyes, "if the Yankees had shown up?"

"I think we would have fought them if they had attempted to harm The Oaks," she said simply. "This is my home, Wesley. I love it and I shall always defend it."

"Just the same, I want you and the children and Mrs. Arnold to be ready to leave within the hour."

Wesley turned to Aunt Polly, who stood in the doorway, listening. "Do you and the rest of the servants want to go, Aunt Polly, or will you stay here and keep the place?"

"Mistuh Wes," she declared stoutly, "I 'magines some of dese trashy niggers is gonna run off when de Yankees come, but I ain't seen the piece of po' white trash I is scared of. If yo'all says stay, den stay I will. Just like Miss Margaret say, this is my home and I intends to take care of it."

Wesley smiled. "I knew what you'd say, Aunt Polly. You darkies have nothing to fear from the Yankees anyway. They are fighting us to free you, you know."

"Free us! Makes me sick!" Aunt Polly mumbled, shuffling off.

"God have mercy on the Yankee who sets his foot inside our door while Aunt Polly is here," Wesley said to Margaret. "Now I have to go, but don't any of you worry for, the Lord willing, we're going to stop them long before they get close to The Oaks and Montgomery."

After scribbling a note for Temple, instructing him to leave three men to guard The Oaks and the surrounding plantations, and to ride fast with the rest of the company for Danville, he watched his family enter the surrey and drive away.

This was something new to Wesley, watching his loved ones fleeing their home because of the Federals. It angered him and he turned away, resolved to fight the enemy with everything he could muster.

He knew he was taking a big chance by pulling his Rangers this far north, but he wanted to come to grips with the invader at the earliest possible moment; and he believed the Yankees would continue south rather than west from Huntsville because they could inflict more damage on the country. If they followed their own pattern they would move on the big plantations between Chicken Creek and the San Jacinto River. Danville was in the middle.

On a fresh horse, he took the north trail through his land almost to Willis, then turned north on a dim road that would carry him across Weir Creek and into Danville. Just as he turned off the Willis Road he saw a Negro boy on a sorrel mare racing from the direction of Danville. Recognizing Wesley, the terrified boy pulled his horse up sharply.

"Lawdy, Mistuh Wes!" he exclaimed, his eyes rolling in fright. "I is sholy glad to see yo'all. There's a heap o' Yankees comin', suh, and Mistuh Dude done tole me to tell de white folks in Montgomery to get ready fer 'em."

"Listen to me, Jimbo," Wesley said sharply. "Now listen. You ride into Willis and tell some of the menfolks there that we're going to try and stop the Yankees at Danville, but for them to be ready to fight anyway. Then—— Are you listening to me, Jimbo?"

"Yassuh. Yassuh, Mistuh Wes. I knows what yo' sayin'."

"All right. Now after you ride to Willis, take the lower road to The Oaks and wait for Mr. Temple and my Rangers there. Tell them to ride as fast as they can to Danville. Now get going."

The boy needed no urging. He dug his heels into the sides of the mare and raced off in the direction of Willis.

As Wesley spurred his horse along the trail he checked the two big .44s he carried in his gun belt to be sure they were loaded. As he approached the south end of Danville's main street he heard a number of rifleshots. Perhaps a quarter of a mile away, he thought, reining his horse into a side road. There he stopped to listen. The shooting continued and he guessed it to be in the vicinity of Richard's store, a strong brick building near the center of the town.

While riding fast toward the sound of battle, he saw several grim-faced, elderly men slipping along the streets and through the alleyways with long muskets. One of the group told Wesley that the Yankees had probably descended upon Danville to replenish their supply of food and ammunition. Wesley said that he certainly hoped such was the case, for the little ammunition the Yankees might find in Danville would not fit a Sharps rifle. Then he left them and crossed another side street.

A moment later he saw several Yankee cavalrymen holding a number of horses and hurriedly reined back out of sight.

He was about to dismount when the very thought of

Federal soldiers standing on Texas soil so angered him that he threw caution to the winds. Drawing one of his revolvers, he spurred his horse around the corner and raced directly toward the nearest soldier.

The Federal trooper tried desperately to draw his pistol, but the holster flap was buckled and Wesley was upon him before any of the other soldiers realized what was happening. Wesley slid to the ground before his horse stopped running. In another moment he was standing close to the Yankee, his big pistol shoved hard into the man's middle. He whirled the soldier so that his back was to him.

"Tell them to drop those bridle reins and unbuckle their guns, quick," he demanded, ramming the gun barrel savagely into the man's back.

The soldier did as he was told, pleading with the other troopers not to fire. When they dropped the reins as ordered and the horses began to stray off slowly, Wesley drew his prisoner back against the wall of a building. Several of the soldiers had raised their hands above their heads, though others, realizing that the horses would offer protection from Wesley's bullets, dived behind the animals, drawing their pistols.

Wesley roughly jerked his prisoner around and, keeping back of him, began a swift advance upon the other soldiers. One trooper attempted to run down the street, but before he had taken a half dozen paces Wesley fired. The soldier fell face up in the weeds bordering the sandy roadway. The report of Wesley's pistol caused the enemy's horses to bolt, thereby clearing the obstacle between the Ranger and the soldiers.

"Now drop those guns and put your damned hands up! High!" Wesley commanded.

The soldiers threw down their arms and raised their hands.

As Wesley pushed forward with the trooper at gun point, he glanced behind him to see five of the old men of Danville, all armed with muskets, moving up at a run. They herded the soldiers together and tied them with their own belts. Then they marched the prisoners to the main street of Danville and turned north toward the sound of gunfire.

As they approached Richard's store, Wesley learned to his surprise that the blue-coated raiders were inside the building, defending themselves against some thirty elderly men and boys. The store was a veritable fortress of solid masonry, its big front door of timber thick enough to absorb a rifle bullet and its roof of heavy slate.

Wesley halted his prisoners a short distance from the building, cupped his hands, and shouted, "Listen to me. We have captured all your horses and men out here. You don't have a chance to get away. Come out with your hands up or we'll set fire to the building and burn you out." Meeting with no reply, he said, "You have one minute to make up your minds."

Before the minute was up, a soldier replied from the store: "We need more time to decide. Some of the men will not vote to surrender. Will you give us an hour?"

Wesley considered the position of the sun and thought he was wise to the Yankees' plan. With nightfall not an hour away, they hoped to rush from the building under the cover of darkness and attempt to take enough hostages throughout the town to ensure their safety. He also thought of his Rangers who would, he hoped fervently, arrive by that time.

"One hour, then," he said. "But no longer."

One of the old men edged up to Wesley and spat disgustedly. "Young fellow," he asked, "can't you see through that Yankee trick? The damned scoundrels are playing for time. It will be dark by the——"

"Yes, sir," Wesley said. "I'm not blind to their game. Now listen." He acquainted the old man with his own plan and asked him to relay it to the people in the buildings across the street.

The old fellow cackled to himself and trotted off to carry the message.

Wesley could well imagine the smirk on the Yankee officer's face as he considered the ease with which he had outsmarted the Rebels. He moved back with his prisoners and their guards, keeping the soldiers between them and the store, then marched the Yankees into an empty smokehouse, where they were locked up and a guard posted.

The sun was almost behind a distant line of trees when Wesley heard the thunder of hoofbeats. He looked down the street at a welcome sight, Lieutenant Temple riding hard at the head of the Ranger company. At Wesley's signal the Rangers swung to the side of the street he indicated and dismounted. Then Wesley deployed his men across the street from the store by using the alleyways back of the stores and dwellings, the enemy none the wiser.

The hour was almost up and the last minutes of twilight were rapidly fading into darkness when Wesley so advised the enemy.

There was no immediate answer from the building, though a minute later the big door swung open and the troopers began to pour out, hands above their heads. "We give up," one of them cried into the night. "Where are you, Rebel?"

"Right here," Wesley replied, not showing himself.

This was the signal for the cavalrymen to scatter. Tugging at their side arms, they began to disperse rapidly

up and down the street. A small group ran blindly toward
Wesley, and he thumbed the hammers on his .44s and
began to shoot. Then the Rangers and the townspeople
began firing also, and the soldiers fell in little heaps all
over the sandy street.

After this deadly volley the Rangers leaped on their
horses and dashed into the street, firing their pistols with
uncanny accuracy as they charged through the dismounted cavalrymen.

The troopers were completely disorganized. Their
officers had been killed or wounded in the first sally and
now, at every turn, they encountered Rangers and townspeople.

Half a dozen soldiers made a stand against the wall of a
building directly across the street from where Wesley
stood. As he directed his fire at them, another pistol at his
side began to shoot. He glanced around, expecting to see
one of the old men of Danville, but standing shoulder to
shoulder with him was a woman. As he looked closer at
her, the pistol she held with both hands exploded and
he saw her face. Betty Irvine, the little girl whose father
and brother had been killed at the battle of Arkansas
Post.

Wesley did not hesitate a moment, but swept the girl
off her feet and dashed for the safety of a brick wall.

"Betty, you brave little idiot!" he whispered huskily as
he stood her against the wall. "Are you trying to get yourself killed? Now stay here and——"

Wesley did not complete the sentence. A Yankee bullet
plowed into him and he fell, face-down, unconscious.

When he opened his eyes, he seemed to be drifting
about in a clean, cheery room. Then a fog swirled in,
blanketing everything white, lifted momentarily, and
swirled in again and again until it finally began to dis-

sipate. He saw the room again, and then his eyes rested on a lamp that burned brightly on a marble-topped washstand in a corner.

Wesley examined all of this carefully, trying desperately to reconcile these strange surroundings to the running fight in Danville. Moving his eyes about, he saw Temple sitting by his bed. And then another figure bent over him and began to probe his shoulder with a hot, blunt instrument.

"I am Dr. Meyers, Captain," the man said. "Now we've got to get this lead out of you without benefit of morphine, so just grin and bear it."

The doctor began to probe deep into Wesley's shoulder muscles, and just when it seemed that he could stand the pain no longer, he felt someone lift his right hand. It was Betty Irvine. As the doctor dug deeper, she squeezed his hand tighter. He loved the child for her timely thoughtfulness. He held his teeth together and looked at her with a fixed smile until the heavy slug was finally removed. Then, with the worst of the pain over, Wesley turned his head and asked Temple how the fight had ended.

"We lost six Rangers, Cap'n." Temple named them. "There was one Danville man killed and one hurt pretty bad—besides you, that is. But we killed a passel of Yanks. They're countin' 'em now. Considerin' them we took with the hosses, we got thirty-seven prisoners. We won't know till daylight if any got by us, but I don't believe they did 'cause we was pretty doggone careful to prevent such."

Wesley thanked Temple and, as the doctor began to apply a pad and dressing to his wound, he looked toward the other side of the bed, where Betty stood holding his hand.

"Now, young lady," he scolded gently, "why did you try to get yourself killed a while ago?"

"Captain Smith," she declared strongly, "those damn-yankees are probably the same ones who killed my father and my brother and shot William Spiller. As long as I live I want to believe that the bullets I fired from Grandpa's gun killed some of them."

The tears brimmed in her eyes, but she fought them back and composed herself just as Mrs. Irvine and Mrs. Susan Spiller entered the room.

"Captain," said Mrs. Spiller after learning that Wesley was not seriously wounded, "we people here and around Danville have every barn, shed, and warehouse full of cotton, and you certainly have our heartfelt thanks for saving it for us."

"Thank Betty, Mrs. Spiller, I think she is the hero of the Battle of Danville."

Though weak from loss of blood, Wesley insisted that he be carried to Montgomery as soon as possible and that no one tell Margaret of his condition. Soon after sunrise he was placed in a cotton-filled wagon and covered with blankets to protect him from the frosty air. Then the slow trip back to The Oaks began.

The wagon was entering the main gates when Wesley sent for William Spiller and asked that he accompany Betty, whom he wished to break the news to Margaret. When they rode ahead, he told Temple to stop the wagon until Betty eased the shock of his return flat on his back. The old Ranger smiled wryly and agreed that, since women were involved, the captain's strategy was "damn good."

By the time the Rangers lifted Wesley and entered the front door of The Oaks, Betty Irvine had fulfilled her mission; admirably, thought Wesley, when Margaret and Aunt Polly put him to bed with little show of the tears, fuss, and bother he had anticipated.

That night, however, the strain Margaret had endured and masked broke through for Wesley to see. He held her trembling hand in his and looked at her sitting quietly at his bedside with no demands but silent entreaty in her eyes.

"Don't worry," he smiled. "I promise to stay close to home for a while, Margaret."

He was right on that score, for despite all old Dr. Young, Margaret, and Aunt Polly could do for him, his wound healed slowly. Christmas was almost at hand before he could muster enough strength to ride more than an hour or two in the fields and pastures with Dude Justice.

25. After Appomattox

WESLEY remained on the sick list while his company of Rangers down on the Rio Grande tried to force a trade-route opening into Mexico. Their task was an urgent one, for the South seemed minus even a ship to run the blockade that was slowly but surely strangling her even as the invader moved deeper and deeper into the very heart of the Southland.

Both Wesley and Major Tarbone, who visited The Oaks often, realized that only one end was in sight. Only a miracle could save the Confederacy, and they as thousands of others hoped for that miracle. Food was scarce, and the major told Wesley that his services were needed more at home than on the battlefields. One could not argue against a glaring fact. Every day news reached Texas concerning Confederate soldiers living on a few grains of corn a day. All news seemed of the worst sort.

A new problem, racial and social, was walking hand in hand with military losses and starvation. In all sections of the South where troops in blue appeared, many Negroes fled before them and many others began to test their new-found freedom. Unused to freedom and not knowing how to deal with this new thing the Northerners said he was at last blessed with, the confused Negro was more to be pitied than blamed for the tragedies that followed.

Despite these things life went on, and the South hoped and prayed even as the Federals penetrated deeper, burning and pillaging and carrying the war to the very hearthstone of the Confederacy, to the supplies behind the lines, to the women and children. The war had resolved itself into the type of merciless conquest advocated by General Sherman, that "the government of the United States has any and all rights which they choose to enforce the war, to take their lives, their houses, their lands, their everything, because they cannot deny that war exists there, and war is simply power unrestrained by constitution or compact."

As this kind of war continued, the Confederate dollar bought less and less. Although cotton brought forty cents a pound in coin, stocks piled up because little got through. The high market price of cotton was offset by such increase in prices that there was more loss than gain. Flour, when one could obtain it, cost two hundred and fifty dollars a barrel. In 1862 the price was forty dollars per barrel. A fifty-cent shirt brought from forty to fifty dollars.

Although Texas felt the economic pinch, she had not experienced the suffering of other states. Thus far no big Union army had marched on Texas soil, which was reason for thanksgiving at The Oaks on Christmas Day of 1863, despite the fact that there was no flour, canned goods, fruits, or toys. But there was beef, plenty of it, and turkey and yams and beans and corn bread. After offering up thanks to the Lord that day, Wesley said the war seemed far distant in one sense and right in one's lap in another.

He knew in his heart that he had done his best, probably more at home than he could possibly have done on the big battlefields. He had shipped every Diamond Six calf and steer he could round up to the men at the fighting front, as had so many other Texans. But this was never enough, for so little of all he sent ever reached the hungry soldiers in gray.

Christmas was only a day in name to the gods of war. The struggle continued on into 1864. In that year the Union made a final attempt to invade Texas. A Federal regiment was put to rout by the Home Guards of Texas and Louisiana at Sabine Crossroads. The old men of the South won a battle here unassisted. Although invasion had once again been thwarted, the good news was offset by bad. On Friday, September 2, 1864, when Sherman's army came to stand in the streets of Atlanta, the days of organized resistance were numbered. The token resistance offered by the tattered and bloody men in gray at Jonesboro was a prelude to the dying gasp of the Confederacy. The tired, sick, half-starved men began to trudge homeward, with no strength and little heart left to resist the invader. When the news of the defeats in Georgia reached Montgomery, the people refused to believe the seriousness of it. Their men were fighting with Generals Johnston and Hood. They could not be beaten. And, too, General Robert E. Lee stood between them and the enemy. Their fathers and brothers and husbands and sons would march with him to win the war.

Even this was but a hopeful prayer, for on the chill, gray Sunday morning of April 9, 1865, General Robert E. Lee surrendered the tattered remnants of his once invincible army at Appomattox Courthouse. The bloodiest war in recorded history was ended. The real test of courage for the South was about to begin.

Wesley, like a majority of loyal Southerners, spent no

time in idle grief over the failure of the Confederacy to win the war. There was much work to do to restore Texas to prosperity, and he undertook his part of the task with vigor. A hard, cruel war had been fought and lost, but now that it was over he realized the importance of the necessary adjustments to a new way of life. Like so many of his neighbors, he had invested all his earnings in Confederate Bonds. This money he knew he had lost, but he thanked God that he owed few debts.

Although the great herds of fine cattle on Diamond Six had been sadly depleted during the war years, there remained more than a thousand good young brood cows that should build his herds up quickly. The barns and warehouses at The Oaks were still half filled with cotton he had been unable to sell during 1864, and this would bring a large sum of money from cotton-starved England and France.

The future looked bright for Wesley and his family, bright for The Oaks, and even brighter for Diamond Six, for by his foresight Wesley was no longer dependent upon the Negro. As long as the "darkies" wanted to stay with him and work, they could, but now that they were free, he was also free of them. With little help, he and Dude Justice could handle a great many cattle, which more than took the place of cotton as a money crop.

No explicit orders had come from Washington relative to freeing the slaves. With the exception of one or two who ran away to taste of their new-found freedom, life went on as usual at The Oaks. Wesley had called his Negroes in, family by family, and told them they were soon to be set free by the Federal Government. None of them were happy over the prospect of shifting for themselves. They begged that they be allowed to continue to live the lives they knew and loved. He told them they could stay and also tried to warn them against the time when unscrupulous employers would attempt to take advantage of their ignorance.

However, destiny did not decree that the South should be left at peace to recover from the disastrous effects of the war. The political leaders of the North, still smarting under the knowledge that a numerically inferior force had taken such a tremendous toll of its manpower and resources, were determined to teach the Rebels a lesson that would make them forever remember and respect the dictatorial power of the Yankee.

The lesson was not long in getting under way. On Sunday, June 18, 1865, General Gordon Granger landed in Galveston and on the following day issued a proclamation declaring the slaves free. Granger quickly established Union soldiers in every community in Texas where there were Negroes. Thus the Reconstruction period had begun.

Lesson number one had been easy, for it had been expected.

Wesley—in fact, all the people of Texas and the entire South—thought that once Federal troops had succeeded in establishing the freedom of the Negroes they would depart and allow the Southerners to lick their wounds in peace. But when President Johnson, a Southerner, appointed A. J. Hamilton as provisional governor of Texas and he, in turn, proceeded to appoint all the local, county, and state officials, then Texans began to feel the tyrant's heel. They realized that their trial by fire was only beginning.

Lesson number two was considerably stronger and totally unexpected.

Anxious to get the Yankees from underfoot, the people of Texas offered every co-operation to the newly organized government, and on Wednesday, February 7, 1866, the duly elected delegates met in Austin for the purpose of declaring secession illegal, the slaves free, and the public debt canceled. These were the requirements of President Johnson under which the people could again control their state governments. Although Wesley and other men sent to this convention knew it would mean bankruptcy for many of them, they agreed after many hours of wrangling, cursing, and fiery speechmaking to accept the ultimatum in exchange for the promised peace.

However, despite the declarations and proclamations issued in Washington and carried out by the military, the Negroes as a whole refused to leave their white masters. Consequently, with good weather over the state, the Texas plantation owners had a bumper cotton crop. But this further displeased the vengeful politicians of the North, and they determined, by an act of Congress, to place the entire South under military government until the Negroes were allowed to enjoy all the rights and privileges of the white man.

This was the attempted beginning of lesson number three, and although it came as a surprise, it was doomed to miserable failure for the simple reason that free men, though easily led, refused to be driven.

But through the clouds of unrest and growing hatred of the oppressor, there came to The Oaks a ray of happiness when Margaret presented Wesley with their fourth child, a daughter. They named her Maggie, after her mother.

Aunt Polly's joy was unbounded. For years she had complained that the Wesley Smith family was not large enough. Now she had another child to pet and pamper, to fuss over and to brag about.

"Dis is the very time dis baby oughta come to us," she told Margaret. "Wid all the trouble these Yankees and trashy niggers givin' us now, we needs dis ray of sunshine. Thank de Lawd for her. And look how she make Mrs. Arnold smile."

True, Margaret's mother, who was getting old, seemed to take on a new interest in life with the arrival of another granddaughter. Wesley had not forgotten how she, a Connecticut Yankee, had worked to keep the plantation and the ranch going during the time he was away with the Rangers. And now she seemed to forget the aftermath of war, causing Wesley to envy her as he looked at the worsening political situation.

The sixth of August, 1866, had seen newly elected officials take office. The false security Texans felt was realized when in January of 1867 perhaps the most malicious group of radicals ever assembled in the U. S. Congress up to that time met and mapped a plan for the complete and thorough subjugation of the South.

Nor was Texas overlooked by these politicians who forced military rule on all Southern states. General Philip Sheridan was placed in command of the occupation troops in Louisiana and Texas. His overbearing manner and harsh dealings with the people made the military governor the most hated man that ever trod Texas soil. He proceeded to set aside the laws he did not like and to remove officers of state and local government who failed to sanction his tyrannical methods. He was never known to appear in public without an armed guard of fifty or more soldiers.

Thus, with no law enforcement except the military, events went from bad to worse. Many offices were filled with Negroes who could neither read nor write. By legislation the slave became the master.

Wesley had been losing a large number of cattle to bands of Negroes who wandered through the country taking whatever they pleased, so he quietly hired twenty-five young Confederate veterans from Houston after thoroughly investigating them. Lately released from a Federal prison in Illinois, these hardened youngsters had been incarcerated for their steadfast refusal to take the hated ironclad oath of allegiance. They came to Diamond Six ready to take up the fight where it left off at Appomattox in 1865.

Wesley armed them and gave them one simple order: They should ride his properties for the sole purpose of protecting it and what it held against trespass. He warned them, however, to keep their identity secret, since the Negroes who composed the marauding bands were protected by the United States Army.

"You don't have to tell us anything, Captain Smith," said one of the men. "We're hiring out to protect your property and we'll take all the responsibilities that go with it."

Wesley knew his cattle were in good hands. He told the men that he would back them up, but warned them that the ex-slaves and whites had been organized into military companies called the Union League, an order created back in 1862 which now worked for radical reconstruction, punishment of Southern leaders, Negro suffrage, and confiscation of property by the blacks. Since the Union League of America was sanctioned by the Federal Government and given the protection of the army, it could do no wrong.

"You don't have to tell us, Captain," said a youngster named Duane Murchison. "The damned Union Leaguers are not only protected by the Yankee army but also by the Freedmen's Bureau. Both of them stand behind the nigger in everything he does, whether it's stealing one of your calves or raping a Southern white woman. I can tell you this much, this job with you will be a pleasure for us all. I just wish I could afford to work for you for nothing."

"We'll move into your pastures a few at a time, Captain Smith," said another of the group who had been a major of cavalry, "but we'll all be there in a night or two. Right after that we ought to ride your fences with your Mr. Justice and get located."

Wesley shook hands with each man and went back to the livery stable to get his horse and begin the ride to The Oaks. As he walked into the big double door of the stable, a man said:

"Hi there, Cap'n."

He turned to see Temple. With warm greetings over, they sat on a bench in the shade of the livery stable and talked.

"I haven't heard from Major Tarbone in a long time," Wesley said. "What has happened to him since the Rangers were disbanded?"

"Well, I thought you had already heard. You know the major always swore he would never knuckle down to a damnyankee, and, Cap'n, he's taken to the other side of the fence, so to speak."

"What do you mean?" Wesley asked.

"Cap'n, right after that damned Sheridan come down here, the major took a few of the boys from old Company A and headed North. Tried to get me to go. They aimed to take the Yankee banks and trains to a good cleanin'."

Wesley was amazed. Tarbone was the man who had given him so many lectures about staying on the side of the law.

"But," Wesley mused, "where is the law?"

He could not condemn Tarbone. As long as the man's lawlessness hit only at the military tyrants, then more

power to him. He thought of the smart-alecky blacks
marching through the streets drunk on whisky, drunk on
power, all armed, all mean in their unrestrained freedom.
He thought also of the replies from Yankee officers when
a Southern white complained of the lawless act of a Negro.
The stock answer was always the same:

"You fought on the wrong side, Johnny Reb. Go on
home and forget it."

The more Wesley thought of it, the less he blamed Tarbone. Were it not for his family, he would join the major
within the week.

"Temple," he said suddenly, "would you like to go to
work for me?"

The old Ranger smiled. "When do I begin, Cap'n?"

He had not asked what the work would be. Wesley
explained: "I want a sort of bodyguard for Mrs. Smith
and the children. I'm away from home a great deal and
we have a lot of mean, strange niggers in the country now
that——"

"If you're startin' for home now, Cap'n," the Ranger
interrupted, "just give me time to catch my horse. This is
a job I'm gonna like."

So far there had been no actual bloodshed around
Montgomery, though Wesley and the other men had
avoided it only by swallowing their pride and paying no
attention to the taunts and gibes thrown their way by the
soldiers, carpetbaggers, and Negroes who loitered about
the military posts because the government clothed and
fed and protected them.

Reason might have prevailed between the Southern
white man and the ex-slave had it not been for the Freedmen's Bureau, which controlled the Union League and
sent Northern whites down to teach the Negroes to hate
their white masters and to regard the properties of their

former owners as their own. The bureau issued an "exodus order," requiring all blacks living with their former masters to find other homes. Those who refused or voted with the white South were beaten and often killed.

Wesley and other citizens of Montgomery County witnessed this reversal of the old social order of the South with amazement on a par with anger. That such a thing could be possible, much less forced on the people by a government founded on principles of liberty and justice, was almost unbelievable. Yet it was happening before their very eyes. The United States Army, the carpetbaggers and scalawags were in control of the South. The Negro was their tool of vengeance and Philip Sheridan was their champion.

"How much more can we take?" one of Wesley's neighbors asked one day. "We know the darkies and are familiar with their problems and characteristics. The Yankee can never know these things, for the Negro was never his problem. Why doesn't the North pass laws we can abide by? That would resolve the issue, for we would abide by it. It's that simple."

Shortly afterward a meeting of the white men of Montgomery County was called. It was decided that the time was near when they would strike back, regardless of the consequences.

The beginning of the trouble came from an unexpected source. On Friday, December 20, 1867, Temple drove Margaret into Montgomery to make a few purchases. Aunt Polly was along to care for Maggie, and the baby, Estelle, born a few months earlier. Temple was tying the team to the hitching rack at Peel's store on the courthouse square when three drunken Negroes, dressed in their Union League uniforms and carrying rifles, staggered down the plank walk. One of them walked too close to the edge and pitched to the ground on his head, squarely at Temple's feet.

The other two straightway accused the old Ranger of assaulting their comrade and began to advance on him, fumbling with their rifles as they did so. Not wanting to draw the .44 he carried inside his shirt, Temple hastily grabbed the rifle of the Negro who had fallen and began to back slowly away, all the while trying to reason with the drunken men.

Aunt Polly, who had climbed laboriously down from the surrey to help Margaret to the ground, jerked the rifle from Temple.

"Lemme have it, Mistuh Temple!" she said. "Dese wuthless, trashy niggers ain't gonna bother me."

So saying, she rammed the barrel viciously into the stomach of the lead Negro. He fell to the ground, groaning, and before he touched the earth, Polly swung the heavy gun and brought it crashing down, stock-first, on the head of the third member of the Union League. All of her two hundred and twenty pounds were behind the blow, and the hapless black collapsed without a murmur.

The Negro who had fallen, thus starting the trouble, and the other whom Aunt Polly had so unceremoniously punched in the stomach regained their feet and lurched in the direction of the surrey, where Margaret sat holding her baby daughter. Just as one of the Negroes reached for Margaret, the old mammy grabbed him by the collar of his resplendent uniform with a big right hand and reached for the other with her left hand. With all the strength of her mighty arms she brought their heads together in a mighty crash.

Luckily, Wesley was in town and came running up as Polly dropped her two victims to the ground, unconscious.

"Aunt Polly," he said with admiration, "you're a wonder."

Then Wesley turned to Temple. "Take my horse and get out of town, quick. Go to Diamond Six and stay close to the boys until you hear from me. Hurry now."

"But, Cap'n," the old Ranger argued, "I didn't touch any of them. I was just startin' to——"

"Don't argue with me, Temple," Wesley snapped. "You know what the soldiers will do to you. Now get going."

The old Ranger nodded, walked across the street, mounted Wesley's horse, and rode up the Fish Trail Road in the direction of Willis.

A crowd of townspeople gathered quickly as Temple rode away, and Wesley took his baby daughter in his arms to quiet her. As he helped Margaret from the carriage, a squad of Union soldiers came shouldering their way through the crowd. When they demanded an explanation from him, Wesley said:

"Why, I was across the street when one of these drunk Negroes fell off the gallery there and the other two got the idea that someone had pushed him. They all started bullying our baby's nurse and she simply defended herself."

Wesley knew there would be no penalty for Negro fighting Negro. But just as he took notice of a fleeting smile on the face of the corporal, one of the blacks whom Aunt Polly had handled rose painfully to his knees and pointed at Polly. "Corp'ral, suh," he said to the squad leader, "dat nigger ain't laid a hand on any of us. It was a white man who was drivin' dat buggy. He pushed me offen de gallery and picked up my gun and tried to shoot us all."

Even the soldiers realized that this was a lie. However, they were stationed in the South with orders to bring the Rebels to their knees. It did not matter that the majority of these men had no stomach for it; they were trained to carry out orders.

"Where is the man who was driving this carriage?" the corporal asked.

"I sent him to take my horse back because I intended to drive home with my wife," Wesley replied. "He never laid a hand on any of these Negroes. I give you my word for it."

"What the hell is your word worth?" the corporal replied.

Wesley's old self-control asserted itself and he masked his rising anger with a tight, inscrutable smile.

Under the calm scrutiny of the Southerner the corporal's indecision mounted with every moment. "Go on," he finally blurted forth. "Get back home and stay there until we can investigate this thing further. And don't leave Montgomery until Captain Clark gets here, for you'll probably be arrested for questioning."

"Don't you worry your head about my leaving, Corporal," he said evenly, still eying the man squarely. "I have never run from a Yankee and I never intend to."

Without waiting for a reply, he took Margaret's arm and moved through the parting crowd toward Peel's store. "Hey, you!" the corporal shouted. "I told you to go home."

Wesley turned as he gently shoved his wife into the open door of the store. "I heard you say that, Corporal," he replied softly. "I heard you say that, and we are going home—just as soon as my wife finishes her shopping."

Something held the soldier. It might have been the deadly softness of Wesley's voice, or it might have been the many grim-faced men who had gathered around the squad of soldiers. But he hesitated to arrest the Rebel whose brand of polished threat put fear in his heart.

Wesley had no sooner entered the store than the cor-

poral marched his men up the street. The three drunk
Negroes followed, leaving their rifles in the street. The
white men exchanged glances before moving out to shield
one of their group from view while he hurriedly placed
the three rifles in a wagon and covered them with sacks.
Then, with three more guns added to the arsenal of the
white citizens of Montgomery, they scattered into small
groups and awaited Wesley's return to his surrey.

Finally Wesley emerged and handed Margaret into the
surrey. Although Margaret seemed occupied in showing
Aunt Polly and the baby the tree decorations, she did not
miss the play between the citizens and her husband. Several men walked by and spoke in low tones, and Wesley
merely nodded and smiled in a gratified manner. Then
they were driving toward The Oaks.

26. Reconstruction Days

WESLEY, Margaret, and Mrs. Arnold were decorating the Christmas tree for the children that evening when the knocker beat a businesslike staccato at the front door.

As Wesley opened the door a Union soldier thrust his foot inside to prevent the door from being closed. "Is your name Wesley Smith?" he asked harshly.

"Why do you want to know, soldier?" Wesley replied.

"Captain C. A. Clark, United States Army, wants to see you."

Desiring no further conversation with the enlisted man, Wesley looked toward a group of horsemen standing motionless in the gloom of the driveway and addressed the man he could not see. "Come on in, Captain Clark."

In a lower voice he said to the soldier who was still blocking the doorway, "Take your foot out of the door. You might trip the captain."

The man obeyed instinctively, and as a footfall sounded on the gravel he snapped to attention. A tall, slender Yankee captain with a heavy, close-cropped beard and graying temples entered and extended his hand.

Wesley grasped the officer's hand, then shut and bolted the door and led the way to the privacy of the library just off the big parlor. When they were seated and Wesley had poured two drinks from a decanter of whisky, the captain began to explain the nature of his visit.

"I should like first, Captain Smith," he said in friendly tones, "to put your mind at ease on one thing. The orders we operate under here in the South are very distasteful to me. Naturally such a statement coming from a Yankee officer must surprise you. But I mean it, sir. I fought you people, beginning as a raw, untried lieutenant of infantry at the first battle of Bull Run. I have never lost the respect I gained for you Southerners that day."

He paused to sip his scotch.

"You people had something to fight for," he continued. "But when the war ended, the majority of us were ready to forget strife and be friends to Johnny Reb."

Captain Clark finished his drink but continued to look critically at his empty glass. "If I and many more like me in the North had known the barbaric treatment you people would be subjected to after we had beaten you, a lot of us might have fought on your side."

He paused again, and it gave Wesley the opportunity to weigh the man's speech carefully. He sounded truthful, and Wesley only wished he could believe him. "Go on, Captain," he said affably.

"What I'm trying to get at, sir," the officer continued, "is how to deal with the incident that took place in town today. I understand you witnessed it and, although you are vitally concerned, because the man accused of the assault is in your employ, I should like to hear your version of it."

Wesley, always suspicious of the enemy and his ingenious traps, outlined the incident briefly, neglecting to say that Jimmie Temple had ever held the rifle with which Aunt Polly had felled the Negroes.

"Where is this Temple now?" asked the officer.

"Very probably riding hell-bent for Indian territory," Wesley lied glibly. "He was reared among the Comanches and will likely go back to them."

This seemed to satisfy the captain, who said with a little smile, "The charges were brought against him, no one else. Unless the men making the complaint change it, we'll make a routine search for the man and close the case."

"I give you my word," said Wesley, "that Mr. Temple is not on this place, so there's no need to do any searching here."

As he spoke Wesley rose and proceeded to pour drinks.

"Captain Clark," he said, extending a glass to the officer, "the North seems to assume that our problem with the Negroes is so elemental and so uninvolved that it can be changed by a simple vote of Congress or a majority vote of the people, many thousands of whom have never seen a Negro, much less lived around him."

He paused and drank deeply before continuing.

"We have lost a war here in the South. I mean by that that we were beaten physically. No war, or the outcome of war, could command us to change our way of thinking. What makes this period of our history so utterly ridiculous is that it has taught the North nothing. Do you follow me, sir?"

The other nodded in agreement.

"The average Yankee knows nothing of the South," Wesley went on. "It would be impossible for him to know it from his crowded homes and factories. He simply assumes that now that the law is passed giving the Negro his freedom the whole question is settled. But that same average Yankee, Captain Clark, must be made to realize somehow that he is not dealing with a simple matter of the statute books. To the contrary, he is faced with an emotional situation of such fierce intensity that it could very well mean the second call to arms in the South. Thank God the Southern people are slow to use violence. They must be certain that no other means of settlement are available before they resort to final extremes. But, Captain, please believe me, if the North persists in steering the course they now have taken, they will have to literally grind our very bones into dust before we cease to resist. There is no law that man can make that will change our thoughts and our deportment on the racial question, now or ever."

When Wesley finished, flushed and angry, the officer rose and extended his hand, saying, "I can't say that I blame you. I have enjoyed this visit, Captain Smith."

They walked through the now-empty parlor and to the entrance hall. As he opened the door Wesley saw the group of mounted men waiting in his driveway, and his resentment of all men in blue returned.

"How is it, Captain," he asked, "that you brought a whole cavalry troop if this was to be a pleasant visit?"

"That order," the captain replied with contained embarrassment and anger, "came from General Sheridan's office, Captain Smith."

Wesley smiled inwardly as the troop thundered down the drive, for what he had seen seemed to verify the rumor that General Philip Sheridan was a coward as judged by Texas standards.

Just as he was about to close the door, Wesley heard a horse coming up the graveled driveway and waited. It was the corporal with whom he had the trouble in Montgomery that afternoon. He dismounted and came to stand on the edge of the veranda.

"I beg your pardon, sir," he said politely, "but Captain Clark has instructed me to rescind the order I gave you this afternoon. You are to feel free to move about as you wish, but the captain also requests you stay within the law. Thank you, sir."

He saluted Wesley and was gone.

As he shut the door, Wesley found himself wanting very much to believe that he had found an understanding friend in Captain Clark. But he doubted this and knew he could only wait and see.

Wesley and his family enjoyed a happy Christmas despite the occupation, carpetbaggers, scalawags, and the despised men who officered the Union League. The soldiers had, for reasons unknown, created no incidents to stir undue resentment among the white people of Montgomery County, who realized only too well that the armistice would be short-lived. It could scarcely be otherwise, since the Negroes were now enrolled as qualified voters and the right to vote was denied all Southerners who had served in the armed forces of the Confederacy. This meant that the coming elections would be fraught with violence and bloodshed.

On Thursday, January 9, 1868, Wesley rode into Montgomery to attend to business matters. He was sitting in the office of Robert Gay, his lawyer, when Old John, one of Reuben Simonton's Negroes, came rushing in from the street out of breath, his eyes wide with fear.

"Mistuh Wes!" he whispered hoarsely. "You and Mistuh Bob better come quick! Please, suh! Some crazy niggers done broke in on us and is stealin' everything Miss Bess got. Dey got Miss Bess in de house wid 'em and——"

Neither of the white men heard the end of the story. Robert Gay reached into a secret compartment of his desk and pulled out a .44, which he shoved into his shirt front. He and Wesley dashed for the rail where their horses were tied. The old Negro followed them, still frightened.

"John," Wesley said as they mounted, "go tell Mr. Peel and Mr. Robinson to meet us out there. Now hurry, and don't say anything to anyone else."

The Negro trotted off in the direction of the Peel store as the two men raced off in the direction of the Simonton place. Reuben Simonton was still being held in a Yankee prison in Chicago because he refused to take the oath of allegiance.

They rode rapidly up the tree-lined road to the big home, dismounted, and were approaching the front door when a pistol fired from the house sent a bullet into the earth to their right.

A Negro cried from the Simonton house, "Stay where yo' is, white men!"

Wesley and Robert Gay sprinted for the comparative safety of a plank wall between the tall front windows. They had scarcely taken cover when six Negroes in the uniform of Union Leaguers rushed from the door and ran for their horses, firing wildly. They held as hostage Bess Simonton, who was fighting them like a wildcat. Seeing Wesley and Gay, she cried frantically:

"Shoot, Wesley! You won't hit me. Shoot them! Shoot them!"

The surge of anger that engulfed Wesley as he saw the wife of one of his best friends mauled about and dragged from her home by a group of Negroes steadied his nerves and prepared him for what he knew he must do.

"Stay where you are, Bob," he said to the lawyer. "Don't miss them if they come by you."

Wesley ran toward the Negroes, paying no attention to their fire, which was still wild. The blacks realized that Bess Simonton was slowing their progress. One of them dropped her arm and ran, letting her fall almost to the ground. As Bess went down, she grabbed the other Negro who was dragging her.

Wesley fired once. The big Union Leaguer spun and fell heavily across Bess Simonton, holding her down and thereby keeping her fairly well protected from the pistol bullets of the five other Negroes who were firing as they ran.

"Keep down, Bess! Keep down!" Wesley yelled.

He knew they had to account for every black involved in the abduction, for if one escaped he would incriminate every white man in Montgomery. Wesley sprinted after the fleeing Negroes, aware that every shot would have to count. When they tried to catch up the reins of their horses, the animals began plunging and rearing, and the Negroes ran. And Wesley brought them crashing to earth, one by one.

Gay, who had been denied a single shot, came running up to Wesley as the last black collapsed to the ground. "Look," he said. "There are seven horses out there. There must be another one."

Wesley made a rapid count, then raced to the front of the house, where Bess Simonton was getting to her feet. "Bess," he said, "how many of them were there?"

"There was a white man with them, Wesley," she said. "I wanted to tell you, but——"

She never had the opportunity to finish her statement. Wesley and Gay were running for their horses. As they swung into their saddles, Bess cried, pointing down the drive:

"There he is, Wesley!"

Wesley jerked his glance around and saw a white man with two lariats about his neck trotting up the drive in front of two horsemen. Peel and Robinson rode up and halted, and Bess Simonton identified the man as the leader of the marauding blacks. Confronted with the problem of how to deal with the prisoner, they debated on whether to hang him or to shoot him down in cold blood. They were not averse to the former punishment and decided to hang him down by Lake Creek.

Suddenly a gun appeared in the scalawag's hand. Removing the ropes from his neck, he ordered them to drop their pistols. "Quick," he demanded. "No tricks, either."

"Sure," Wesley replied. "My gun isn't even loaded."

As he and the others dropped their pistols to the ground, the scalawag struck out across the lawn.

Wesley knew that if the man went free it was tantamount to signing the death warrants of himself and the men with him. He had to act at once. He did. Falling from his horse, he grabbed up Gay's gun and fired twice. The second bullet toppled the rider to the ground. He got up, staggered, and ran for the corner of the house. Peel's gun roared, and the man leaped into the air. He was dead when he fell.

"Well," Wesley said, "the poor devil certainly solved that problem for us, didn't he?" He lit a cigar and smoked thoughtfully for a minute. "Now, we have another problem," he continued. "What are we going to do with them?"

He swept a hand in the direction of the scalawag and the Negroes and then turned to Bess, who was now beginning to look faint. "How many of your darkies are here on the place, Bess?"

"None of them except Jennie Lee and Aunt Ellen," she replied. "And here comes Old John."

The old Negro rode up and surveyed the carnage about him without flickering an eyelash. He seemed to know what he would find when he saw Wesley and Robert Gay ride out of Montgomery.

"Miss Bess," he said, "I can git rid of de evidence for yo'all if you let me handle it my own way."

"Let Old John handle it, Wesley," said Bess. "I don't know what he's planning, but he is pretty ingenious. He has been my mainstay for years now."

The four men waited at the Simonton home for more than an hour before Old John returned and began industriously to clean the big lawn and stamp out all the hoofprints. As they walked out of the house, Wesley noticed that not even the attackers' horses were to be seen, and he asked the old Negro about them.

"Ever'thing has been took care of, suh," he replied politely. "Dat ole quicksand is a evidence-hidin' thing. Yassuh, it sho is."

The old white-haired darky smiled and went on with his work.

The four men rode away from Bess Simonton's singly, each taking a different route. As Wesley moved in the direction of The Oaks, he pondered the change that had come over the South. The very thought of a white woman unsafe in her own home had once seemed unimaginable in the settled South. But it was happening, and it would happen again and again—as long as Northern troops ruled the South.

Wesley spurred his horse to a faster pace. This same thing could take place at The Oaks, he realized. Then he remembered the words with which Reverend Milo Walker had closed his benediction on the night he and Margaret were married:

"And keep the tyrant's sword forever away from this door. Amen."

It made him feel better, gave him new strength as he rode up to the gates of The Oaks.

27. General Philip H. Sheridan

As Wesley dismounted to open the gate, one of his blacks addressed him from a position behind a big oak:

"Mistuh Wes, I wouldn't go up to the big house if I was yo', suh. There's a smart-alecky Yankee soldier waitin' fo' yo'. He got Miss Margaret just plumb scared to death. Her and Mrs. Arnold done run to their rooms and locked up wid de chillun."

A dark, deep anger seemed to consume Wesley in that awful moment. He sat his horse several minutes, trying to forget that his family had been terrorized by the Federals. He knew that self-control was his best ally, that he had to think clearly. But his troubled gaze returned to the house on the hill—his, The Oaks.

Calmed somewhat, he quickly checked the loading of his .44, dismounted, and moved to the tree, where he eyed the frightened youth speculatively.

"Henry," he said at last, "you can help me a great deal if you'll do what I tell you. Now take this gun and place it under the back of your shirt, in your trousers."

He showed the Negro how to carry the pistol so that

his shirt covered it. "Now, Henry, get close to me while I practice taking it from under your shirt."

After several attempts Wesley said, "That's fine. Good. Now you remember well, for my life may depend on you today."

"Yassuh, Mistuh Wes. I knows just what to do. I'll be there wid it too."

"Be sure you are, boy. When I ask for coffee or anything, you tell Aunt Polly I said you were to bring it. Understand?"

"Yassuh. Coffee or anything. Yassuh!"

Wesley rode up the hill as though he knew nothing of the presence of the Federal soldiers. Dismounting at the front of the house, he saw a large group of cavalrymen sitting their horses farther down the drive and on the lawn. As he moved to the door a pair of troopers marched up and advised that he was under arrest.

They ushered him into his own hallway, through the big parlor, and into the library where a short, stout man in the uniform of a cavalry officer looked up from a seat at the fine chestnut-oak desk that once belonged to Wesley's father. Seeing the officer's spurs indenting the smooth shining desk top, Wesley was hard pressed to still the anger clamoring inside him.

The man had a very prominent nose set above a huge black mustache that drooped far below his receding chin. His eyes were cruel and narrow, the cruelty accentuated by heavy black eyebrows set too low in a forehead on which the hairline had receded except directly in the center. Wesley realized that he had for company the most passionately hated man in Texas, General Philip Henry Sheridan.

The two soldiers who had escorted Wesley in ranged

themselves on either side and stood at rigid attention while the general looked him over.

"What's your name?" he roared in a voice calculated to unnerve the prisoner.

Wesley never moved a muscle, and when he answered his voice was so soft it was almost silky.

"If we are going to talk I'm going to sit down. These soldiers are going to leave the room, and you are going to take your damned spurs off the top of my desk."

The general's feet hit the floor, and he rose angrily. "These men stay where they are!" he stormed. "I don't trust any of you damned Rebels."

"I'm not armed, as you can plainly see." Wesley held his coat back. "And I'm not given to barroom brawling. But I don't understand fright like you do, I suppose."

"Search the insolent Rebel," the general ordered, glaring at Wesley.

One of the soldiers carefully patted Wesley from shoulder to ankle, taking everything from his pockets. "He is not armed, sir," he said, "except for this little penknife."

He laid the knife on the desk.

"Get out," the general ordered. "Take your positions by the door to this room."

The two soldiers clicked their heels together, saluted, performed a right-face, and marched out of the room, closing the door behind them. Then Wesley dropped easily into a heavy chair just as a knock sounded on the door and one of the guards stuck his head in.

"Begging your pardon, sir," he said, "there's a boy here with coffee. Shall I let him in?"

"Let him enter," Sheridan replied brusquely. "Who ordered it?" he demanded, eying Wesley menacingly.

"A custom in the South, sir," Wesley replied just as

Henry entered with a pot of steaming coffee on a big tray. The Negro moved to the desk and lowered the tray.

As he poured, he put his back to Wesley, who rose leisurely and walked to the desk as if to take his cup. He stood behind Henry and quickly transferred the gun from the Negro's shirt to his own waistband beneath his coat. Then, taking the cup Henry proffered, he sat down again.

"That's all, Henry," he said. "Thank you."

The Negro bowed again and departed, closing the door behind him.

"Now, General," Wesley said as pleasantly as possible, "to what do I owe this visit?"

"I'm here to arrest you on three charges of assault on United States citizens with intent to kill."

"Would it be presumptuous on my part to ask who filed these charges?" asked Wesley.

"It would," the other said contemptuously. "You'll learn that at your trial. Finish that coffee so we can go."

Wesley realized that he was going to have to act quickly if he acted at all. "General," he said evenly, "there is something you had better know before we go any further."

The big revolver suddenly appeared in his hand, pointing unwaveringly at the astonished man's middle.

"The people of this state, town, and county have had a bellyful of your dirty Yankee malevolence. They don't propose to put up with it any longer."

He paused for a moment to enjoy the effect of his statement. "Go on, call your men if you like. But remember, the first sound you make to bring them here, I'm going to put a bullet into a part of your body where it will take a week of hell for you to die. Go on, call them if you like."

He paused again, silently daring the man to make some move, but the big revolver pointing steadily at him

seemed to hypnotize the general into a silent and un-
moving state of shock.

"Now, General, I want you to keep in mind how fast I
can draw this gun, then call one of those soldiers in here.
Tell him we have discovered that we are old friends, that
you are ordering the troops back to their quarters because
you are spending the night here with me. Remember this
and believe me when I say I will kill you, for, so help me
God, I will."

The menacing revolver disappeared and Wesley pointed
a finger at the door. The general did as he was told, and
soon one of the cavalrymen entered.

"My compliments to Major Brinkfield, orderly," he
snapped at the soldier. "He is to take the troops back to
quarters. I am spending the night here with my friend,
Captain Smith. Dismissed."

When they were alone once more, Wesley said, "Now
we will sit here for a minute and then go watch your bodyguard ride off. I hear you seldom venture forth without
them, General."

Just as two old friends might have done, they stood in
the front doorway of The Oaks and watched the troops
ride away. But General Philip H. Sheridan must have
known that the cold, quiet man beside him would have
shot him instantly had he made an outcry. The general
possessed one human trait, Wesley reflected—he wanted
very much to live.

After the troops disappeared from view, Wesley led the
way to the library, where he said:

"It is going to be just this simple, General. Both of us
want to live. Both of us can live, as long as you and your
troops treat us with a little common courtesy. For your
information, General, and I urge you to believe this, there
are more than twenty men scattered over Texas and Loui-

siana who have sworn to kill you if anything ever happens to me. If a robber were to enter this house and shoot me tonight, or next month, or next year, these same men would hunt you down and one of them would kill you."

"You're bluffing," scoffed the little general.

"You can't defend yourself against them," Wesley went on, ignoring the other's remark, "for the simple reason that you don't know who they are. Just get this thought well established in your mind. It will be to your distinct advantage that I keep on living, for when I die, you die also."

Sheridan might have disbelieved another man, but the one who faced him so calmly and steadily across the desk must have impressed him forcibly with the knowledge that he meant every word he uttered. There was no idle threat here. This calm, deliberate man would be fully capable of ordering his execution, even to performing the chore himself.

"You know, Smith," he said with a great effort at self-composure, "you have signed your own death warrant. Why, all I have to do is leave Texas for a little while——"

"Just a minute, General," Wesley cut in quickly. "Just a minute. Just let me remind you that some of the men of whom I spoke could very well be in that splendid bodyguard that rides with you. You are too well known to hide, and I assure you that one or more of them will be near you, no matter where you go. Now, suppose we take a gentlemanly approach to this thing and agree that no mention be made of our conversation. You protect me, I protect you. There is one other thing."

Wesley paused and took his time in lighting a cigar. Then he sat and watched the smoke drift slowly between him and the general before saying: "There is one other thing. The Negroes in Montgomery County are not going to run over me, my family, or my friends. All we ask—

require is a better word—is that you keep an officer at the head of your troops in this county who will be fair and impartial to white and black alike. In return, you have my word that the white people here will recognize the fact that the Negroes are free and will take no undue advantage of them."

The heavy-set little cavalryman looked long at the ex-Ranger, trying hard to ferret some weakness, Wesley realized. He found none and, by his expression, he felt his position unimproved.

"If the situation were reversed, General," Wesley continued, "you would be quick to defend the honor of your home and your community against any and all, be they red, white, or black. The people of the South have been goaded to the limit of their endurance. I have also reached mine, and unless you Federals ease up a great deal you are going to drive the South into guerrilla warfare. When people are hungry, General, and their families are mistreated and insulted, there is no limit to what men will do."

Sheridan sat in deep thought for several moments. "I admire your courage," he said finally, "and I'm going along with you under certain conditions. Condition one, this deal is between you and me and is strictly confidential. Condition two, I want your word that you will confine your political activities to Montgomery County. And condition three"—he laughed a little bitterly through a thin smile that brought his receding chin forward—"under the conditions you have outlined, you must take care of your worthless Rebel hide."

"I will, General." Wesley laughed good-naturedly. "I enjoy living too. I give my word on the other two conditions also." He arose and extended his hand. "It's getting late. I'll show you to your room."

After breakfast next morning Sheridan prepared to leave. As he swung up into his saddle, he shook hands with his host. "I will say again that I admire your courage," he told Wesley. "My visit here has been of immeasurable benefit to me in a way you cannot know."

He touched the spurs to his horse and rode slowly down the hill. Wesley stood and watched until Sheridan was halfway to the main gates. As he turned to go inside, he met Margaret in the doorway.

"Wesley darling," she said with a shadow of reproof in her voice, "whatever possessed you to have that man spend a night under our roof?"

Wesley looked at his pretty wife and smiled tolerantly. "My dear sweet wife," he replied, "I did something last night that I hope fervently will bring a measure of relief to the good people of Montgomery County."

"Oh, Wesley," Margaret cried, "surely you haven't traded your soul to that unspeakable man?"

"No, Margaret, I have not. Far from it. Now listen to me. I am sending you and the children away for a few days. There is a remote possibility that we may have some trouble here, and I want you to visit with the Spillers until I see what results will come from my conversation with General Sheridan."

"All right, Wesley," she said, placing an arm about his neck. "And I'm sorry I doubted you."

While Margaret and Aunt Polly packed, Wesley sent Henry into town with a message for Robert Gay. He attended to harnessing the team himself and within the hour the Negro was back. Soon the surrey was whirling down the Fish Trail Road behind a pair of fine bays, Henry driving and Wesley following on his horse.

They moved at a brisk trot until they forded the San Jacinto River and reached the intersection of the Danville Road that ran through Diamond Six Ranch to join the Spiller lands. As the driver turned the team north, Wesley heard a hail from the woods, and two of his men came riding out of the pines.

After greeting the two youngsters, Wesley introduced them to Margaret and instructed them to give her protection to Danville and then to return there for her and escort her back to The Oaks one week later unless they heard from him to the contrary. Then he kissed Margaret and the children and, as the surrey trailed by the two armed men moved in the direction of Danville, he took the Fish Trail Road to Montgomery.

Although many of Wesley's friends had responded to his call, nothing happened to justify his distrust of Sheridan and he began to breathe easier. The only thing that worried him was that he could not tell his friends why he had asked for their help. Sheridan kept his word, and one week later Margaret and the children returned to The Oaks. Life was now a great deal brighter, despite the fact that some of Wesley's friends said he was acting like a damned scalawag. These remarks cut him to the quick, though he kept his silence.* He had pledged his word.

* He kept this confidence, until many years after the war, when he told his son Bubba the whole story.

28. The Lawmakers

N O T H I N G could be accomplished at a convention such as the one called on Wesley's thirty-ninth birthday, Saturday, June 6, 1868, so Wesley had a good excuse for declining to go as a delegate. The convention developed into a fight between A. J. Hamilton, the abolitionist, and E. J. Davis, the radical, both regarded by most Texans as the biggest traitors Texas had ever known. The fight finally grew so bitter between the Negroes and the scalawags, who were the only ones allowed to vote, that the convention finally dissolved and the delegates went home.

This gave Philip Sheridan the opportunity which he had endeavored to bring about, and he had the secretary of the convention write the constitution of Texas just as he dictated it. With no white men allowed to vote, the Negroes, scalawags, and carpetbaggers ratified this document on Saturday, November 13, 1869.

In this same hectic year of 1869, state officers were elected. In the most unsavory political contest ever held in Texas, E. J. Davis won the office of governor over his opponent, A. J. Hamilton, the abolitionist. Although it was a serious and unhappy time for Texas, Wesley in later years humorously referred to it as "The Race of the Rat and the Reprobate."

During these trying times many of Wesley's friends wondered why he refused to take an active part in politics outside Montgomery County. They finally came to realize, however, that white people could walk down the streets of all the towns in Montgomery County without being pushed and shoved about by the Negroes and the trashy whites. They also realized that their taxes, some of which had been raised more than fifteen times the prevailing rate at the end of the war, were now lowered considerably.

The people of the county were not long in learning that they had an ally in Captain Clark, who remained in charge of the local military force. They blessed the day that such a fair and impartial man had been assigned to their district.

There were happy times in 1869 in spite of the oppressive and shameful treatment still heaped upon the South by the radical leaders of the Federal Government. On the morning of Saturday, August 28, Margaret presented Wesley with their sixth child, a son, whom they named William after Wesley's friend William Spiller. Their eldest, Irene, now almost eighteen, had become engaged to J. E. Pace, a fine young cotton broker from Waco. Wesley, a strapping boy of thirteen, Owen, a husky youngster of nine, Maggie, a little lady of seven, and Estelle, a pretty toddler of two, composed the rest of the family.

But tragedy was soon to follow. Just a month after the birth of William, Mrs. Arnold complained of a violent headache and took to her bed with a raging fever. Although Dr. Young called in learned consultants and Aunt Polly and Margaret constantly ministered to her, she never rallied. On Wednesday, September 29, 1869, she passed away at the age of sixty-seven.

Margaret and Wesley took her to Haddom, Connecticut, for burial beside her husband. Upon their return they found Aunt Polly sick. Despite her protests, she was put to bed with the same ailment that had caused Mrs. Arnold's death.

The same loving care was given the old matriarch of The Oaks, the same doctors called in. On a Sunday morning, October 24, Aunt Polly asked to see Margaret and Wesley. They stood at her bedside, the tears rolling unheeded down their faces. The doctors had told them there was no hope for her recovery, and they could not imagine their world without Aunt Polly. As long as Wesley could remember she had been his confidante, nurse, and the nearest thing to a mother. And every day of his and Margaret's married life, nineteen wonderful and happy years despite the war and the sorrows and adversities of Reconstruction, she had been a pillar of strength to them and their children.

She rallied as she saw them standing there beside her. Seeing them crying, she began to cry also.

She found her voice and told them she was glad to see them once more, that she praised the Lord for putting her in a home like theirs. Her speech was broken by sobs as she said she knew the good Lord had "privileged" her when He let her be mammy to their children. Then she asked Wesley to be kind to the good Negroes, just for her, and to remember that they were all like children.

Her voice trailed off and she was gone. A happy smile remained on her face, as if she were in the midst of a pleasant dream. An era had passed.

The death of Margaret's mother, followed so closely by Aunt Polly's, seemed to bear down like a great burden on The Oaks. An emptiness, all too sudden, left both Margaret and Wesley in a state of despair. But as winter drew near, another problem arose, one which demanded Wesley's attention.

Rounding up his cattle and culling them for market cleared his mind of the double loss. With Margaret it was not so easy, and Wesley was quick to realize that unless he did something to relieve her sorrow she might suffer a nervous collapse. So he took his family to Houston for a week and outdid himself in showing them a good time. Margaret began to smile, then laugh and plan again for the future. Her children and Wesley felt the outpouring of her love, though only Wesley realized that the extra measure had once belonged to her mother and Aunt Polly. But that was life, and life was good.

Upon his return, there was more news concerning the rash of cattle thievery that had swept East Texas that fall. Wesley was glad he still had the twenty-five Confederates on his payroll, that he had augmented this purchase of power and authority with nearly a dozen men of the dissolved Ranger Company A. They rode in secret over his far-flung acres and protected him from loss.

Loss? He thought often of the actual loss of operating a ranch at a time when the United States had placed an embargo on any Southern product that could be obtained elsewhere. He sent his oldest and poorest-grade steers along the Atascocita Trail to New Orleans and foreign ships, keeping his best cattle in that long gamble for the day when the embargo would be lifted. When that day came, if he survived financially until that time, he would have thousands of fine Herefords on Diamond Six. But it was costing him while he waited, costing him a great deal of scarce money for protection atop all else. On the other hand, when the cattle thieves struck close by, almost ruining aspiring ranchers, Wesley wondered if the money spent for protection wasn't a sound investment after all. Only time—which could spell his own ruin or success —would tell.

Christmas came, and in appreciation for the fine work his riders had done, he sent word to them to meet him at a given place. He sent Henry and other Negroes ahead with a wagon loaded with food and gifts of shirts, hats, boots, guns, and cigars. Then he arrived in time for the feast and spent several companionable hours with the ex-Confederates and Rangers, talking of Indians on the trails, the Yankee wagon train and other events of the war.

As the cattle thieves continued to give Diamond Six a wide berth and the Union League left Montgomery County alone, Wesley began to look toward the future with more hope than he had at any time since the end of the war. He failed to reckon with the political situation, however. Although he realized that Sheridan was determined to force Texans to their knees, he thought perhaps the general had bitten off more than he could chew, until reports from Austin convinced him otherwise.

On Monday, February 7, 1870, E. J. Davis, who had taken the oath of office on January 18 and became the governor of Texas, convened the legislature, which promptly ratified the thirteenth, fourteenth and fifteenth amendments. All political barriers to Texas' readmittance into the Union were dissolved. On the thirtieth of March, Texas became a state again and her representatives and senators were allowed to take their seats in Washington. Although Texas was again officially in the Union, its government was still in the hands of carpetbaggers, scalawags, and ignorant Negroes.

To forestall any effort on the part of the white people to gain a foothold in local and state politics, the radical whites and Negroes in the legislature gave Davis the power to appoint every county and city official in the state. It seemed to Wesley that he exercised this prerogative with deliberate and meditated malice toward the white people, his purpose to do all the harm possible.

The scalawag governor had organized a band of outlaws and desperadoes into what he called the State Police. To this group he added other companies of Negroes, one of which served as his personal bodyguard. These men performed his outrages against the white people of Texas in return for amnesty from the many crimes they committed. Honest law-abiding farmers and merchants acting to defend their lands and properties against these ruffians were turned into outlaws; those who were not killed or imprisoned fled with a price on their heads. Davis had another and equally important reason for organizing his State Police, that being the forceful installation of his Negroes and scalawags as state and county officials.

As spring turned into summer, Wesley and the citizens of Montgomery County realized that their days of comparative peace were drawing to a close. They met and discussed the forthcoming trouble and waited for Saturday, July 9, when it would come.

Ordinarily on Saturday the streets were filled with farmers and townspeople. But on this hot afternoon not a white man was seen on the streets of Montgomery. True to form, Governor Davis had dispatched ten members of his State Police to install his fifteen appointees, nine of whom were Negroes. These men felt safe, since a detachment of United States Cavalry was stationed in Montgomery, and they marched to the courthouse steps at around a quarter to three that afternoon to await the swearing-in ceremony scheduled for three.

A buggy rolled to a halt a block away, then moved on out of sight. The ten State Police knelt, facing the street with rifles ready. A merchant gazed at the fifteen men selected by the governor as county officials, all lined up against the wall of the courthouse, closed and locked his front door, and moved to the rear exit. The appointees looked up and down the empty street, removed their hats and used them as fans. Not a breath of air stirred on the portico, and the sun burned hot on them.

The Federal judge selected to preside and give the oath of office walked slowly from the courthouse and stood facing the group. In a long harangue he endeavored to convince the new county officials that they were better than the people they were to govern, for they had not fought against the United States. He spoke also on the subject of social equality and predicted that within a few short years the Negro race would, with the assistance of the understanding people of the North, become the ruling class in Southern states.

Finally, the presiding officer came to the end of his exhortation and raised his hand. The appointees were instructed to do likewise.

The office of Captain Clark, military commander of the district, was one street removed from the courthouse square. At around a quarter to three the captain looked up to see Wesley and a dozen other Montgomery men dismounting at the hitching rail outside. Any small fear that these men whom he called friends might be paying an unfriendly visit because of the tense situation in the town was quickly dispelled when they entered smiling and placed two quarts of whisky on his desk.

"We're here to drink to your health, Captain, and to tell you we're sorry you're leaving Montgomery."

The captain seemed more than pleased, since he had not expected these men to regret the end of military rule, much less to show any fond regard for a Yankee soldier, however helpful or friendly he had been.

"Thanks," he said. "You know, Captain Smith, I've come to like your town and its people. So have my men, whom all of you have treated with kindness. And I can truthfully say they have no stomach for the harsh measures employed against the white people of the South."

After sending an orderly for glasses, he looked the men over one by one before saying, "I don't suppose you men rode in to greet the new county officials."

Out of the silence that gathered, Wesley said, "What officials?"

Captain Clark emitted a wise chuckle and reached for a bottle. Pouring into all glasses, he said, "To better days, gentlemen."

"To better days," the men chorused.

The minutes slipped by with no further mention of the ceremony soon to begin at the courthouse. Dr. Young proposed a toast to the health and long life of Captain Clark. When the men drained their glasses, the doctor said, squinting shut an eye and leveling the other on the captain:

"You, sir, are one Yankee we would like to keep in our midst. I mean come to Texas and live. We realize that we haven't made your job easy, but we do believe we've been fair with you. And, by grabs, you've been pretty fair with us."

"Well, I'm retiring from the army soon, Doctor, and you are likely to have me for a fellow Texan. And if the South should ever——"

A volley of rifleshots sounded from the courthouse square. The captain paused an instant, then completed his unfinished statement. Neither Wesley nor any of his friends got up or so much as changed the expressions on

their faces. Storekeeper Peel was talking about the opportunities Texas offered a newcomer when the corporal
whom Wesley had once defied entered and saluted.

"Captain, sir," he said, "the new county officials, the
Negro State Police, and the presiding judge have just been
shot dead on the courthouse steps."

Captain Clark lowered his drink and looked sharply
from the corporal to his guests. "Who shot them, Corporal?"

"I don't know, sir. Some fifty men raced out of the
building across from the courthouse and rode out of town.
I didn't recognize any of them. They were wearing long
white robes and high, peaked white caps that came down
over their faces."

Clark smiled wryly and drummed the desk top with
his fingers before darting half-accusing glances at his
guests. Turning to the trooper, he said, "Corporal, I have
an idea that the men responsible for that shooting came
from Houston. Take your squad and see if you can intercept them on the West Montgomery Road. Don't go too
far, as they will probably be well hidden in ten minutes
anyway."

"Yes, sir," the corporal replied, hiding his smile also. He
knew the men he was to intercept had ridden boldly north
along the Fish Trail Road. Nevertheless, he departed and
cantered south in the direction of Houston a few miles
and returned to report that no trace could be found of the
Klansmen.

Had the cavalry ridden north in the direction of Danville, the soldiers might have seen Betty Spiller's red-
headed husband William and other respected citizens of
that community rapidly divesting themselves of Klu Klux
Klan regalia. And they might have seen also thirty-seven

riders wave a salute to the men of Danville and move into Diamond Six land along the San Jacinto River.

When Wesley and his friends rode off, both the Yankee captain and his corporal knew full well that the guests had accomplished their mission. They had resorted to desperate measures, but they had been driven to it. And while Captain Clark did not condone murder in cold blood, he believed that justice had been done. As a result, Governor Davis had failed to grind Montgomery County under his heel.

On the following day Captain C. A. Clark departed for the New Mexico Territory with his troops, but not before he used the incident to deal out further proper justice. He had arrested and jailed every Union League member the troopers could locate. They were stripped of their resplendent uniforms and charged with the murder of the fifteen appointees of Governor E. J. Davis, their ten guards, and the presiding judge.

However, Captain Clark allowed the few scalawags and carpetbaggers who came forward in behalf of their comrades to post bond for them. He knew this would be the end of carpetbag rule in Montgomery County, for as soon as the prisoners were released, bailee and bondsman alike would leave hurriedly for parts unknown. He was correct in this assumption. By Sunday afternoon not a single undesirable remained in the county.

The incident did not end there, however. The enraged scalawag governor dispatched other members of his police force to investigate the killing of his henchmen, though every man he sent disappeared suddenly and completely. When the news spread and Davis was unable to induce any of his private police to invade Montgomery County, the case was closed and forgotten owing to lack of evidence.

The citizens of Montgomery County chose to forget the affair also. When it was mentioned, men remembered and repeated a remark made by Wesley Smith: "Whoever the men were, they took their lesson in creating new laws from General Philip H. Sheridan. He rewrote the laws of Texas, but Montgomery County simply outwrote him."

29. Hangman's Noose

THE reward for faith and patience in waiting came to Bess Simonton on the day the military detachment rode out of Montgomery. A tall, gaunt man rode up to her door and rapped.

The news of Reuben Simonton's return spread fast. Many citizens, including Wesley, were surprised and delighted, for they knew Simonton's stubbornness and pride might never permit him to take the despised iron-clad oath of allegiance. They had despaired of him for several years, during which they tried to cheer Bess at every opportunity with predictions that he would wear the Yankees' patience to a frazzle and win his freedom.

Wesley learned that Reuben had done just that. He had been set free without taking the oath. But Bess was more interested in his return. When Wesley and Margaret arrived, she was stunned and overjoyed and kept saying: "Just think of it, he's home! He's home!"

Margaret suggested a big party to celebrate Reuben's return. Riders were sent to invite their friends in Willis,

Danville, Swartout, Hempstead, and other communities to The Oaks on the night of Monday, July 18, 1870.

On the day of the party Wesley was sitting on the veranda with a group of the guests when he saw a lone horseman coming up the long drive from the main gates. He looked closely, wondering who the man was. As the rider came on, he still could not recognize him. He was dressed entirely in black, from expensive boots and the close-fitting pants and shirt to the wide, curled-brim hat on his head. The hat was laced with a thin leather chin strap that hung down his shirt front, and at his waist was a heavy black gun belt which held pearl-handled .45s at each hip.

As the rider came close to the veranda and dismounted, Wesley's keen glance detected familiar mannerisms that, despite the heavy beard the man wore, revealed his identity. Then Wesley bounded from his chair to embrace Major Tarbone.

"Hope I'm not intruding, Wesley. Was on my way West and wanted to see you. It's been a long time, hasn't it?"

Wesley laughed, took his friend's arm, and began introducing him to the guests. They gradually made their way through the crowded house to the library and closed the door.

"I suppose," Tarbone said after lighting one of his evil-smelling cigars, "you have been hearing some awful tales about me, Wesley."

"Only in a roundabout way, Major. I did hear that you had gone off the deep end, sort of. But that's your business."

"Well, a great deal of what you have heard is true. I used the Yankee oppression of the South as an excuse, I suppose, and gave way to the very thing I used to warn you about. I have a clear conscience on one point. Not once have I ever taken anything by force from a Southern white man. All my efforts have been directed toward the Yankees, carpetbaggers, scalawags, and the smart-alecky niggers. I've led a rough life the few years past, rougher and more exciting than with the Rangers. And now, very comfortably fixed at the expense of the people who tried so hard to grind us under their damned heels, I'm going West to live quietly and peacefully—I hope—the rest of my life."

Wesley looked intently at his old friend. It was difficult, almost impossible, to reconcile Tarbone the Ranger with Tarbone the outlaw of the Reconstruction period. And yet in another sense—when one considered the times and conditions and the fact that hundreds of law-abiding Texans had been forced by circumstances attending the Davis tyranny to do the same—it seemed quite natural. Further thought on the subject was cut short when Tarbone returned Wesley's stare and said with an accusing smile:

"Seems Montgomery County made a good stand against the Union Leaguers and old Davis. I don't reckon you had anything to do with the courthouse affair, you being a good ex-Ranger and all that."

Wesley kept a straight face. "Certainly not, Major. Have another bourbon."

They laughed together. Then Wesley said thoughtfully, "So you're headed West." A little later he said, "I wish I could go with you, Major. There's one thing I was never quite satisfied about that happened above Las Cruces. I still admire the Yankee colonel, but I'm still convinced that he might have lied to me."

Tarbone's leathery face was suddenly alive with interest. "You mean the one in charge of that wagon train back in 1863?"

"Yes. Was anything ever heard about the rumored gold shipment reaching the Yankees, Major?"

"Not a thing. But there was supposed to be gold in that wagon train. But if it was there, it's bound to have been in the wagon the Yankees managed to get into the river before you could save it. What are you driving at, Wesley?"

"Major, would you like to try and salvage that gold if it's there?"

The old Ranger smoked thoughtfully for several minutes. "If the colonel carried gold, don't you think he would go back and try to find it? Beyond that, I have no idea which ford you came up on the Yankees at. There are many crossings on the road north from Las Cruces, you know."

"A gamble is a gamble, Major. Maybe the colonel was exchanged and possibly killed in the war or maybe he did return and couldn't find it. Anyhow, that was a big wagon, and if the Yankees had nothing but gold loaded in it, they must have had more than a ton. That, even at fifteen dollars an ounce, would run up to half a million dollars. Now, my proposition is to outfit an expedition made up of the ten members of Company A who still work for me, you in charge. You and I will split whatever you find fifty-fifty on half the total, and the other half will be divided equally among the ten men you take with you."

"Just one thing, Wesley. Would you trust me with that much money after what I have been doing?"

"Why, you old goat!" Wesley laughed. "If it's there, yes." Then he said seriously, "I reckon you've got a short memory, Major, else you'd remember that I trusted you with my life many, many times. In fact——"

A gentle rap on the door claimed Wesley's attention. A moment later his eldest daughter entered and gave him a pouting smile. "I thought I was to have the first dance with you tonight, Father. The music is starting and here you are in a business meeting."

Wesley laughed and introduced the pretty girl to Tarbone. They then moved to the dance floor, leaving the old Ranger in the door of the library, smoking his cigar.

On the morning following the party for Reuben Simonton, Wesley sent Temple to bring the other ex-Rangers. As he returned to the dining room for breakfast, the only overnight guest at the table was Betty Spiller. Wesley sat down after wishing her a good morning.

"It was a lovely party, Captain!" she exclaimed. "And it was so good to see Mr. Simonton again. Why, I hardly knew the poor man, he was so skinny and frail. I just hate damnyankees, Captain Smith. I shall always hate them."

Suddenly Betty was in tears. Wesley knew she was thinking of her father and brother who had lost their lives at the battle of Arkansas Post. Presently she regained control and dabbed daintily at her eyes with her napkin.

Other guests joined them, all talking about the party. After breakfast they began to leave for their homes around the county. Wesley was anxious to resume his planning with Tarbone for the trek into Apache country. As the last carriage pulled away, he took a chair on the veranda and lifted Estelle to his lap, while the major sat down beside him and produced one of his black cigars. Owen and Wesley, Junior, raced away to Montgomery for the papers and mail, while Maggie played on the broad green lawn with the pig-tailed daughter of Nicey, who was trying so hard to take Aunt Polly's place in the Smith household.

"Wesley," Tarbone said, "I'm damned near jealous of you. I'm getting old. Be sixty my next birthday. If I could just turn back the clock and have a wonderful family like this——"

Just then Margaret and Irene came out of the house, followed by Henry, who brought two cups of steaming coffee on a silver tray.

"Don't get up," said Margaret with a happy smile. "You old Rangers looked entirely too comfortable, so we came out to break up your gossiping."

"I'm delighted, ma'am," Tarbone said, rising and bowing. "I was just telling Wesley what a lucky man he is to have such a fine and wonderful family. I'm downright jealous of him."

They had not been on the veranda long when Wesley saw the ten ex-Rangers turn in at the main gates. "Here come your Rangers, Major," he said, watching the happy expression on Tarbone's face.

The next two days were busy ones at The Oaks. The wagons were greased and a false bottom was built into each vehicle. Then they were loaded with camping equipment, ropes, chains, grappling hooks, lanterns and food. Wesley had told the ex-Rangers of his plan and explained the division of the gold, if it was found. Never had he seen a more enthusiastic group of men.

The trip would take them through Comanche country and into the land of the Apaches, but this prospect did not worry them nearly so much as the fact that they would very likely encounter patrols of Union cavalry, who had caused so much strife and bloodshed between the Indians and the settlers before the great war.

Early on the morning of Friday, July 22, 1870, the train of five wagons and ten rough, hard-bitten men led by the still tougher Major Tarbone, ex-Ranger and ex-robber, pulled away from The Oaks. Wesley and his two sons, Owen and Wes, rode a short distance with them then waved farewells as the wagon train plodded westward. Watching them depart, Wesley felt a momentary desire to share the stirring adventure with the old Rangers. Then he was glad he was returning to The Oaks to be with his family rather than riding into Indian territory on what more than likely would prove to be a fruitless mission.

The weeks following Tarbone's departure were busy ones for Wesley. A cattle drive was forming for New Orleans and he decided at the last moment to send several hundred of his oldest steers. The gathering and cutting out of these steers kept his cow hands busy for two weeks, since the cattle were scattered over thousands of acres along the San Jacinto bottoms. The drive hit Danville on Saturday, September 3, 1870, and Wesley's men drove the big Diamond Six steers into the huge herd and placed themselves at the disposal of big, jovial Pat Lindley, the trail boss. The cattle moved slowly out of sight to the east, and Wesley and his eldest son, Wesley, Jr., whom they called Buck rode back to the roundup, where the new calves were being branded.

Working shorthanded now, with ten of his best men on their way to New Mexico Territory and ten more in the trail drive, Wesley found himself dependent on the Negroes who had continued to cast their lot with him. To the fifteen white men on hand other than his foreman Dude Justice, Wesley assigned three Negroes each to help with the handling of the cattle. There were several thousand calves to be rounded up, castrated, marked, branded, and weaned, and the men engaged in this work were necessarily confined to the pastures. This also meant that the chuck wagon should follow the work and be at the appointed place in time for all meals.

All went well for about a week after the cattle drive left Danville for New Orleans. Then one night one of Wesley's riders came to The Oaks.

"Hate to bother you at home, Cap'n Smith," he said, "but I'm afraid we're going to have some trouble with the niggers."

"How is that?" asked Wesley.

"Well, sir, the chuck wagon got lost off from us today and didn't catch up with my bunch until about three o'clock. One of the niggers—the one they call Ike—started grumbling. He said if he couldn't have his meals on time he was going to quit. I didn't pay much attention to him at first, but by the time the wagon showed up he was getting pretty nasty. Said he didn't eat slop like what the cook had fixed for us, and threw it in the fire, plate and all. I might have done wrong, Cap'n, but when he did that I walked over and knocked hell out of him and run him off. Duane was with me, with his three niggers, and all three of them left with Ike, hollerin' that they'd be laying for me. I started to shoot one or two of 'em, 'cause I don't take much stock in anybody makin' threats toward me, but I figgered it would be better to see you first."

Wesley sat quietly for several minutes, turning his cigar over and over between his fingers.

"Ernest," he said finally, "we can expect more and more of that as time goes on. All of my darkies were told that they were free to leave in '65, and only one or two of them left. But now they're getting the idea they should be paid a monthly salary. That I will never do as long as I live. I'll feed them, house them, clothe them, and give them everything I'm able to, but that's as far as I ever intend to go. The darky is not ready to be treated like a white man, Ernest, and if he were, I would still refuse, for the damned Yankees never consulted us on how to deal with the problem they created. The Negro didn't have anything to do with it either. The Yankees just freed him over our protest. Now that they're free, if they can't work for a living, let them go North and live with the people who profess to love them so goddamn much.

"You had better stay here tonight, son," he continued, "and I'll ride over with you in the morning and help you get straightened out. They'll probably come back in the morning wanting to go back to work, and I plan to be there."

Wesley and his man had breakfasted and were on their way before daylight. About an hour after sunrise they rode up to the line shacks where the men were finishing a breakfast of steak, potatoes, hoecakes, and coffee. Wesley and Ernest dismounted and walked over to the fire and poured coffee. Wesley sat down on a box just outside the lazy curl of smoke from the cook fire and counted the Negroes gathered around a folding army table enjoying the food which Ike had called slop.

He counted only forty, which meant that five of them had left. He finished his coffee and walked over to them.

"Good morning, boys," he said pleasantly.

When they chorused a cheerful "Good morning," Wesley detected no sullenness or discontent. He had known every Negro in the group since birth and liked them all.

"I want you boys to listen to something I have to say this morning," he began. "I want you to listen carefully. Now when the war was over I told every one of you that you were free to leave any time you wanted to. That's still true. You can leave now, next week, or next year, but as long as you stay on this place you are going to work just as hard as the white gentlemen you are working with. You'll be fed the same food I feed them and you'll wear clothes as good as theirs. I'll take care of you when you're sick, and when you get too old to work you know you'll have a home where I'll take care of you as long as you live. But if I ever hear of one of you getting uppity and mean, I won't ask one of these white men here to run you off. I'll come do it myself, and I won't be as nice about it as they would."

Wesley placed a cigar in his teeth and took his time about lighting it.

"Now if those boys who left come back," he continued, "or if any of you see them, I want you to tell us, for they could cause you and us a lot of unnecessary trouble."

The Negroes understood and nodded their heads and grinned. Then Wesley saw Dude Justice riding into camp. As soon as the work pattern had been established for the day, Justice came over and sat down beside Wesley.

"Mr. Wes," he said, "I wasn't planning on coming out this way this morning, but some hard-looking customers rode into Willis last night. I figgered them to be ex-soldiers or maybe Yankee deserters, since they're all wearing cavalry boots and hats. They got pretty rough in one of the saloons, but when they saw nobody was scared of them, they began talking about going into the cattle business. They laughed a lot about it while they carried on. I just got to thinking they might try to go into business at your expense."

"Let's hope not, Dude," Wesley said, "but at any rate we had better——"

"Well, I'll be damned!" interrupted Justice suddenly. "Speak of the devil, there they are now, Mr. Wes."

Wesley glanced up and saw a half dozen men riding slowly through the pines. They rode deliberately up to the fire, where the two Negro cooks were cleaning the breakfast dishes.

"How about some vittles?" one of them asked.

Dude was right, decided Wesley as he calmly looked them over. They were either ex-soldiers or deserters from the Union Army. Every man wore new cavalry boots and campaign hats, and some other part of each man's gear was government issue. They were indeed a mean-looking lot, and Wesley was relieved to see Justice ride off into the trees as if he had not seen the men. He knew Dude was going after a few of the Diamond Six cow hands.

"Get down," said Wesley curtly. "The cooks will find you something to eat."

He would have enjoyed refusing them, for soldiers in those same uniforms had cost him many hours of worry and grief and many thousands of dollars. However, he had never refused a meal to any man who asked to be fed.

The strangers had paid no attention to Justice as he left camp. Now, as they sat waiting for the Negroes to serve their breakfast, Wesley saw Dude slipping through the pines with three Diamond Six men to take up positions behind trees within pistol shot of the camp.

Then the unexpected happened. One of the Negro cooks was pouring coffee into the tin cup of one of the strangers when the man looked away for an instant and unconsciously moved his hand directly under the boiling liquid. With an oath he dropped the cup and slapped the cook's face, causing him to drop the big coffeepot.

"Lawdy, mistuh!" the black said. "I didn't mean to spill dat on yo'all." As he backed away with a look of terror in his eyes, the offended man strode after him, cursing vilely.

"Leave that darky alone!" thundered Wesley.

The man whirled to face his host. "That goddamned nigger burned me purposely and I am going to punish him. You keep out of this or we'll give you the same treatment."

As Wesley rose and walked calmly toward the speaker, one of the ruffians shoved a pistol in his back and said: "You just calm down, you damned Rebel. If Josh says he's going to whip that nigger, then, by God, he's going to whip him."

The terrified Negro cook began to run. As he did, the man he had burned drew his pistol and leveled it at his back. But before he could pull the trigger a shot rang out from the pines and the man turned completely about-face, a look of astonishment in his eyes.

"Who in the hell fired that shot?" he asked.

He looked from one to the other of the men who had ridden into the camp with him. Then his eyes fell on the gun in the hand of the man behind Wesley. Thinking that he was the one who had shot him, the man half raised his weapon. Then his knees buckled and he collapsed suddenly and fell face down, dead.

Another shot rang out from the woods. The weapon in the hand of the man at Wesley's back spun away from him and he grabbed his torn hand, screaming. Before any of the others could size up the situation Wesley had drawn his two .44s and covered them.

"Tie them up, boys," he instructed as his men came out of the pines, "until we decide what to do with them."

"Let's hang them and get it over with, Mr. Wes," suggested Dude.

This suggestion produced a very distinct effect on the youngest of the men. He began to whine and plead.

"Shut up, you fool!" cried one of his companions.

"I'll do no such thing. I'm not going to be hung for something I didn't do."

This conversation aroused Wesley's curiosity and he quickly pursued the point. "Keep talking," he ordered, "if you want to save your dirty hide."

"It's just like this, sir," the wretched youth said. "We are all deserters from Fort Davis, way down on the Pecos River. I had been stationed there ever since the war and I left to get back to my folks because I'm homesick and tired of the army. These men said they were going to run off and go back home too, but they lied to me. They are just a bunch of murderers and thieves. They killed three men a few days ago just this side of Houston and——"

"Shut up, you lousy——" yelled the man at his side.

"Keep talking," Wesley commanded.

"If you don't believe me," the youngster said, "just look in their pockets and you'll find the wallets of the men they killed. They were planning to kill you too when we rode in here."

One of the Diamond Six men searched the visitors. "Mr. Wes," he said, holding up a wallet, "this belonged to Paul Hackett. Paul was the best friend I ever had. This man murdered him just like the kid said."

Wesley examined the wallet, knowing as he did so his men were not to be denied much longer. "Hold on a moment," he said softly to his veteran cow hand. "Just take your time and we'll attend to this thing in proper fashion."

Wesley turned again to the confessor. "Did you have anything whatever to do with the killing of these men?" he asked.

"No, sir," the boy cried in anguish. "I swear I didn't. I never killed a man in my whole life, even when I was in the war."

Wesley untied him and pulled him to his feet. "Get on your horse and get going before I change my mind."

As the wretched man ran for his horse, Dude Justice touched Wesley on the shoulder and said in a whisper: "Mr. Wes, the boys want to attend to this little thing by themselves if you don't mind. It's kinda personal with them, you know. And besides, we've got to get them away from the darkies."

Wesley nodded, and Justice gave the three Diamond Six men a signal of approval. They hustled the murderers to their feet, helped them on their horses, and rode off into the pines. As they went about their mission Wesley and

Dude sat down to another cup of coffee and the Negro cooks began to prepare the noon meal.

The Negro who had accidentally spilled the coffee on the man Justice had killed came up with the steaming pot to refill their cups.

"Yo' know, Mistuh Wes," he said, "I kin see more than ever what de difference is between de Southern gent'man and de Yankee white man. De white gent'man in de Souf treats us niggers good. They loves us as indivijuals and just kinda tolerates us as a race. De Yankee white man hates us niggers as indivijuals and pretends to love us as a race. Does I make sense wid dat remark, suh?"

"You certainly do," Wesley said, grinning. "You certainly do." He turned to Justice. "You know, Dude, he has summed up the whole difference between the thinking in the North and South in one sentence."

"I've never heard it said better'n that," Justice replied.

Wesley stared thoughtfully into the fire. "Dude," he said, "we are witnessing a passing era."

"What do you mean, Mr. Wes?"

"Simply this. The North has succeeded in freeing the Negroes suddenly, with no thought being given as to how they will make their way in the world. The entire economy of the South was built around the Negro. We needed him for hand labor. He needed us. But now we are going to see the South built on a new foundation that will not see the Negro supported by whites. The Negro is no longer free of responsibility. From this time forward his plight is going to be a sad one. The North doesn't want him and the South can no longer afford him."

Wesley puffed on his cigar and discovered it had gone out. Dude struck a match and held it for him. They sat silently watching the white smoke lifting up into the pines.

"I've said before and I'll say again," Wesley continued,

"that slavery is not all right and it's not all wrong. A great deal depended on the man who owned the Negroes. If he treated them fairly and kindly—and a large percentage of them did—the Negroes stayed on even after they were set free. But think of all the thousands of slaves freed by their owners before the war. Most of them picked up and went North, but how many of them stayed? Only a handful. The others came back South because they were mistreated. When the darky has no place to run, Dude——"

He puffed his cigar back to life and smiled broadly at his capable old foreman. "Hell's bells," he laughed, "I'm not the one to settle this thing, and besides, I've got to get back to Montgomery."

Wesley got up just as Dude pointed toward the Diamond Six men riding back into camp, leading five riderless horses.

30. Holiday Visitors, 1870

THE hot, sultry days of 1870 blazed their way across Texas, leaving barns and warehouses filled with one of the best crops since the beginning of the war. Cotton bales were stacked high at every gin, waiting for the buyers who came late every fall to grade and sample and bid on this one Southern product the Northern mills needed. Reports from other Southern states indicated a sore lack of Negro labor necessary to produce cotton. The same was true of the tobacco crop in Virginia and the Carolinas, though Texas sweathouses bulged with the golden-brown leaves.

The cash crops at The Oaks, as on most other Texas plantations, were sold at a great profit and, in spite of Governor Davis and his tax collectors, a great part of the proceeds were banked against future years that might not prove so prosperous.

Cool nights and balmy days continued until the day before Christmas. A cold norther blew in and Wesley spent the day with his family around the glittering Christmas tree and before the big logs blazing in the fireplaces. Then a freezing rain began to fall, turning to ice as it hit the earth. This was one of the hardest freezes Wesley had ever seen in Texas, and he hoped the men on Diamond Six would be able to haul sufficient feed to the cattle from the big barns near Willis.

The second day after Christmas was clear and very cold. The children were kept inside to play around the Christmas tree, and while Margaret went about her household duties Wesley had his horse saddled and rode to the post office for mail and newspapers.

He had just returned and pulled off his heavy overcoat when four-year-old Maggie, who was industriously helping her father with his hat and gloves, pointed through the glass of the front door.

"Man's at the gates, Father, man's at the gates. They cold, ooooohhh!"

Wesley looked through the door, wiping the glass for a clearer view. He saw a group of men and wagons begin the slow drive up the slick, icy hill. His heart gave a bound. These men could be none other than Major Tarbone and the ex-Rangers returning from their long trek into New Mexico Territory.

They were still far down the drive when he drew on his coat and went out to meet Tarbone, who had pushed his horse ahead. The old Ranger slipped wearily from his horse and embraced Wesley with a great hug.

Under the press of excitement and curiosity, Wesley forgot the bitter cold. He did not ask Tarbone whether or not they had found the gold, and the old Ranger divulged nothing more than pleasure at seeing Wesley again. The wagons came up slowly and the men extended cold hands to Wesley.

Tarbone said dryly, "Maybe you don't have a damned

fire inside, Wesley. Maybe that smoke coming out of the chimneys is just my imagination."

Wesley laughed. "Well, I suppose I'll have to thaw the lot of you before I learn anything. Come on in, boys, and gather around the fireplace while I pour something to warm your insides."

Once in the house, Wesley noticed Tarbone and Temple move alternately back and forth from the fireplace to a window for a look at the wagons.

"Coldest I ever seen it," Temple said, launching into an account of the long trip home. Following a pause, he looked into the fire. "Remember the wagon that rolled into the flooded river, Cap'n? Well, weren't much of a job findin' the place. And there's still signs of the battle that day. But the wagon—you know they made good wagons. That one weren't carried far by the flood."

Wesley remembered the scene in vivid detail. He saw again the big wagon gathering headway backward for the plunge. "Why wasn't it carried far, Temple?" he asked.

"It went plumb to midstream, Cap'n, dumped its load and turned over, I reckon. Leastwise that's the way we found it, some hundred yards downstream from where it hit the water. Course the canvas was washed off and a wheel was gone and half the timber tore out, but there she was—empty as a whisky jug after election day. Then we started pokin' around in the sand and gravel. The river was pretty low. Never seen it so dry out there. How was it here, Cap'n?"

Wesley narrowed his glance on Temple. Not a word had been spoken regarding their success or failure. Suddenly aware that they were baiting him and enjoying every minute of it, he decided to have a little fun himself.

Rising, he left the old Ranger's question unanswered and allowed the pause to lengthen before saying:

"I'm expecting company. But maybe it's too damned cold for the State Police today."

Tarbone whirled on him. "State Police! The hell you say!" He turned to Temple in a hurry. "Get that stuff out of the wagons! All of you. You there——"

Wesley threw back his head and roared. He laughed louder when Tarbone glared at him and sat down weakly.

"You know, Wesley, I reckon we had it coming. We planned to keep you jumping, planned it all the way from Las Cruces." Then he said, "We found it. Found even more than any of us hoped for, you included. Three thousand pounds if there's an ounce."

Wesley lowered his glass and whistled in surprise. A little stunned, he sat down and tried to adjust the major's statement in his own mind. It was difficult to imagine so much gold, and harder to realize that it belonged to the men gathered in this very room. But three thousand pounds of gold! He eyed Tarbone a moment.

"Major, I don't doubt your word. Not in the least. But it's not easy to hear a man say he found that much gold and just believe it right then. Wait a minute, Major. Let me finish. When I suggested this expedition, all I had to go on was supposition, and that based on doubt of the Yankee colonel. I just gambled that he lied to me. I would have done the same thing in his place.

"But after you men left, I got to thinking. Suppose there was gold in that wagon, the United States Government would have torn that river up trying to find——"

"Somebody damn near did," Tarbone cut in. "But you forget, Wesley, the Yankees thought we had captured the whole train. And remember, the colonel was a prisoner through the rest of the war."

"I suppose that accounts for it," Wesley said. "Anyhow, I was a little ashamed of myself for sending my friends out on a wild-goose chase."

"It danged near was," said Temple, chuckling. "We gave up more'n once. The boys will vouch for that."

Wesley walked to a window and gazed out at the wagons. "I wouldn't mind seeing some of it, Major," he said. "Or were you planning to let it freeze out there?"

Then he turned an appraising gaze on the men. They were standing before the fire, each lost in deep thought, as though trying to place an estimate on his share of the wealth.

"Well, Wesley," Tarbone replied, "we've talked about it all the weeks we've been on the trail back, and I reckon today, right now, is as good a time as any to divide it."

The ex-Rangers began to unload the wagons with enthusiasm. When all the heavy sacks were deposited on the library floor, scales were brought in and the weighing began. Soon Tarbone said to Wesley:

"I want the men here to answer any question you might wish to ask about it, but not wanting to haul my share here and back West again, I buried it out there. I took a counted one hundred thousand dollars. The men helped me and witnessed it, and they will verify my figures."

"But, Major," Wesley protested, "if there's as much here as you say, you didn't take your full share. You have a great deal more coming to you."

"That's all I need and all I'm going to take. You and the men divide the rest of my share any way you like."

The weighing continued, and as a share was decided, the recipient's name was tagged to the sack. Wesley's and Tarbone's shares, with the metal figured at only fifteen dollars an ounce, were over one hundred and eighty thousand dollars each, but the old Ranger would not accept any more than he had buried in New Mexico Territory. Finally, at Wesley's suggestion, the remainder of Tarbone's share was divided equally among the ten men who had served so long and faithfully with him in the Texas Rangers and on Diamond Six.

Wesley produced another decanter of whisky and they drank to their success and to the future. Margaret entered a little later and led them to the big dining room and a belated Christmas dinner. After they had eaten and were seated around the roaring log fire in the parlor with coffee and cigars, Wesley eyed the men speculatively for some time before saying:

"Well, Temple, you and the men here who rode with me in old Company A can look forward to living in comfort the rest of your days."

"Now hold on a minute, Cap'n," Temple said, removing a cigar from his mouth. "If you think we went out and got rich on your hunch just to high-tail it off, you got another guess a-comin'. We all been thinkin' and talkin' about this here thing all the way back from New Mexico. We decided we'd like to stay on at Diamond Six for the time being. Leastwise till times change and you can find good hands to take over our jobs."

Touched by their true loyalty, Wesley did not dare look at Temple or those he spoke for. As a sudden mist clouded his vision, he muttered a word: "Thanks."

The men were as good as their word. They stayed on at Diamond Six, with lariat or branding iron in hand, with experienced guns ready to defend the now famous Diamond Six Ranch. Each buried his share of the gold at a spot known only to its owner, and for a reason that also remained his secret. Perhaps for a wife and home, perhaps for his declining years. Whatever the reason, his depository was the earth, a bank likely to retain forever in the palmetto flats along the San Jacinto River one cache or many.

But on that same bitter-cold day in which the treasure of the Rio Grande was divided, Major Tarbone took leave of his friends and companions of the many campaigns during the days of the Republic of Texas, the state of the Union and the Confederacy. Something in his expression and manner, a reluctance to let go of a man's hand in farewell, and the deep look he gave one, seemed to say he was riding out of their lives forever. Before he rode down the drive to the gates of The Oaks he told them he had decided to become a rancher in New Mexico. The cattle brand he planned to use was, with Wesley's permission, Diamond Six.

31. Loss and Gain

In the spring of 1871 Texas cotton planters devoted their energies toward two important objectives. The first was an effort to produce a bumper crop equal to that of 1870, while the second was an organized attempt to regain control of state politics. The harvesting of the cotton crop and the necessary vote to oust the scalawag government seemed simultaneous. While the cotton gins hummed, men banded together at the Taxpayers Convention in Austin to offer the first united protest against radical rule and waste of public funds. In the October elections they were rewarded with success. All Democrat candidates to Congress won. The only flaw was the inability of Texans to oust Governor Davis, because his term of office did not expire for two more years. However, the opening wedge had been driven and the people of Texas took new hope.

Wesley had taken a leading part in the work of the Montgomery County delegation. He realized that the gain of the 1871 convention, while something to be proud of, could very easily be lost to Texans in 1873 unless the united effort was kept enthusiastically alive. He worked tirelessly in this direction, often traveling to other parts of the state when cattle and cotton demanded his presence on the far-flung acres of Diamond Six.

It was during this time that Margaret told him she was expecting an addition to their family. His happiness seemed in no way marred when she jokingly said she hoped he would be at home when she presented him with another child.

"I'll be here," he promised. "And I'll name the boy after your father—Eliphlet Arnold."

"Why, Wesley Smith, I never thought you would consent to naming one of your children after a Yankee," she teased.

Wesley was at The Oaks on that Friday, February 2, 1872, when a husky boy was born to them and, as he had promised, he named him Eliphlet Arnold. But the boy seemed destined to carry another name throughout his life, for his five-year-old sister Maggie, in an effort to say "brother," came up with "Bubba." The nickname caught on and Eliphlet Arnold seemed a forgotten name at The Oaks.

Bubba was not quite two when his father joined a delegation of angry and armed citizens and left hurriedly for Austin. The reason—to place the elected Democratic nominee Richard Coke in the governor's office.

Coke, a man who had served Texas and the South both during and after the war, won over Davis by an overwhelming majority in the election of 1873. But Davis charged that Coke's election was due to wide-scale illegal voting and sent the case to the State Supreme Court, a body composed of his appointees. The court, as expected, declared the election void. The Democrats rose in a body over the state and moved on Austin for the inauguration of Coke and Lieutenant Governor Richard Hubbard by force of arms if necessary.

Wesley and his group reached Austin on the afternoon of January 12, 1874, five days before the constitutional date of inauguration, and learned that Davis had not altered his determined stand. Instead, with the Supreme Court of Texas backing him, he further contended that his term of office would not expire until four years after his last inauguration, which would be on April 28, 1874. Furthermore, it was learned that he had concentrated his private police force, mostly Negroes, in the basement of the capitol building.

Dr. Young of Montgomery and Temple returned from a scout of the building and reported to Wesley that holes had been drilled in the ceiling of the basement in order to enable the State Police to fire into the hall of the capitol.

The angry Democrats milled about, all expecting, and rather anticipating, a real gun battle for the capitol. All the while, the Fourteenth Legislature, composed of a majority of Democrats, advised of no change in its plan to meet in the capitol on the thirteenth.

That night the movement of men toward the capitol began. Wesley's group moved with them. When within range of the Negro police, one of the leaders of the Democratic army sent a message to Davis:

"Let one Negro trooper fire a gun and the next shot will be aimed directly at your heart."

Guns were readied for use. The men waited, tense and alert. Temple, at Wesley's side, said, "You know, Cap'n, this is better than a passel o' Comanches to shoot at. I hopes to draw a bead on one of them State Police." As they edged on step by step, Temple said, "Too bad Jack

Spangler ain't with us. He'd shore love a kinky-headed scalp."

Wesley's brow wrinkled. It had been a long time since that night in 1862 when he shuddered at the sight of scalps in Spangler's tent. Christmas night, he reflected. It had been a long time since he had so much as thought of Jack Spangler. And now, almost in detachment, he was tracing the course of events backward to their first meeting. It brought Joe to mind. He wondered again where his brother was and what he was doing.

The order came to move on. The Democrats marched into the capitol. The State Police held their fire. Evidently Davis valued his life more than the office he coveted, for no gunfire impeded the occupation of the second floor of the Capitol.

The legislature met at noon on January 13 and shortly thereafter declared Richard Coke the duly elected governor of Texas. Thus thwarted, Davis barricaded himself in the capitol and in desperation telegraphed President Ulysses S. Grant for Federal troops. He held out even after his plea was ignored, despite the laughter of the elected officials who carried on the affairs of state.

Davis slipped out one night, under the protection of Wesley and other Texans whom he had both hurt and offended. They kept a would-be lynching bee from forming and escorted him to his home. Wesley and others believed that, as time went by, the fact that he had made a laughingstock of himself was all that saved him from being shot later by his many enemies.

Back at The Oaks after the affair in Austin, Wesley discovered that a number of his Negroes had left him to investigate the doubtful security of freedom. These he replaced with white men, putting them to work with the other cow hands as he turned more of his cotton acreage into pasture land for his increasing herds. Wesley required that every man on the Diamond Six payroll be a Confederate veteran or the son of a veteran, and by this one stipulation he organized and welded together a group of men solidly behind him in everything he did.

As more and more of the Negroes continued to seek their happiness and fortunes in the North, Wesley began to center his operations in Willis, where he was closer to his cattle. He was torn between two loves, The Oaks in Montgomery—where he and Margaret had lived happily all their married lives, where all their children had been born, and where so many of their old friends had been a part of their happiness and sorrows—and Diamond Six, the breadwinner in those lean years. He realized the possibilities of even greater returns if he moved to Willis, where he could better manage the cattle and other enterprises he had centered there.

The International & Great Northern Railroad had finally begun construction of a line from Houston to St. Louis, Missouri, and this meant a ready market for his beef, cotton, and grain. However, Wesley could not reach the decision to make the move to Willis by himself, for he knew how much The Oaks meant to Margaret. So he did nothing about it. Fate, however, decided it for him.

Their eldest child, Irene, graduated from William and Mary College in the latter part of May 1874. She and her fiancé, J. E. Pace, had set their wedding date for Saturday, June 6, 1874, her father's forty-fifth birthday. When Irene arrived in Montgomery, The Oaks immediately became a beehive of women in frantic preparation for the wedding.

Wesley kept as close to home as his business would permit during the few remaining days, for Irene, his firstborn, held a place in his heart no other could quite fill. He and Margaret approved of the well-to-do young cotton broker, despite the fact that his business was in the distant city of Waco, which meant they would see their daughter very seldom.

On the day of the wedding The Oaks was decorated just as it had been when Wesley and Margaret were married. The ceremony was read by a venerable minister of Montgomery who reminded Wesley of Milo Walker, long since dead. When the reception was at its height the young married couple slipped away and dressed for travel. Returning to the head of the stairs, Irene tossed her bouquet to the bridesmaids. Taking advantage of the happy scramble for the flowers, she and her husband ran for the carriage under a barrage of rice to begin their journey to Houston and New Orleans.

As expected, the guests hurried to the veranda to see them whisked away. No one was in the empty house and no one saw the big coal-oil lamp that had been pushed across a table in the rush for the door. As it came in contact with the heavy window drapes, the material flared quickly. By the time the excitement on the veranda had subsided and the guests re-entered the house, the wall was blazing fiercely.

Both guests and servants battled the flames with everything at their command, but lack of water made the fight a hopeless one. When it became evident that The Oaks could not be saved, they began moving out furniture and personal belongings, stacking them well away from the flames.

The fire mounted higher and higher, and the men were forced to leave the building long before the last of the fine colonial pieces could be removed. Just as the little red fire engine from Montgomery dashed up the drive the first section of the great roof collapsed and an enormous shower of sparks cascaded upward out of the roaring flames. Then the fire seemed to slow and take its time in consuming the mansion.

Driven from the house by the intense heat, Wesley sought out Margaret to assure her that he had been through the entire house and that no one had been hurt or trapped in the flames. He found her sitting with Bess Simonton and the children in chairs placed far down the slope of the lawn. Margaret burst into tears at his approach. He knelt at her side and took Bubba, crying because his mother was crying, in his arms to quiet him. The great love and sentiment they held for the grand old home was strong and could not be destroyed by the flames. They continued to sit with sorrow in their hearts until only charred timbers and smoldering ashes remained between the tall brick chimneys now standing stark and lonely against the starlit night.

The hospitable people of Montgomery threw their homes open to them that night, and they chose to stay with Bess and Reuben Simonton. On the way to the Simonton home Wesley tried to placate his wife with promises of a finer and even more beautiful home.

"No, Wesley," Margaret said through her tears, "I never want another home as big as The Oaks. You know nothing could ever take its place with us. Just build a home that we will be proud of, but make it one that I can manage without a large number of servants. I want a place that Henry, Nicey, Hutsie, and Deacon can keep for me."

As she continued to sob, Bubba slept in perfect contentment at Nicey's bosom.

The next day, Sunday, Reuben Simonton once again volunteered his services and architectural ability, and Margaret and Wesley planned their new home while Bess served coffee and supervised the preparation of the Sunday meals. Bess endeavored also to take Margaret's mind off her sorrow, and long before the day ended she observed that she had been more than mildly successful, for Margaret finally entered enthusiastically into the planning. Late that evening Simonton finished the general layout and promised to begin the working drawings next day.

Before they retired for the night Wesley drew his eldest son Buck aside and advised him regarding the management of the business in and around Montgomery. "Son," he told him, "you are old enough to shoulder responsibility. So while we are building the new place in Willis, I'm going to leave you in charge of everything here. Just name the ones you need to help you."

The young man thought for only a moment. "There's only one man I want, Father. That's Mr. Temple."

The next morning Wesley and Margaret drove to Willis to select the site for their new home. They chose a spot at the top of a long, sloping hill overlooking the town from the south. Dude Justice immediately began to clear and level it, leaving only the big live oaks to grace the front lawn.

The home they built consisted of entrance hall, parlor, music room, dining room, Wesley's office and study, and their bedroom, dressing room, and bath on the first floor, with four bedrooms and two baths on the second floor. All were large, airy, and comfortable. A big kitchen and pantry were connected to the dining room by a latticed porch. Across the front of the house, which faced north, and the east side, was a wide veranda upstairs and down. There were three gables in front, supported by large columns. The servants' quarters, a small barn, and the stables were back of the house, and a huge rose garden flanked the main structure on the east and ran some three hundred feet to the line of engineer's stakes marking the new railroad right-of-way.

The railroad had crossed Spring Creek some twenty miles to the south when the foundation was laid for their home. Shortly thereafter, Wesley signed a lucrative contract to do the grading of the roadbed from Conroe north through Willis to the Danville station.

On none of the work that Wesley Smith performed was there any supervision of his men by other than Confederate veterans or sons of Confederate veterans. Wesley gave his section close supervision, but as he was also busy building a home for his wife, a great deal of the responsibility was delegated to his favorite veteran, Duane Murchison.

Their new home was completed before Christmas of 1874, and Margaret, aided by her four faithful domestics, made Christmas a holiday her family would long remember. The new home was a veritable Christmas wonderland for the children, and the entire day was given over to them.

On the following Wednesday, December 30, the Wesley Smiths were hosts to friends from Swartout, Montgomery, Hempstead, and other communities for a very special occasion.

At about two o'clock in the afternoon a shrill whistle sounded to the south. Hosts and guests rushed for their carriages in order to cover the short distance to the brightly painted little depot where they would welcome the first train into the thriving town of Willis.

Fearing that the teams would bolt at the unfamiliar sight, Wesley ordered them hitched at the back of his store. Then the Smiths and their guests walked across the graveled street to see the flag-bedecked train pull grandly in and roll to a grinding stop amid clouds of steam and cries of wonderment and happiness from the large crowd.

As the cars came to a halt, a brass band seated on benches bolted to a little flatcar struck up "Dixie," and every throat swelled with it. As the stirring song ended, the crowd cheered long and loud. Then Governor Richard Coke appeared on the platform of the one passenger car. He stepped to the car on which the band was now standing to cheer him and raised a hand to silence the enthusiastic crowd. The cheering finally subsided and the governor began to speak.

"My good friends of Willis and Montgomery County, this is indeed a happy day for you, for this fine community, and for Texas. This great achievement marks the beginning of a new era for the entire South, for as I speak to you there are literally hundreds of miles of railroads being built throughout the length and breadth of the great Southland. Before many decades these railroads will transform the South into a mighty industrial giant. A giant that will be able to lend the strength needed to make Texas and the other great Southern states secure against those who might otherwise dare to violate the rights and privileges for which our forebears fought and died. There are many of you here who will witness the day when Texas, with its enormous potential of natural resources, will be far the richest and most powerful state in the Union. I predict that——"

The governor paused as the applause swelled into a roar. When it subsided, he concluded his speech with:

"This railroad will make next-door neighbors of the good people of Austin, Houston, San Antonio, and other places. Yes, my friends, you have witnessed the beginning of a new era for Texas and the entire glorious South, an era we shall bless as long as we live. Thank you."

He bowed and returned to the platform of his private car.

The band struck up "Dixie" once more and the engineer pulled the throttle, and the little train began to puff noisily. Governor Coke waved, and the people stood and cheered, watching until the train disappeared around a curve in the rails. Then they began walking back to their conveyances.

Margaret knew Wesley was excited by the great event. They held hands tightly as they crossed the street to their surrey.

As Henry drove them homeward, Wesley turned to Margaret. "Darling," he said happily, "it's good for a man to have his faith justified. That train today brought with it the fulfillment of a dream I knew would come true someday. First of all, we'll have a market for everything we raise right at our doorstep. Second, the things we send to market in the North will arrive there within a few days. Why, when we have good demands for beef, we can deliver it while the prices are still good."

He smiled with a measure of self-satisfaction and put a cigar in his mouth. "Best of all, we have the beef the Yankees want. Good, sleek, heavy beef that will bring good prices."

The year 1875 was an eventful one for Wesley's family. On Tuesday, February 2, when Bubba was three, Wesley put his family on the train at Willis and they were off on a glorious adventure that took them all the way to St. Louis, Missouri, and back. Nicey was taken along to care for the small children, and she summed up the trip with the simplicity and expressiveness of the Southern Negro: "I ain't never dreamt of movin' so far so fast in all my life. Ain't nuthin' 'cept a bird could made such a trip any faster."

The greatest event for the Wesley Smiths during 1875, however, came when their daughter Leila was born. The most important event for Texas in 1875 was the meeting of the state convention that drafted a new and permanent state constitution. This meant that the last yoke of Federal oppression had been thrown off and that Texans could again govern themselves by and under laws of their own making.

32. Law and Disorder

THE future looked bright for Texas, though it was more in the minds of her citizens, who after long years of disaster and oppression had inaugurated a government chosen by the people. On the factual side, the state was heavily burdened with debt and taxation and the frontier was all but defenseless against Indians and lawless bands of renegade whites.

Wesley frowned over reports of frontier raids, though he was glad the Texas Rangers had "come to life," so to speak, when Coke became governor. The Rangers were kept busy; the so-called Special Force was called upon to put down banditry on the Rio Grande, while the larger Frontier Battalion was sent out to stop the Indians, cattle thieves, and train robbers operating out of Denton County.

With memories of his days behind Captain Wade's Ranger badge and the many times Tarbone had called him back to service, Wesley forgot that he was getting older. Often he looked down the road, expecting to see Tarbone. At such times he smiled, glad the call to serve again was not forthcoming. Then he thought of Temple and turned his reflections to his son Buck, who had shown himself to be such a good manager that Wesley was seldom called to Montgomery.

In 1876, however, Buck asked for his share of the estate. Wesley and Margaret deeded it to him. That same year Owen, a quiet, studious boy, entered the Agricultural & Mechanical College at Bryan when it opened its doors for the first year; and Bubba, now four, began tagging after his father.

As the years went by, the bond between father and son grew stronger. Before the husky, nerveless boy was ten Wesley realized that every time he looked at young Bubba he was seeing himself at that age. In 1883 William died, leaving a heartbroken mother and sorrowing father. He had been the antithesis of Bubba, and for some unexplained reason his death made the bond between Wesley and Bubba stronger than ever.

Bubba appeared to be as much at home on a horse as a Comanche. Before he was thirteen he amazed Wesley with his speed and accuracy with a .45. He was faster than Wesley had ever been with his deadly .44s. Wesley did all he could to encourage the boy to master the six-shooter, for in 1885 there were still many bands of outlaws preying on the law-abiding people of Texas, and men still protected themselves or died.

Banks and stores were robbed daily, thousands of head of cattle were stolen, and many peaceful citizens were beaten or killed. Teaching his young son to ride and shoot was nothing more than a protective measure, for Wesley knew Bubba was even-tempered and slow to anger and therefore not likely to provoke trouble. The lessons progressed until Wesley had taught him all he knew and the student began to improve on his master and teacher.

On Bubba's thirteenth birthday, Monday, February 2, 1885, much to Margaret's chagrin Wesley gave the boy a handsome, well-balanced, pearl-handled .45 Colt revolver. With simple admonition he said, "Son, I have gone against your dear mother's wishes in giving you this gun and I don't want you to wear it unless you are with me until you have reached the age of recognized responsibility. That age may come when you are fifteen, eighteen, or twenty-one. I don't know now, but we'll be able to tell. But there's one thing you must always remember. Never draw this weapon in anger."

The youngster took the handsome weapon and examined it with unconcealed elation. The gun came alive in his hand as he flicked it from the scabbard, whirled it on his index finger in the trigger guard, and allowed it to slip smoothly back into the scabbard after the hammer had fallen rapidly on the empty shell chambers.

"I'll always remember what you said, Father," he said. "And thank you ever so much."

The boy developed a method of shooting that, while most unorthodox and scoffed at by many gun fighters, was lightning fast and extremely accurate. He had taken his gun to an old German shoe-repair man, and together they worked out a simple catch of metal and leather which held the pistol securely in a leather vise and which still allowed the cartridge cylinder to turn freely and offer no resistance to the moving parts of the gun.

The barrel protruded past the end of the short scabbard, which was swiveled to the wide gun belt in such a fashion that it gave free vertical movement to the weapon. Bubba then filed the trigger release until the hammer fell freely. Then he removed the trigger entirely.

After long weeks of practice under the critical eyes of his admiring father, he was able to walk ten full paces, whirl, and in the twinkling of an eye send two shots, never more than an inch apart, crashing through a target. The boy's right hand would instantly level the revolver, and the palm of his left would sweep rapidly across the hammer to speed the slugs on their way. Bubba had to shoot twice when he fanned the hammer in this fashion, for some muscular reaction demanded a second sweep of his palm over the hammer. If he held to a single shot it was usually far from accurate and he gave it up, letting the big .45 explode two shells every time he shot.

Wesley grew to love the youngster more and more. He could not help it, for the boy always worked hard and happily toward pleasing his father. His quick smile and ready wit endeared him to everyone and made him welcome in every home he visited.

Bubba idolized the old Rangers of Company A who had worked so hard and long for Wesley. As the years passed, they quit, one by one, and bought land and cattle of their own to live out their declining years in peace and comfort. That is, all except Jimmie Temple, who had asked that he be allowed to come back to Diamond Six. And now, when Wesley mentioned his quitting and using his share of the Yankee gold to ensure a tranquil and easy life, he would say:

"Well now, Cap'n, I don't know as how I could hit it off any better than right here with yo'all. Yore whole family treats me like I was somebody, and I'd be downright lonesome anywhere else. Reckon I'll just stay on a spell longer."

Only a half dozen of the Confederate veterans Wesley had hired many years back were still with him. These men now formed the core of his whole organization and with Dude Justice, who was also getting too old, they kept the wheels of the big Diamond Six operation turning smoothly. The hiring of additional men to help with the cutting, marking, and branding of the thousands of cattle more often than not turned into a real chore, since many of these men would work for only a day or two, then drift on. "Plain ornery saddle bums," Temple declared. "They ain't worth the powder and shot it would take to blow 'em to hell."

As the situation grew more desperate and the bands of outlaws grew bolder, Wesley appealed to the sheriff, but to no avail. The outlaws were too numerous and moved too fast. However, his letter to the governor brought ready action, and a small band of Texas Rangers was sent into the area. The depredations ceased just long enough for the Rangers to be withdrawn.

Late on the rainy and blustery night of Friday, April 3, Duane Murchison staggered to the veranda and knocked feebly. As Wesley, in nightshirt and robe, opened the door he saw Murchison collapse as he worked his lips in an effort to speak. With the lamp in one hand, Wesley tried to catch him with his free arm, though Murchison slipped to the floor across the threshold, his bloody head and shoulders inside on Margaret's bright green carpet.

Wesley had placed the lamp on a table near the door and was lifting Murchison inside when he heard a slight noise behind him. Turning, he saw Bubba standing midway on the stairs.

"Is Duane hurt bad, Father?" the boy asked.

"I'm afraid so, son," he said. "Go fetch Henry quickly so we can get him to a bed."

Bubba dashed down the stairs and out the back of the house, and Wesley brought the wounded man inside, placed a pillow gently beneath his head, and opened his shirt to see the extent of his injuries. Blood bubbled black and thick from an ugly bullet hole in the upper part of his chest. Another bullet had cut his scalp, but this wound had ceased to bleed. Wesley felt of Duane's back and discovered a small lump. Judging the course of the slug, he wondered how the wounded man lived.

After rousing Henry, Bubba returned to the house, only to be sent after a doctor. As Henry hurried sleepily into the room, Duane Murchison opened his eyes and looked at Wesley. He moved his lips, and Wesley held his ear close. "Ambushed us," Murchison whispered weakly. "Right near—Danville—cutoff. Taking cattle—upriver. Hurry, Cap'n."

His head rolled slightly and the neck muscles stiffened, as if trying to hold back death by sheer force of will. Then the muscles relaxed and his face contorted. A pinkish foam bubbled on his lips and Duane Murchison died.

Wesley rose slowly and faced Margaret. Her long curly hair, caught up with a ribbon at the neckline, hung to the waist of her silk negligee and shimmered in the light of the lamp.

"What on earth, Wesley?" she asked, scarcely breathing.

"A bunch of murdering cutthroats killed this boy, Margaret, and God only knows how many more. He told me they were ambushed. I'm going after them."

Margaret did not reply as he raced up the stairs to dress, but sank slowly into a chair by the parlor door, never taking her eyes off the handsome man whose lifeblood had spread over the carpet of the reception hall. As she continued to stare silently at the dead man she caught herself wondering if Wesley would ever come to such an end. The very thought terrified her.

Then Wesley appeared, buckling the black leather gun belt she had seen him wear so many years. Each time he had put it on, since her very first days at The Oaks, she had prayed for his safe return, and each time he hung it in his room she prayed he would never have to wear it again.

She rose and kissed him. "Be careful, Wesley," she whispered. "Please be careful."

Wesley drew her close, then moved off, Henry ambling after him, saying, "Mistuh Wes, I'd be only too glad to ketch that ole hoss for yo'all, but he is so mean, and I is kinda crippled."

"Yes, I know, Henry," Wesley said crisply. "You're a house darky."

Aware that he had hurt the old Negro with this remark, he was immediately sorry. But Duane Murchison's death had been a terrible blow to him. He vowed to offset what he had done to the old "darky" in the near future.

In less than five minutes he had caught and saddled his bay gelding and was riding hard in the direction of Danville. He stopped at Sam Beard's home on the outskirts of Willis, asking him to notify his neighbors to ride hell-bent for William Spiller's place, Esperanza. A half hour later he arrived at the Spiller home in Danville. Then he and William roused the men of the town and went back to the Spiller home to await them and the party from Willis.

Within two hours, thirty men armed with Winchesters and revolvers were assembled and ready to ride. Wesley placed the shooting at around ten o'clock, judging from the time Duane Murchison had knocked on his door. Driving cattle up the San Jacinto River at night, the outlaws could not possibly make a herd of any size move more than two miles an hour. At that rate, Wesley decided, they should have progressed about six miles. It was now almost one o'clock. In another hour the outlaws should be approaching the ford on the Danville–Anderson road. And in less than an hour Wesley and the men with him could be waiting for the thieves when they came to this crossing.

With Wesley and William Spiller riding at the head of

the column, they soon reached the ford on the San Jacinto. Wesley advanced into the pines alone. Finding no tracks, he returned to the horsemen and approached Sam Beard, banker and lumberman of Willis.

"Pick half a dozen men and get down on the sand bar at the ford, Sam. The rest of us will close in behind them as they move toward you. Don't any of you shoot downstream, and none of us will shoot toward you. Now when they show let's do our damnedest to kill every one of the sonsabitches and put the fear of God into any other murdering shunks who might think of coming to Montgomery County in the future."

Beard selected his men, and they rode down into the deep shadows along the river while Wesley led his group downstream to close in behind the outlaws and the stolen Diamond Six cattle.

They had longer to wait than Wesley predicted. It was almost three o'clock when he heard the rustle of cattle plodding through the palmettos of the river bottom. He knew then why the rustlers were late. The large unwieldy herd they had taken could not be driven fast.

Aware that the thieves would have outriders flanking the side of the herd opposite the river, Wesley took Charlie Pugh and Carl Abercrombie and rode almost to the edge of the woods to intercept them. The cattle moved slowly past them as they sat their horses. Soon the outriders began to close in. Wesley and the two men clubbed their big revolvers and rode silently among them. Three outlaws crumpled and dropped soundlessly from their saddles.

The cattle had just moved past Sam Beard and his men at the ford when the air was split by the crack of seven Winchesters. These shots were followed by the sounds of many more rifles, then a smattering of pistol shots. A few of the cattle, scattered here and there through the big herd, began to run wildly away from the menacing sounds. Within a matter of seconds the main herd was stampeding up the river in a northerly direction, with a smaller bunch turning east toward the open fields a few hundred yards away.

The outlaws were taken completely by surprise. While they were not averse to fighting, they could locate no one to fight. A shadowy figure would appear from behind a big pine. Then a rifle would crack, and the rustler would fall from his horse. The thieves began shooting wildly at everything that moved within their vision, and some of them shot their companions.

Wesley and his friends drew the ring slowly tighter until, in desperation, the outlaws made a dash for the ford, only to run into the withering fire of the seven Winchesters.

"We give up! Hey, we give up! Quit shooting!" one of the rustlers shouted.

"Hold your fire, men," Wesley yelled. "But if even one of them tries to get away, shoot all of them." Then he addressed the outlaw who had done the talking: "If you really want to give up, drop your guns, get off your horses, and walk out one at a time to that sand bar just below the ford. Try any tricks and we'll kill every goddamned one of you, so help me."

The desperadoes began dropping down onto the sandy strip at the river until there were nine congregated there. Wesley's men rode up slowly behind them to draw the ring tight. Feeling reasonably sure that none of their quarry had escaped, Wesley reined his horse close to the bank of the river where he could dimly see the men standing near the water.

"One of you bastards come up here," he demanded harshly.

Presently a man detached himself from the group and

scrambled up the bank. When he reached Wesley a rope fell about his neck.

"Now, pick some dead brush and wood to build a fire," said Wesley.

He was thinking of his men Duane Murchison had said were ambushed, and he was anxious to get to them, knowing all the while what he would find. Wesley followed on his horse as the outlaw gathered wood and tossed it down to the sand bar. Soon a fire was blazing, and Wesley and Pugh dropped down to the edge of the river where the rustlers had been made to lie face-down on the sand. After trussing them securely, Wesley left Pugh, Spiller, and Beard to guard the men and took the others with him to drive the stampeded cattle back down the San Jacinto.

They found the cattle fairly well grouped and succeeded in turning them downstream by midmorning. Then, with the prisoners tied securely in their saddles, they rode slowly but steadily until the last of the cattle were driven through the gap in Wesley's fence. After replacing the rails, they headed across Diamond Six property in the direction of the Danville cutoff where it joined the Willis–Montgomery road. By four o'clock that afternoon they came upon the remains of the ambushed Diamond Six riders.

Dr. Loggins rose to meet them, saying: "I just covered them up the best I could with their slickers and blankets. I wanted you to see what a thorough job these murderers did, Wesley, which is the reason we haven't taken them to Willis."

Wesley walked slowly down into the little draw where the still bodies of his riders lay scattered about. Two here, half a dozen around the ashes of a small fire on which a coffeepot still sat, one here, another sitting with his back to a big pine, a tin cup partly filled with cold coffee hanging from a lifeless forefinger. He dreaded a look under the blankets and slickers, for under some of them he knew he would find his friends of many, many years. The Confederate veterans, and Jimmie Temple and Dude Justice. The thought made his heart go cold and he closed his eyes for a long moment.

"Oh, God," he whispered prayerfully, "don't let Dude be one of them."

But he opened his eyes and saw the high cordovan boots with the heavy pull straps. And under the edge of the green slicker he glimpsed gray- and black-striped trousers tucked into the boot tops. This could be no one but Dude Justice. He raised the wide-brimmed hat and looked down into what was left of the face of his old friend.

An icy rage swept Wesley, though he managed somehow to control himself. He went from one still form to another until he lifted a saddle blanket and saw Jimmie Temple, whose chest and head were riddled with pistol and rifle slugs. Wesley shook his head slowly and said:

"Temple, how did they ever catch you in this trap?"

He let the blanket fall and moved on. "Temple was too smart to get caught like that," he muttered to himself.

Outwardly Wesley was calm, too calm. His friends had seen him in these silent rages before, and they knew he was a killer when he looked as he did now. They wondered what outlet his rage would seek.

"Wes," said Sam Beard as he walked up beside Wesley, "we're wasting time. Let's get this thing over with so we can get back to town."

Wesley looked at his friend and nodded. Beard waved to the men guarding the prisoners, and they began to lead the outlaws' horses under convenient, sturdy limbs. Then they adjusted ropes about the killers' necks.

"Wait a minute," Wesley ordered suddenly, his gaze

fixed on the mutilated form of Dude Justice. All the men paused, looking at him, waiting for him to continue. "How many of these dirty sonsabitches had shotguns?" demanded Wesley.

"There was only one, Wes," Charlie Pugh told him. "I took it out of this fellow's saddle boot." He pointed to a tall, hatched-faced man of about thirty-five.

"Did you use that shotgun here last night?" Wesley demanded, staring balefully at the desperado.

"Yo' gonna hang me anyway," the man replied, "so I might as well tell you the truth. Hell yes, I used it."

"Untie him and get him off that horse," snapped Wesley, "then give him his shotgun. Loaded."

One of the men obeyed, and as the outlaw stepped out of the saddle Wesley detected a flicker of hope in the mean, close-set eyes. Then Wesley's attention was drawn to Charlie Pugh, who had reloaded the shotgun and was about to hand it to the desperado.

"Wes," said Pugh, still holding the weapon, "this gun's loaded with buckshot."

Wesley made no reply. His gaze was fixed on Dude Justice's murderer. Then he was addressing the man. "I just want you to know that no matter how much I despise a contemptible bastard like you who would use a shotgun to kill a man, you're going to have the chance to kill me with it. Right now." Facing Pugh, he said, "Give him the gun, Charlie, and get back."

The murderer took the weapon from Pugh without looking at Wesley, who stood some fifteen feet away, and slyly pulled both hammers back while the gun still hung downward in his hand. Wesley heard the clicks and readied himself by flexing his finger muscles. But the man made no attempt to swing the gun into firing position. Instead he addressed Wesley, saying:

"You know I can't pull this gun up and shoot as quick as you can draw that pistol. So you're just figgerin' on murderin' me."

"Your gun is in your hands. Mine's in my scabbard," Wesley replied. "I'm waiting on you."

Then he deliberately looked away from the outlaw, who in that instant swung the shotgun level. But before he could finger the triggers, the .44 sped from Wesley's holster and sent two slugs crashing into the man's chest.

The muzzle of the shotgun dropped. Then, as the desperado began to fall, his dying fingers triggered both barrels. The gun roared and the heavy charge tore into the turf in front of Wesley, throwing a shower of grass and wet earth into his face.

Wesley reloaded his revolver and slipped it back into the holster. Then he walked to where Dude Justice lay, and sat down on the wet ground beside him.

"I just wish that what I've done could bring you back, Dude," he said. "I'll miss you." Folding his arms across his knees, he lowered his head and remained still until Sam Beard touched him on the shoulder.

"It's all done, Wes," he said. "Let's go back to Willis and send some wagons out here to get your boys."

Wesley got up and walked slowly toward his horse. Gazing at the figures of the outlaws swinging from the pine limbs, he wondered if the time would ever come when thieving and murdering and marauding would cease and people could live secure and peaceful lives.

33. The Sheriff

SEVERAL days after the burial of Dude Justice, Jimmie Temple, Duane Murchison, and the other Diamond Six men, Wesley received a letter bearing a Houston postmark. Mildly curious, he opened it and read:

Wesley Smith: You and your men murdered two of my cousins and some of my good friends the other night. The ones you caught you hanged the next day. I was the only one to get away from you, but I want you to know that I will be back to kill you. Keep your gun ready.

John Wesley Hardin.

The letter was written in a neat, legible hand on cheap blue-lined paper.

"Hardin!" Wesley's brow arched.

He knew the name, for John Wesley Hardin was the most famous gun fighter in Texas. Wesley had seen the man only once. That was after Duane Murchison had been forced into gun-fighting Hardin on the streets of Willis on Wednesday, June 19, 1872. Duane had outdrawn Hardin, shot the gun out of his hand, and seriously wounded him in the side. Wesley wished that Duane had killed Hardin then and there. If he had, the Diamond Six men might be alive today.

"So Hardin's out to get me," Wesley said to himself. "Well, I might have thought twice about going up against you, Mr. Hardin, had you not admitted to a part in murdering Dude Justice, Duane Murchison, Jimmie Temple, and the rest of my boys. But not now. I'll shoot you down like a mad dog if I ever get the chance."

Slowly Wesley folded the letter and placed it in his wallet. "I thought Hardin was supposed to be in the penitentiary for killing a deputy sheriff named Charlie Webb," he mused. He thought about this for a moment, then dismissed the matter from his mind.

Cattle rustling and organized crime had come to an abrupt end in Montgomery County following the incident on Diamond Six. The cattle rustlers decided they would fare better elsewhere. But the cattlemen realized that it was too good to last, for their area raised some of the finest beef in the state. Beyond this important fact, which alone was enough to tempt the rustlers, the country to the north and east offered ideal hiding places for stolen cattle.

Wesley hired a number of new men who had come to him highly recommended from various parts of East Texas, and when the outlaw bands began to move back into the county he was once again able to cope with them. He appointed a tall lean man named Bob Butterfield his foreman, and Butterfield coached the riders well. Their first encounter with the rustler band on the night of Wednesday, September 9, 1885, resulted in the slaying of five outlaws and the capturing of several more, who were promptly hung. None of the Diamond Six men were killed, and only one suffered a wound.

The following Sunday a group of Wesley's friends from

all sections of the county called upon him at his home and urged that he declare himself for the office of sheriff of Montgomery County.

Somewhat surprised, he laughed and said they were surely joking, that he had never had any desire for public office or the entanglements of local politics. They knew this, or should have known it by this time.

"Yeah, we know that, Wes," Sam Beard said. "We know a couple of other things as well. First, any candidate for the office will have his past dragged hide bare over the coals. We don't think they'd skin you much. Beyond that, we know how you have dealt with the rustlers and bad men. So we feel that you might as well take the county under your wing the same as you have Diamond Six."

"Hold on," Wesley protested, rising to refill their glasses. "I don't have to tell you how much I appreciate your offer of support. But listen to me. Now the way I'm used to dealing with rustlers in protecting my land and cattle is a defensive measure the law wouldn't condone. I'd be under oath to bring the scoundrels in for costly trial. Some would squirm free. No, I don't see it, boys."

"You didn't refuse to help your state when the Rangers needed you, Wesley."

"Now wait a minute, Jim. You're hitting me in a tender spot. That's gone and done with. I just don't want to be sheriff. That's a job for a young man. Here I am, fifty-six years old, with a family and——"

"We don't want a youngster, Wes," interrupted Sam Beard. "We want you. If we wanted young fellows, we could get them at a dime a dozen."

His friends continued to persist, and Wesley thought seriously on the matter, saying at last, "I'll run for this office on one condition, and that is if my wife sanctions it. I'll talk to her now if you wish."

Excusing himself, he went upstairs to Margaret's sitting room. As she lowered a book he pulled a chair close to her and explained the object of his friends' visit. She listened attentively until he was through.

"Sheriff. So that's it," she said with a smile. "It's not for me to say what you should do, dear. Any time these awful men strike, I know you're going to be there to oppose them anyway. You've always been in favor of strict law and order, and I know you'd make a fine sheriff. But please, don't ask me to make the decision for you. I cannot and will not, darling."

Wesley rose and kissed her tenderly. Then he returned to his friends and said he had decided to go along with them. "For only one term, mind you."

The elections of 1886 swept Wesley Smith into office with a clear majority over his three opponents. He appointed Clint Rose his chief deputy and set about organizing the entire county into a small army of deputized citizens with which to combat the lawless gangs that were still riding roughshod over most of East Texas.

After a few attempted raids the rustlers began giving Montgomery County a wide berth. And for good reason. The citizens under Wesley's plan were able to combat the outlaws on better than even terms in various sections of the county simultaneously. Then something else, at first very unpopular with ranchers, proved to be of considerable help in curbing rustlers. Barbed wire was becoming commonplace in Texas, and as more and more of the farmers and ranchers made use of it, it became increasingly difficult for the outlaws to drive off large herds of cattle. At each fence they were forced to cut three, five, even seven strands of the tough barbed wire. With the old rail fences, the cattle could be crowded against them to make them collapse without any loss of time.

Before Sheriff Smith's term of office ended he was approached by the same friends and urged to run again. He argued against it, only to meet with the kind of persuasion he did not know how to combat. So he bluntly refused and glared at the delegation.

"Sure, Wes," Sam Beard, their spokesman said. "Sure. We understand, Wes. And we ought to be ashamed of ourselves, riding a good horse to death. But we appreciate a good sheriff. Why, since you've been in office we haven't lost a dozen head of cattle, and none of our stores or banks have been robbed that we didn't catch the devils who pulled the job. You have this county at peace with the world now and we want to keep it that way."

As Wesley's face softened, Beard seized the opportunity and said, "So if you don't run, Wes, we're going to put your name on the ticket and elect you anyway."

Before Wesley could reply, Beard herded the delegation out of the sheriff's office. Wesley's perplexed expression vanished as he watched them go. A slow smile tugged at the corners of his mouth as he said to himself:

"You can jail a thief and hang a murderer, but how can you deal with men like that?"

Wesley put the matter out of his mind, deciding instead to show Sam Beard and his cronies that his refusal to run again was final. As he sat down to the paper work attending the job of county sheriff, Bubba entered the office with his closest friend, Mabin Anderson. As Wesley pushed the stack of papers aside and looked up smiling at the inseparable pair, Mabin said:

"We just heard the good news, Captain Smith. I'm sure glad to hear you're running again. Maybe you can use me during your next term of office."

"Who the devil told you I was running again, Mabin?"

"It's all over town, sir. Mr. Beard——"

"Sure, sure," Wesley said wearily. "I suppose I'm running again in spite of myself. But what's this about deputizing you?"

As the youngster talked, Wesley listened in a detached manner. The two boys, their traits and bearing and long association, occupied his mind. Since Bubba's first day in school Mabin had been his constant companion. They were almost like brothers, as Wesley and Joe had been, Sheriff Smith reflected, looking from one to the other.

Mabin was tall and thin, gangling, while Bubba was of medium height and muscular in appearance. However, the boys had every trait in common. Both were well mannered, often mischievous. They never hunted trouble but never ran away from it. Neither knew the meaning of fear, yet each was gentle, kind, and considerate of the feelings of others, and honest to a fault. While learning seemed by comparison of no great importance to them, they had attended school in a dutiful manner. Perhaps, Wesley thought, because their parents expected it of them. Everything they did together was in a spirit of competition, be it work or play. Though Mabin was three years older than Bubba, the latter looked and acted as old, if not older.

Wesley could find no fault with them. Rather, he could not mask his pride of the boys. But their bid through Mabin for a pair of deputies' badges was out of the question, though his reply to Mabin was freighted with more encouragement than he intended:

"It's mighty gratifying to know you conniving youngsters are on the side of law and order. I'll remember that, Mabin."

Wesley ran for sheriff again and was elected. He was a busy peace officer and rancher, though never too occupied with the affairs of Diamond Six or his office to keep an eye on the progress of two boys turning into men. It was like watching a good crop mature.

Bubba's eighteenth birthday was an occasion for Wesley. It fell on a Sunday, and Mabin had accepted an invitation to the Smith home. Having celebrated his twenty-first birthday only a few days before, Mabin appeared around eleven o'clock that morning, riding a new fine embossed saddle, complete with rifle boot, from which projected the shiny stock of a .30-.30 Winchester carbine. As he dismounted and handed the reins to white-haired old Henry, he hung a gun belt holding his old-style Colts .44 on the saddle pommel.

Wesley and Bubba were on the veranda when Mabin rode up. Wesley darted a quick glance at his big son and realized that Bubba was jealous of Mabin, very likely for the first time. Mabin had reached manhood, and with it came the right to bear arms without the supervision of his elders. This gave him an edge over Bubba, who, despite his love for his loyal friend, could not quite hide his covetousness. But he tried, and Wesley admired him for it.

After dinner Margaret touched the little bell at her elbow to summon Henry. As prearranged, the Negro appeared with an armful of wrapped packages. The very first gift Bubba opened contained a new .30-.30 Winchester carbine, identical to the one he had examined on Mabin's saddle. His delighted smile advised his father that all jealousy he had felt had suddenly vanished. Bubba tore excitedly through the packages of boots, shirts, a hat, and other presents, and finally picked up a sealed envelope Wesley had dropped at his plate. It was addressed simply "To Bubba" in Wesley's handwriting. The boy ripped it open and read:

My dear Bubba: Your mother and I feel that you have earned the right to be treated as a man from this day hence. We arrived at this decision after much prayerful deliberation. We ask only that you justify our faith in your ability to be a man beyond your years. Father.

Bubba read and reread the note. Then, bounding up from the table, he kissed his mother and father and executed a dance with his fifteen-year-old sister Leila, who had jumped delightedly from her chair to help him celebrate. Both Maggie and her husband, J. E. Caldwell, smiled happily, while Bubba's older brother Owen, seeing no reason for such child's play, finished his second dessert.

When the noise of the celebration subsided, Mabin said, "Now, Bubba, I have a little birthday present for you too, but I didn't wrap it and bring it in. Want to see it?"

Bubba did, and they walked outside with the family at their heels. At the front gate Henry stood holding the finest blood-bay stallion Bubba had ever seen. Speechless, he placed an arm about Mabin's waist and moved as in a trance to the big, sleek animal. The stallion stood neck high and nostrils quivering as he delicately inspected his new master.

One of the Negroes brought Bubba's saddle and bridle and Mabin's horse, but before the boys mounted, Wesley gave them the surprise of their lives.

"I need two deputies," he said, smiling at them. "So raise your right hands and be sworn."

The pair exchanged incredulous glances, then hastened to repeat the oath after the sheriff. They were still dazed when he pinned a bright silver star on each of them. "Now," he said, "this will make law-abiding citizens of you two hellions."

"You know, Captain Smith," Mabin said when the shock finally subsided, "I really appreciate this star. I'm going to do my best to prove you didn't make a mistake. And when you get tired of the job, I'm going to be sheriff of Montgomery County, somehow or other."

Wesley was about to make a reply when his attention was arrested by two riders who had pulled off the road separating Smith property from the railroad. The pair were now riding slowly toward him. When they were some twenty yards away, they drew up and surveyed the group standing at the gate for several moments. Then the smaller man dismounted, handed his reins to his companion, and took a few steps toward the family gathering.

"Are you Wesley Smith?" he asked coldly.

"Why, yes, I'm Wesley Smith," the sheriff said pleasantly. "What can I do for you?"

The visitor worked the muscles of his face and jaw in a manner that sent his rather weak chin forward. The result was a strange and menacing expression. Wesley was trying to recall when and where he had seen that vaguely familiar face, when the stranger said:

"I wrote you a letter a long time ago, Wesley Smith. Before you were sheriff. Do you remember a letter from John Wesley Hardin?"

Wesley remembered the letter. In fact, he had never quite forgotten it. It had hung like a thin but constant warning, distant but there, during the five years since he had received it. And now he was thinking that the writer of the threat was even more deadly because of his long patience and determination. Racing like an idle memory through Wesley's mind was a similar threat, one conveyed to him long years in the past by his friend Marion Nagle. But this one was as sudden as real. Worse, it had caught him unprepared. But an answer was due.

"Come to think of it, Hardin, I did get a letter from you."

"You didn't have to think to remember it, Smith." Hardin stood with his hands dangling at his thighs, a little tense, a little awkward, as he said after a pause, "I told you I was coming back to kill you. Well, here I am, John Wesley Hardin in person. Go after your gun."

Margaret and the family could scarcely believe all they were seeing and hearing. Their glances shuttled back and forth, from Wesley to the notorious gunman and back again. Mabin and Bubba eyed only Hardin, their eyes pinpointed.

"I'm not armed," Wesley said. "I wish I was, Hardin, so I could shoot you down for murdering my men that night on——"

"I never murdered any——" Hardin checked himself suddenly. Then he said, "You expect me to believe the sheriff of Montgomery County goes around unarmed? For the last time, Smith, go after your gun, damn you."

He began to raise a hand slowly outward, his fingers tense and clawlike.

Wesley went cold all over, for he realized he was looking death in the face, with no chance whatever to defend himself. He wanted to ask Hardin for time to get a gun, but some stubborn streak of pride, however strange and foolish, would not allow him to seek a favor from the man whom he blamed for the death of Dude Justice and Jimmie Temple. So in that instant when he hung between his turbulent past and the hereafter he stood motionless, glaring back at the most famous gunman in the Southwest.

Bubba felt his heart skip a beat. He stood by his new stallion with the bridle reins about his left arm. There was not time enough to free his arm if he were to save his father's life. Caught in this awkward position, Bubba dropped his right hand to the handle of the Colt .45 and he fanned the hammer with his left palm. Both shots went true before the bay reared and bolted, dragging Bubba off his feet before he could straighten his arm and let the reins slip free.

Mabin's pistol was still hanging on his saddle pommel, and his horse had whirled to run off with the stallion. The man holding Hardin's horse was quick to take advantage of the confusion. He threw Hardin's reins to him and spurred his own mount savagely toward the main road. Bubba's bullets had struck Hardin high in the left shoulder, knocking him down, but he managed to pull himself into the saddle and race after his fleeing companion before Bubba and Mabin could reach their mounts.

Mabin caught his horse and vaulted into the saddle. Bubba's stallion was fractious and reared as he tried to mount. Consequently he was fifty yards behind Mabin as they raced after the fleeing men.

"Arnold, come back here!" screamed Margaret. "Come back!"

If Bubba heard, he paid no heed.

Margaret tugged frantically at Wesley's arm. "Why, Wesley? Why did you let him go?"

Wesley placed an arm about her and tilted her chin with a finger. The uneasiness and fear in her eyes touched him deeply, more than ever before. For the first time he realized that neither he nor Margaret was able to bear up any longer under the strain and trials of the violence they had so long endured. They had passed the prime of life, had finally grown old.

"Why, Wesley, the moment he was eighteen, the moment we called him a man, did you pin a deputy's star on him and send him into danger?"

Wesley grimaced and wiped a tear from her cheek.

[365]

Then he stared into the haze of the distant trees. "It's a long story, Margaret," he said, as if in a trance. "A long story."

His hand clutched at her waist and she saw in his expression the need of a man for the full understanding of his mate and companion.

"In the first place, Margaret, Bubba and I were riding down in the river pastures the other day and my horse shied from a big cottonmouth moccasin. I shot twice and—well, I missed, Margaret." He paused. "Bubba didn't."

She looked both curious and perplexed.

"In the second place," he went on, "I'm getting a little careless. Too careless for a family man and a sheriff. Today I was caught unprepared. I was at the mercy of one of the fastest and deadliest gunmen in the Southwest. John Wesley Hardin has killed at least thirty-nine men. By the grace of God and the quick wit of our son, I was not his fortieth victim. I was lucky. But a man can't depend on luck, Margaret. I never did. A man may shape his luck to a degree. Hardin's luck in staying alive is due to something he might not understand. Bubba could have shot him in the head or the heart. But he didn't."

He looked far in the hazy distance, his eyes unfocused.

"Our son didn't want to kill a man, Margaret. He only wanted to defend and protect."

He looked at his wife then.

"So the deputy's star was not a mistake, Margaret darling. It was pinned on a man."

Wesley swallowed hard, and the weariness of the years seemed to surface in his face in that moment. But in his eyes was the brightness of hope.

"Bubba is the kind of man who will defend law and order, Margaret, and preserve the things I have fought for since I was fifteen. As long as there are people in this old world there will be Tobins and Hazeletts, Spanglers, Philip Sheridans, E. J. Davises, and others, each in his own way a menace to society. By the authority of money, office, and a gun."

As he gazed unseeing in the direction where Mabin and Bubba were last seen, Margaret studied him with wonderment and pride in her eyes, for he seemed to wrap up his past in his demands for the future. He further proved this to Margaret when he said:

"But there'll always be men like my father and yours, Margaret, like Mr. McGowen, William Spiller, Major Tarbone and——"

She interposed, smiling now, "And Wesley Smith."

"Like our son, darling," he said, as if he had not heard. "Like Mabin Anderson. Young men with ideals and convictions of right and wrong, with their feet planted as solidly on the ground as were Dude Justice's, Duane Murchison's, and Jimmie Temple's. Young men to shape the right kind of future."

He breathed a heavy sigh, then smiled down at Margaret. "You know I won't be running for sheriff again. I mean it this time. Montgomery County needs a man like Mabin Anderson. He's old enough. And I know a young fellow who'll back him all the way; one who can knock the head off a damned cottonmouth at fifteen paces."

Margaret understood him then. She realized that she had never failed to understand her man, not even before their wedding. It was merely that he possessed the faculty of presenting an old and constant side of himself in a new light, the light of perhaps a trivial circumstance, as the moccasin in this case. She knew he thought a great deal, and deeply, about many things of the past, of their bearing on the future.

Looking at Wesley then, she thought of the one thing

he seldom mentioned any more, and she wondered about it. Then she said: "Wesley, I'm glad you're turning law enforcement over to younger men. I'm glad you're a man who knows when and how to quit, the same as you knew when and how to go after the things you wanted and thought were right. But there is one thing I am wondering if you've learned to quit doing. It's hating the Yankees. Do you still hate them, Wesley?"

He darted her a glance, then looked up the road again. A faint humorous smile tugged at his mouth.

"There was a time," he said with feigned crispness, "when I would have answered by saying that's a man's business, woman, or 'Hell yes.' But——" He turned very serious. "Maybe I'm getting soft, Margaret. I can't ever hope to forget the hundreds of friends I lost during the war. I can't forget the way of life the North took away from us, or the life of hell they made us live after the war was over. But hate them? Well——"

Margaret watched his face harden, then soften.

"I don't hate them. I don't hate anybody, Margaret. But I'll say this much," he said, drawing from his wallet an envelope containing a large check, "I get a grim satisfaction that goes beyond the acquisition of money every time Diamond Six cattle bring one of these back from a damnyankee."

Margaret tried to suppress a smile as she scolded him in the manner of a parent reprimanding a boy. "Wesley Smith, you're incorrigible!"

His eyes twinkled and he said, "Yes, ma'am."

A minute later she looked anxiously up the road. "Wesley dear, do you think Arnold is——?" She broke off and bit her lips nervously before glancing up at him. Her expression changed in that instant from one of uneasiness to calm acceptance.

"What were you going to say?" His glance was gentle but firm.

"Nothing, Wesley."

He knew then she loved him enough, trusted him enough, to place the care of their young son's future in his hands. It was a good feeling.

"I'm going to the house, Wesley," she told him. "The boys will want coffee when they return."

He held her to him for a minute and planted a kiss on her forehead. "And I'll want a cup too, Margaret Smith," he said, releasing her.

He watched her go, then moved toward the east gates, wondering how long his fledgling deputies would be gone; wondering if they were a match for the two men they followed. His anxiety mounted and, try as he did to put it down, he was on the verge of going after his horse when he saw them.

"Thank You, God," he said aloud.

The boys rode up to Wesley, leading the horse that belonged to Hardin's companion, the owner tied across his own saddle, dead. The scene spoke for itself, but Mabin looked downcast as he eased his tall frame from the saddle.

"The other fellow got away from us, Captain. Broke for the woods before we could get close enough to stop him. Shall we get some men and smoke him out?"

"Look, Mabin," Wesley replied, looking from the dead man to each of the youngsters, "have you boys any idea who the other man is?"

"No, sir, except he said his name was Hardin."

Wesley told them what he knew about John Wesley Hardin and saw them exchange surprised glances and swallow hard when they realized the size of the game they had been chasing.

"Now, do you still want to go after him?" asked Wesley.

"Yes, sir," the pair replied in unison.

"Why?"

"Because he was wrong, Captain," replied Mabin.

"You two seem to qualify," Wesley said, nodding significantly. "You've learned all I or any man can teach you." Then he said, "I've been doing a lot of thinking while I waited for you boys to come back; I don't believe now that Hardin would have killed me today. I think I know where he will be in the morning and I'm going to let him tell me why he came here. As far as I know, John Wesley Hardin has never killed a man who was unarmed, nor has he ever killed a man who was not an enemy of Texas. I hope he's where I think he is, in the prison barracks on William Spiller's plantation. It will be interesting to talk to him." Then he said to Mabin, "Take your man there to the undertaking parlor, then come back here for coffee, Mabin."

As Mabin rode off, leading the horse carrying the dead man, Wesley and Bubba stood looking at him in silence.

"Father," Bubba said, "I never saw Mabin shoot as he did today. He shot that man from a running horse at nearly two hundred yards. And he can't hit the side of a barn with a pistol."

Wesley smiled at his husky son.

"Tell me something, Bubba," he said, "did you hit *your* man where you intended to?"

Bubba eyed his father closely and inquiringly for a long moment before he replied.

"Yes, sir," he said slowly. "I—I—Father, I just couldn't——"

"I know, Bubba. I know. And I'm proud of you."

Father and son turned and walked toward the house arm in arm.

34. Trail's End

JOHN WESLEY HARDIN was intercepted the next morning by Wesley and Bubba as he approached the Esperanza post office. They found, as Wesley had suspected, that Hardin was in prison and that good behavior had earned him a job as trusty, which gave a prisoner opportunity to leave when he chose. He submitted readily to being searched for weapons by Bubba and then began to answer Wesley's questions as Dr. Loggins dressed his shoulder wounds.

"Hardin," said Wesley, "I want to hear you tell just why you came to Willis to kill me yesterday."

"Sheriff," began Hardin, "what I'm going to say is the truth. I swear it. I wasn't in that raid on your cattle—back in 1885, I believe it was—I was right up yonder in those prison barracks the night it happened. There were three of my cousins there, however. One of them got away and came up here to tell me about it. It made me mighty mad, and that's when I wrote that letter."

"How did you mail it from Houston?" asked Wesley. "Had you escaped?"

[371]

"No, sir," he replied. "I haven't tried to get away in over ten years. I gave it to that cousin of mine to mail." Then he said, "I think the thing that started me to hating you happened long before the raid on your ranch. You had a man named Duane Murchison who gunned me down in Willis years ago. It was a fair fight, but I always hated him for it, and hating him made me hate you, for he represented the things you had. Maybe I was jealous of you, maybe it was because I had such a time getting over the wounds I got, I don't know. One thing I do know, I'm glad I didn't kill you yesterday."

"I might as well tell you that I hold no grudge, Hardin," Wesley said. "I talked to a friend of mine about you last night. His name is Ben McCulloch. What Ben told me keeps me from arresting you for attempted murder or from reporting you to the officers at the barracks up yonder. Ben told me the type of men you had killed before you shot a deputy sheriff and went to the penitentiary—scalawags, carpetbaggers, and old Davis's State Police. But it's good for you that I didn't have my guns on yesterday, for I would have killed you. I wouldn't have shot you in the shoulder like my boy did."

Hardin opened his mouth to speak, but Wesley continued with, "Do the officers at the barracks know you've been hurt?"

"No, sir."

"I didn't think so," replied the sheriff. "That's why I brought the doctor along. I won't report you because I hear you're up for pardon for good behavior. I think you will still make Texas a good citizen. Ben McCulloch tells me you're studying law. Keep at it. A man like you should make a good attorney. When you get out of prison and need any help, call on me."

Hardin muttered his thanks, and Wesley watched with

Bubba and the doctor as the convict rode slowly toward the post office before turning his horse toward Willis.

The weeks that followed found Mabin Anderson serving as chief deputy under Wesley. He had appointed Mabin when Clint Rose, badly wounded in a gunfight, decided to retire. The young man filled the job beyond Wesley's expectations, handling his duties well and making friends everywhere he went. Pleased, Wesley met Sam Beard and his cronies on the day they came to draft him again with an announcement: He was retiring from office to support the next sheriff, Mabin Anderson, and that was that, final. Even Sam Beard could not prevail upon him this time.

The announcement of Wesley's retirement from office was followed by a wild scramble of men who filed in the race for sheriff. Eight men ran for the office. Mabin won. He held the office for many years, with Bubba his staunchest supporter in every campaign. He finally stepped down after qualifying as one of the most capable peace officers Texas had ever known.

Once free of the responsibilities of office, Wesley concentrated his energies toward the production of better beef cattle. He sent Bubba, his constant companion, in search of fine bulls and cows. Together they bred, culled, branded, laid out more pasture land, all with one aim— improvement and progress. These were happy and rewarding years. Beyond the pleasure of watching trainload after trainload of Diamond Six beef departing for the Northern markets at top prices, Wesley was thankful that the country remained peaceful. Law was winning over outlawry. A man could walk in peace. This was something new to Wesley Smith, who since 1844 and on up to 1891 had witnessed the opposite. Nearly fifty years of his life filled with turmoil and violence.

On June 6, 1895, Wesley celebrated his sixty-sixth

birthday. He had lived nearly fifty-one years in Texas and had made friends in each of these years. Many of them came to Willis on that early summer's day. His family— Margaret, their sons and daughters and grandchildren— were there. Each brought cheer and pleasant memories. All of Wesley's children except Owen and Bubba had married.

Only Estelle's marriage had been marred by unhappiness. She had married a ship captain who had decided to quit the sea, but who could not. Captain Watson left her and their baby Margaret and was never heard from again, and Owen remained with his sister to help comfort her and to rear Margaret.

And Bubba—Wesley searched him out with his eyes that day—had not married because, in spite of his many excuses, he felt his parents' need for him in their declining years. In addition, he had learned to enjoy the life of a handsome, eligible bachelor.

As now, Wesley observed, drawing Margaret's attention to their son. "Look at him, Margaret, eating up all that attention from the pretty ladies."

Bubba thought nothing of riding the big blood bay stallion twenty-six miles to a dance at Cold Springs, eighteen miles to a dinner party in Montgomery, or to visit some pretty girl in Point Blank, forty miles away. And when he was not courting, he and Mabin Anderson and "Scrap" Powell were fox hunting behind the thirty-three hounds he kept penned back of the stables. Owen frowned on his activities and told Bubba so many times. Owen even gave his hounds to one of Judge Hightower's sons. Upon learning of this, Wesley promptly sent Owen after the dogs in a spring wagon. He brought them home from Liberty County after a hectic week on the road and hated the sight of a dog for the remainder of his long life.

"The more I look at Bubba, darling, the older I feel," Wesley said, drawing a smile from Margaret, that and a realization that old age had been and was kind to them. She no longer had to worry about her husband's departure with gun belt buckled at his waist. He was free of all that and she was as grateful as he.

In the winter of 1897 Margaret developed a serious hacking cough, and Dr. Powell ordered her to bed for treatment and complete rest. The cough persisted, and in spite of every attention she continued to fail. The doctors finally recommended that she be placed in a fine new hospital in San Antonio.

Wesley immediately turned his business over to Owen and Bubba and took Margaret to the old city of the Alamo. It wrung his heart to see that the treatment was unavailing and that, before very long, he would be parted from his most treasured possession. He kept the family informed of their mother's true condition, and when she died suddenly on the bright, clear morning of Wednesday, April 6, 1898, he brought her home to Willis and placed her in a huge burial vault.

Wesley now realized just how entwined his life had been with Margaret's. Nothing he did brought respite from the great sorrow that engulfed him, and he came to realize that his remaining days were few. He pondered this feeling which he had never so much as imagined, then shook it off. But it returned, and the knowledge seemed to cheer him. He set about with a passion drilling Bubba in the ways best to prosecute the business of Diamond Six.

"I am giving a full share of the estate to each of your brothers and sisters, Bubba," he said. "But the best of the cattle and the grazing lands I am giving to you. You are also to get the Diamond Six brand, which I want you to leave to the one of your sons who is the most like you. Advise with him on how to improve the land and the cattle he raises. I would prefer that Diamond Six continue with the great Herefordshires we now have established, but of course that will not be for me to say."

Bubba listened patiently while his father talked. Even the mention of the possibility of his parent's death hurt beyond word expression.

Wesley grieved deeply and constantly for Margaret, but aside from the hours he spent each evening at the burial vault, sitting beside her casket in his old wicker rocking chair and reading the newspapers by the light of a green-shaded oil lamp, he gave no indication of the great anguish his body and soul were enduring. His mind remained clear and sharp, allowing him to conduct the manifold enterprises in which he had prospered for so many years to the very day of his death.

The torment of Wesley's sorrow began to take its toll from his physical being in spite of all he could do, and one day Bubba suddenly realized that his beloved parent was an old man. And it was not good for him to spend more time each day at the burial vault. Memories and love were wonderful things, but not when they began to consume a mortal. Thinking perhaps he had been neglectful, Bubba sent one of old Henry's boys after their best squirrel dog and yelled to his father:

"How about a ride down into the pecans on the San Jacinto?"

Wesley walked outside, smiled, and wrinkled his brow as he gazed out over the thin March haze in the trees. "Nothing would suit me better, Bubba." Looking from the dog to the rifle in his son's hand, he said, "I can take my old .44 and get more squirrels than you, son."

In their saddles they rode off toward the budding pecans,

talking and laughing as of old. Wesley stopped his horse often to point to a herd of cattle and to wedge in a word of advice. They crossed a little stream and dismounted to wait for the dog to tree a squirrel.

"Now," said Wesley, creeping forward with Bubba at his side. In a few moments he spied a fat brown squirrel sitting on a high limb.

"Shall I gun him out, Bubba?"

"Go ahead."

Wesley jerked the pistol up and fired. The strange, tired look of an old man came into his eyes. "You kill him, son. Seems I've really lost my touch."

Bubba fired and missed purposely. "Seems that we're both out of practice. We're going to have to shoot more often."

Wesley's glance was stern. "Don't ever do that again," he said. "And don't deny that you could have hit him."

Bubba thought fast. He had listened to the detailed story of his father's life, had written much of it down, and in doing so had learned exactly the type of man his parent was, even to the way he thought. So it would never do to admit the truth, for that very truth would remain a wedge between them. Nor could he deny it. So he said with a good-natured laugh:

"What the devil do you expect after you scared the little fellow so he showed only his head?" He added, "Thanks for the compliment to my shooting just the same."

The reply brought a smile to Wesley's face. It remained there even when hours later they dismounted at a creek to water their horses. As they rode back toward Willis, Wesley said:

"Just how serious are you about William Spiller's daughter, Allie?"

"Huh?" Bubba glanced at his father, saw the old smile

wreathing his face, and relaxed. "She has consented to marry me," he replied, "but we haven't set the date yet. Why?"

"No reason at all. None at all, except"—he hesitated— "except I'm glad to know you're marrying such a fine young lady. William and I have been close friends for many years, and it makes me happy to know that a part of what we have accumulated will be held together by you and Allie. Why don't you two set the date for your wedding? I'd like to be your best man."

"Well," Bubba began, "I don't know, Father. We probably well be married real soon. And I certainly want you to be my best man."

Then Bubba looked away, for he could not tell his father the real truth, that he could never leave him, because Wesley needed him more now than ever before.

Bubba's marriage to Allie Spiller was never again discussed by father and son, for when they arrived home and Henry came to take the horses Wesley had to be helped into the house. He was put to bed with a raging fever. When Dr. Powell bustled in and laid a professional hand upon the sick man's brow he shook his head. He took Wesley's temperature and looked at the mercury. One hundred and five degrees, a killing fever. The old doctor shook his head again and then turned to face Bubba, who stood across the bed from him.

"Wesley is a mighty sick man," he said softly. "I don't want to alarm you, but I believe you should call your brothers and sisters."

"What's the matter with him, Dr. Powell?" Bubba asked.

"Actually nothing," the doctor replied rather pensively. "If you can call a broken heart nothing. In my honest opinion, Wesley is letting Margaret's death kill him."

He handed Bubba a little glass vial filled with tablets. "Give him one every two hours. They should help bring his fever down. I'll be back in a little while."

Bubba walked downstairs with the grave-faced medical man. "Dr. Powell," he asked anxiously, "just how sick is Father?"

The old doctor put a hand on the youngster's shoulder. "Bubba," he said, "Wesley has talked to me a great deal about your mother's death. It has preyed on his mind for years. I saw his decline start the morning she died in San Antonio and—well, it's been downhill ever since. I wish medicine could do something to relieve a man's mind of grief and worry and heartache, but it never will. Never."

As Bubba opened the door for the doctor, tears streamed down his cheeks, and his mouth was drawn into a tight line to keep back the racking sobs in his breast.

"I'll be back soon, Bubba," the doctor told him, "and I'll wire Miss Irene and Buck if you wish."

Bubba nodded and shut the door. Then he threw himself into a chair and loosed the welling flood of tears. Although he was nearing his thirty-first birthday, he sobbed unashamed. Like the child who had toddled after his father since his memory began.

Bubba alone knew the complete story of the great and good man who was his father, and he raised his head with the memories of the many events he had heard recounted. He almost saw young Wesley Smith at fifteen avenge his own father's death, saw him with Joe on the road to Texas. The names Spangler, Tarbone, Magruder, the Republic of Texas, and the Confederacy were woven with McGowen, Simonton, and the many other names he had heard and knew. The legacy went beyond cattle, Diamond Six Ranch, and wealth. It gave him knowledge and insight, a cherished picture of the great man he loved more than any one person in the world—his father. And it prepared him for the inevitable.

Just before dawn on the cool, crisp morning of Thursday, March 20, 1902, with Buck, Owen, Estelle, Maggie, Leila, and Bubba at his bedside, Wesley Smith died quietly at the age of seventy-three. Seventy-three years of violence, love, heartache, and happiness had come to a peaceful end.

Epilogue

IN THE spring of 1903, following Wesley's death, Bubba married Allie, the daughter of Betty and William Spiller. For a happy and carefree month the bride and groom lost themselves in the old city of the Alamo.

Allie and Bubba returned to Diamond Six to begin a happy and eventful life and to plot the destiny of the now-famous ranch that was to see years of drought and years of plenty. For a time they chose Willis as the headquarters of Diamond Six and there, in 1904, their first child, Margaret, was born.

The division of Wesley's estate into equal shares for the seven children who survived him left Bubba too little land on which to prosecute the operations of Diamond Six, and at Betty Spiller's suggestion she and William deeded lands to Allie and Bubba adjoining the land inherited from Wesley. The headquarters of Diamond Six was then moved to the new and thriving community of Esperanza, and the additional acreage again allowed expansion and growth. These new lands also provided another shipping point on the International & Great Northern Railroad for cattle bound to the Northern dinner tables. On the north end of the ranch, cattle could be gathered and shipped from Esperanza, and a short drive from the south end would put the fat white-faced steers in the stock pens at Willis.

In the hallowed shadows of Esperanza, the big, handsome old home of William Spiller's mother, the author's sister, Margaret, died in infancy. In these same surroundings William Fielding Smith was born. Here also his two brothers, Thomas Wesley and Eliphlet Arnold, were born. The three brothers and their mother, Allie Spiller Smith, all survived Bubba, who died suddenly on Saturday, June 1, 1929, after piloting Diamond Six through twenty-seven years of its thrilling and sometimes bloody history. Twenty-seven years spent with horse, rope, and gun, his working tools, his eldest son, William Fielding, his constant pupil and companion.

In 1935 the author married Ella Frances McMurrey, the granddaughter of James McMurrey and Robert McGowen, two of Wesley's closest friends. With their two children, Roslyn Starlett and William Fielding, the Smiths still carry on the Diamond Six cattle business founded by Wesley well over a century ago.

The present headquarters of Diamond Six Ranch is located at Point Blank, Texas. This lazy, peaceful little village was once the home of the illustrious George T. Wood, second governor of Texas and the notorious Texas gunman, John Wesley Hardin.

Point Blank is a name that stirs the imagination. Its narrow, winding streets and paths once resounded to the thundering hoofbeats of outlaws' horses, bank robbers, thieves, and murderers, all riding hell-bent for hiding places in the edge of the Big Thicket along the Trinity River. Point Blank, literally defined, means straight, direct, honest, blunt. In a way the name symbolizes Wesley Smith, for his every act and deed were aimed directly toward the mark. It therefore seems fitting and proper that Diamond Six finally came to Point Blank.

In the southeast corner of Diamond Six, bordered by the broad Trinity River, are the scattered remains of the long-deserted town of Swartout. Here Wesley and Joe had their second encounter with Jack Spangler. And it was to these same acres that Robert McGowen brought his wife to dwell in the mansion he had built for her on the land he loved so well.

Diamond Six still raises Hereford cattle, just as Wesley wished.

God rest his soul.

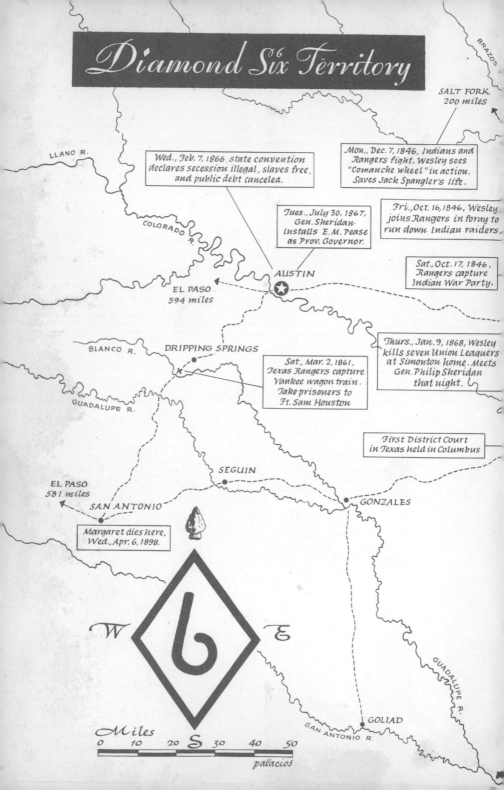

Diamond Six Territory

BRAZOS

SALT FORK
200 miles

LLANO R.

Wed., Feb. 7, 1866, state convention declares secession illegal, slaves free, and public debt canceled.

Mon., Dec. 7, 1846, Indians and Rangers fight. Wesley sees "Comanche wheel" in action. Saves Jack Spangler's life.

COLORADO R.

Tues., July 30, 1867, Gen. Sheridan installs E. M. Pease as Prov. Governor.

Fri., Oct. 16, 1846, Wesley joins Rangers in foray to run down Indian raiders.

AUSTIN

EL PASO
594 miles

Sat., Oct. 17, 1846, Rangers capture Indian War Party.

BLANCO R.   DRIPPING SPRINGS

Thurs., Jan. 9, 1868, Wesley kills seven Union Leaguers at Simonton home. Meets Gen. Philip Sheridan that night.

Sat., Mar. 2, 1861, Texas Rangers capture Yankee wagon train. Take prisoners to Ft. Sam Houston

GUADALUPE R.

First District Court in Texas held in Columbus

SEGUIN

EL PASO
581 miles

SAN ANTONIO

GONZALES

Margaret dies here, Wed., Apr. 6, 1898.

W   E

GUADALUPE R.

GOLIAD

SAN ANTONIO R.

Miles
0   10   20   S   30   40   50

palacios